SELECTIVITY AND MOLECULAR MECHANISMS OF TOXICITY

F. De MATTEIS

MRC Toxicology Unit
Carshalton, Surrey SM5 4EF, UK

and

E. A. LOCK

ICI plc Central Toxicology Laboratory
Alderley Park, Macclesfield, Cheshire SK10 4TJ, UK

MACMILLAN
PRESS

First published 1987

Published by
THE MACMILLAN PRESS LTD
Houndmills, Basingstoke, Hampshire RG21 2XS
and London
Companies and representatives
throughout the world

Typeset by
TecSet Ltd, Wallington, Surrey

Printed in Great Britain by
Camelot Press Ltd,
Southampton

ISBN 0-333-41780-1

SELECTIVITY AND MOLECULAR MECHANISMS OF TOXICITY

Contents

The Contributors

W. N. Aldridge
Medical Research Council
Toxicology Unit
Carshalton
Surrey SM5 4EF
UK

F. Berends
Medical Biological Laboratories – TNO
Lange Kleiweg 139
P.O. Box 45
2280 AA Rijswijk
The Netherlands

A. P. DeCaprio
Wadsworth Center for Laboratories and
   Research
New York State Department of Health
Empire State Plaza
Albany, New York
NY 12201
USA

F. De Matteis
Medical Research Council
Toxicology Unit
Carshalton
Surrey SM5 4EF
UK

D. Dinsdale
Medical Research Council
Toxicology Unit
Carshalton
Surrey SM5 4EF
UK

D. Henschler
Institute of Pharmacology and Toxicology
University of Würzburg
Versbacher Strasse 9
8700 Würzburg
West Germany

M. K. Johnson
Medical Research Council
Toxicology Unit
Carshalton
Surrey SM5 4EF
UK

P. Jenner
Institute of Psychiatry
and King's College Hospital Medical School
Denmark Hill
London SE5 8AF
UK

E. A. Lock
Central Toxicology Laboratory
Imperial Chemical Industries plc
Alderley Park
Macclesfield
Cheshire SK10 4TJ
UK

L. L. Smith
Central Toxicology Laboratory
Imperial Chemical Industries plc
Alderley Park
Macclesfield
Cheshire SK10 4TJ
UK

C. D. Marsden
Institute of Psychiatry
and King's College Hospital Medical School
Denmark Hill
London SE5 8AF
UK

F. Stirpe
Instituto di Patologia Generale dell'Università
    di Bologna
I–40126 Bologna
Italy
and
Drug Targeting Laboratory
Imperial Cancer Research Fund
London WC2A 3PX
UK

B. Nemery
Medical Research Council
Toxicology Unit
Carshalton
Surrey SM5 4EF
UK

Present address:
Université Catholique de Louvain
Unité de Toxicologie Industrielle et
    Médecin du Travail
Clos Chappelle-aux-Champs 30–54
1200 Brussels
Belgium

R. D. Verschoyle
Medical Research Council
Toxicology Unit
Carshalton
Surrey SM5 4EF
UK

A. H. Penninks
Department of Veterinary Pharmacology,
    Pharmacy and Toxicology
Faculty of Veterinary Sciences
University of Utrecht
P.O. Box 80158
Utrecht
The Netherlands

J. G. Vos
Laboratory for Pathology
National Institute of Public Health and
    Environmental Hygiene
P.O. Box 1
3720 BA Bilthoven
The Netherlands

Preface

A symposium was held in September 1985 at the University of Kent to mark the retirement of Dr W. Norman Aldridge, the Deputy Director of the Toxicology Unit of the Medical Research Council and the first Chairman of the British Toxicology Society. The title of the Symposium was *Selectivity and Molecular Mechanisms of Toxicity* and it was intended to highlight the major guiding principles in Norman's distinguished scientific career which made him a recognised pioneer of toxicological research both in the UK and worldwide. Most of the contributors had been closely associated with Norman, either as students or as collaborators, and we were very happy to organise the scientific programme with the help of Martin Johnson, which we gratefully acknowledge.

This book is aimed at providing a more permanent tribute to Norman's influential achievements. It is a collection of short reviews which have been written by the contributors to the symposium, all specialists in various fields of human and experimental toxicology, and which illustrate some of the most interesting and topical problems in present-day toxicological research. Examples are given of the molecular basis for tissue-selective toxicity in the lung, peripheral nerves, kidney and immune system; and the mechanisms of toxicity of toxic lectins, organo-phosphate inhibitors, genotoxic chlorinated hydrocarbons and suicide substrates of cytochrome P-450 are then considered. Finally, human and experimental studies on the toxicity of three classes of compounds (MPTP, hexane and impurities of commercial parathion) are reviewed: these have received a great deal of interest in recent years for their involvement in human toxicity, being associated with the development of previously undescribed toxic syndromes.

Our thanks go to the British Toxicology Society who supported the symposium and encouraged the publication of this book.

Carshalton and Alderley Park, 1987   F. De M.
                                                                             E. A. L.

Part I

Tissue-selective Toxicity

1
Cellular Specific Toxicity in the Lung

Lewis L. Smith and Benoit Nemery

INTRODUCTION

The architectural structure of the lung is designed to provide and protect a vast surface area within the chest cavity which allows the effective exchange of respired gases with the bloodstream. This means that the lung has numerous cell types with specific functions and when the cell types in the blood are taken into consideration, over forty individual cell types have been identified (Sorokin, 1970). Since the total cardiac output passes through the lung, the lung can be exposed to toxic xenobiotic compounds and their metabolites present in the blood. The lung is also exposed to gases, vapours and particles (if small enough) present in the inspired air. Even toxins present at very low concentrations in the atmosphere may present a risk to the lung, especially when one considers that the adult human lung respires approximately three tons of air per year (Mustafa and Tierney, 1978).

The selective vulnerability of lung cells will depend on several factors. These will include:

1. The route of exposure (i.e. inhalation or via the bloodstream).
2. The mean aerodynamic diameter (particulates).
3. Solubility of inhaled gases (e.g. sulphur dioxide compared with ozone).
4. Selective uptake mechanism (e.g. paraquat).
5. Selective metabolic activation (e.g. 4-ipomeanol).
6. Susceptibility of individual cell types.
7. Species susceptibility (e.g. butylated hydroxytoluene, BHT; trialkylphosphorothioates; α-naphthylthiourea, ANTU; 4-ipomeanol; paraquat).

It is the purpose of this review to consider in some detail the mechanism of toxicity of some chemicals which damage the lung. In doing so we shall attempt to highlight the cellular specific toxicity which these chemicals provoke. In particular we shall

3

discuss the pulmonary toxicity of hyperoxia, ANTU, BHT, 4-ipomeanol, and para-quat.

OXYGEN TOXICITY

Prolonged exposure to elevated oxygen tensions is toxic to most animal species including man (Clark and Lambertsen, 1971). The effects of hyperoxia on various aspects of lung structure, function and biochemistry and its mechanism of toxicity have been the subject of numerous experimental studies. Indeed the investigation of pulmonary oxygen toxicity is of direct relevance to man, not only because humans are often exposed to high levels of oxygen (usually for therapeutic purposes), but also because hyperoxia can be used as a model of the pathogenesis of adult res-piratory distress syndrome, pulmonary fibrosis and for processes such as inflam-mation, ageing and carcinogenesis (Autor, 1982; Parke, 1982; Pryor, 1982).

Pathology

Several ultrastructural studies (Kistler *et al.*, 1967; Kapanci *et al.*, 1969; Meyrick *et al.*, 1972; Crapo *et al.*, 1978, 1980) have shown that breathing high concen-trations of oxygen leads to the initial destruction of the alveolar capillary endo-thelial cells with few signs of damage to the alveolar type I epithelial cells. This process provokes interstitial and alveolar oedema and haemorrhage, some infil-tration by monocytes and polymorphonuclear leucocytes and eventually fibro-blast proliferation. If the animal survives this early destructive phase, a proliferative phase follows characterised by hypertrophy and proliferation of type II epithelial cells and a large increase in the number of interstitial fibroblasts.

There is considerable species variability in susceptibility to pulmonary oxygen poisoning. The time-course of tissue changes and the survival times vary with species (rats being more susceptible than monkeys), age (immature animals being often more resistant than mature animals, Frank *et al.*, 1978) and other factors such as nutritional levels of antioxidants (Deneke *et al.*, 1983) or the induction of oxygen tolerance as a result of prior exposures to oxygen or other pretreatments which increase the levels of antioxidant systems (Frank, 1983).

Mechanism of toxicity

The primary mechanism of oxygen toxicity is thought to result from an imbalance between the increased generation of toxic oxygen radical species during hyperoxia and the available cellular defence mechanisms against these species (Frank, 1983; Fisher *et al.*, 1984). Toxic oxygen species result from the reduction of molecular oxygen to superoxide anion (O_2^-) and this radical may in turn dismutate, either spontaneously or catalysed by superoxide dismutase, to form hydrogen peroxide (H_2O_2). Superoxide anion is also able to reduce transition metals such as Fe^{3+} to

Fe^{2+} and the ferrous iron is capable of reacting with H_2O_2 to form the hydroxyl radical ($OH^{\cdot}$) by processes which have been well described by Freeman and Crapo (1982) and Halliwell and Gutteridge (1984). The $OH^{\cdot}$ is thought to react with, and modify structural, metabolic and genetic material. In this way it may lead to perturbations of cell function and cause cell death, if the protective mechanisms (low-molecular weight scavengers and enzymatic systems) are overwhelmed.

Although it is generally accepted that the primary mechanism of oxygen toxicity is the increased generation of free radicals of oxygen, the cellular source of these radicals, during hyperoxic exposure, is not known. There are at least two hypotheses which have been advanced: one is that high concentrations of oxygen lead to an excessive production of oxygen radicals *within the alveolar cells themselves*; and the other is that oxygen radicals are generated, mainly by *activated polymorphonuclear leucocytes* which accumulate in oxygen-damaged lungs.

This latter hypothesis would explain the apparent paradox that the endothelial cells appear to be damaged by hyperoxia before the more directly exposed epithelial cells. Neutrophils are well equipped to inflict tissue damage, since they can release potent oxidants (including reactive oxygen-radical species) as well as proteolytic enzymes, metabolites of arachidonic acid and other amplifiers of the inflammatory response.

Circumstantial evidence incriminating the neutrophil comes from the observation that circulating leucocytes are sequestered by the lungs of patients developing adult respiratory distress syndrome, thus resulting in high numbers of neutrophils or their products in broncho-alveolar lavage fluid and in the lungs at autopsy (Anon., 1984; Tate and Repine, 1983). In rats exposed to greater than 95% oxygen a close temporal relationship was observed between the chemotactic activity of the lavage fluid, the influx of neutrophils to the lavaged lung compartment and the subsequent mortality (Fox *et al.*, 1981). In sheep, the chemotactic activity for granulocytes in lung lymph increased eight-fold within 72 to 96 h of oxygen exposure (Newman *et al.*, 1983). This neutrophil recruitment to the lungs has recently been attributed to an increased elaboration of chemotactic factors by macrophages as a result of hyperoxic exposure (Christman *et al.*, 1985) although the respiratory burst of alveolar macrophages is in fact decreased by oxygen exposure *in vitro* (Suttorp and Simon, 1983).

The importance of the infiltration of inflammatory cells into the lung has been further supported by the observation that neutropenia results in a decreased severity of lung injury from hyperoxia and that the degree of lung injury correlates with the number of remaining circulating polymorphs (Shasby *et al.*, 1982). Lung vascular permeability changes induced by other treatments have also been shown to be attenuated in leukopenic animals (Brigham, 1982; Eiermann *et al.*, 1983).

It is not generally accepted that lung injury is mediated by neutrophils in oxygen toxicity (Fisher *et al.*, 1984; Glauser and Fairman, 1985). Indeed ultrastructural evidence of endothelial cell injury seems to precede the accumulation of inflammatory cells, and the correlative studies of Fox *et al.* (1981) indicate that neutrophil infiltration is associated with onset of mortality rather than with the initiation of lung injury. Also, much larger numbers of neutrophils may be seen in lobar pneumonia and inflammatory conditions other than adult respiratory distress syndrome. Moreover, pulmonary oxygen toxicity and the adult respiratory distress syndrome have been shown to occur despite neutropenia in animals (Raj *et al.*, 1985) and patients (Braude *et al.*, 1985; Rinaldo and Borovetz, 1985). Oxygen toxicity can also clearly occur *in vitro* without the participation of inflammatory cells (Martin *et al.*, 1981; Block and Stalcup, 1981; Housset *et al.*, 1983; Block *et al.*, 1985), and signs of oxygen toxicity may occur *in vivo* without evidence of pulmonary inflammation, as shown by analysis of bronchoalveolar lavage from human volunteers exposed for 17 h to $> 95\%$ O_2 (Davis *et al.*, 1983).

In conclusion, it seems likely that blood leucocytes are not essential for the initiation of acute lung injury but they may enhance pulmonary dysfunction by the self-propagating effects of the released tissue-damaging proteases and oxygen radicals. The two concepts, i.e. direct injury by the intracellular generation of oxygen radicals or inflammatory cell mediated injury are not necessarily mutually exclusive, since hyperoxia may cause the initial damage which in turn causes an influx of inflammatory cells. This combination of injurious processes is strongly supported by the *in vitro* experiments of Suttorp and Simon (1982), Bowman *et al.* (1983) and Krieger *et al.* (1985). The latter authors showed a synergistic interaction between hyperoxia and granulocytes in producing acute lung injury, with hyperoxia priming the lung for further injury by granulocytes.

α-NAPHTHYLTHIOUREA

α-Naphthylthiourea (ANTU) was developed as a selective rodenticide following the observation that phenylthiourea killed rats in low doses while being virtually non-toxic to man (Murphy, 1980; Gosselin *et al.*, 1984). Rats and dogs are the most sensitive species tested but even in rats there is considerable variation in the LD_{50} of ANTU, depending on the strain, age and diet (Roszkowski, 1967). This factor and the rapid induction of tachyphylaxis (Van den Brenk *et al.*, 1976) have detracted from the use of thioureas as rodenticides. However, ANTU has been widely used as a model toxin for the study of the pathophysiology of pulmonary oedema since it produces pulmonary toxicity by causing massive, non-haemorrhagic pulmonary oedema with fibrin-rich pleural effusion.

Pathology

The most characteristic feature of ANTU toxicity is the rapid onset and resolution of pulmonary oedema. In rats, pulmonary oedema and pleural effusion begin 2 h after injection and are maximal by 4 h; death generally occurring between 8 and 10 h. In survivors the exudate is reabsorbed by 24 h (Cunningham and Hurley, 1972; Van den Brenk *et al.*, 1976). The same pattern of toxicity has been described in mice (Mais and Bosin, 1984).

Cunningham and Hurley (1972) and Meyrick *et al.* (1972) have described the ultrastructural characteristics of rat lungs at various time-points after ingestion of lethal or sub-lethal doses of ANTU. The earliest changes (2 h) consist of peri-vascular and interstitial oedema with localised sub-endothelial blebbing (i.e. accumu-lation of fluid between the endothelium and its basement membrane). Later, inter-stitial oedema and endothelial blebbing become more marked. Ultimately, intra-alveolar oedema containing fibrin becomes apparent. This classical (Staub et al., 1967; Staub, 1974) sequence of events in pulmonary oedema is interpreted as follows: interstitial fluid is normally drained away from the gas exchange region to juxta-alveolar sumps formed by lymphatic capillaries in the perivascular, peri-bronchiolar and septal connective tissue beds, possibly as a consequence of the interstitial pressure gradient created by the distribution and interaction of mech-anical forces in the alveolus-capillary region (Weibel and Bachofen, 1979). If altered haemodynamics or altered permeability cause the rate of fluid accumulation in the interstitium to exceed the rate of lymphatic drainage, then the peribronchial and perivascular spaces will become dilated, forming 'cuffs'. Fluid will then accu-mulate in the alveolar walls and eventually it will enter the air spaces causing alveolar flooding and severe impairment of gaseous exchange. Thus, pulmonary oedema is best defined in functional terms as a condition of altered fluid dynamics in the lung leading to excessive accumulation of fluid within one or more lung compartments. Using a dog lung lymphatic preparation, Rutili et al. (1982) have recently con-firmed that the oedema caused by ANTU is produced by increased vascular per-meability.

Despite the evident fluid leakage, definite signs of endothelial cell injury (swel-ling, loss of organelles, vacuolation, breaks in endothelium, increased electron density) are either uncommon (Cunningham and Hurley, 1972; Machado et al., 1977) or occur only at a late stage (Meyrick et al., 1972). The pulmonary oedema caused by ANTU is remarkably short-lived. By 24–48 h after an oedemagenic dose the exudate and pleural effusion are reabsorbed and minimal signs of injury are present (Cunningham and Hurley, 1972). No long-term sequelae seem to result from a single dose of ANTU (Van den Brenk et al., 1976), but a recent study has demonstrated right ventricular hypertrophy after four weekly doses of ANTU (Hill et al., 1984).

Mechanisms of toxicity

The mechanism by which ANTU causes endothelial dysfunction is still unknown. Boyd (1980a) and Neal and Halpert (1982) have reviewed the experimental evi-dence indicating that the lung toxicity of ANTU is brought about by its metabolism and in particular that its desulphuration results in the formation of reactive inter-mediates.

Resistance to ANTU toxicity has been induced by pretreatments with small doses of ANTU itself, with other thiourea derivatives, sulphydryl compounds including glutathione, 2-aminoethylisothiouronium bromide, possibly cysteine, 3-methylcholanthrene, or piperonyl butoxide (Boyd and Neal, 1976; Van den Brenk et al., 1976). On the other hand, depletion of glutathione by diethylmaleate potentiated the toxicity of ANTU (Boyd and Neal, 1976). Administration of (carbonyl-^{14}C) and (^{35}S)-ANTU led to covalent binding of radioactivity to macro-molecules in the rat lung and liver, with relatively more binding taking place in the lung. In contrast, little radioactivity became bound after the administration of the non-toxic (carbonyl-^{14}C) labelled α-naphthylurea (Boyd and Neal, 1976). The latter observation provides compelling evidence that the thiono-sulphur group is required for both covalent binding and toxicity.

Incubation of (^{14}C) or (^{35}S)-ANTU with rat liver or lung microsomes also led to covalent binding of radioactivity to protein (Boyd and Neal, 1976). Most of this binding was NADPH dependent. The proportion of bound sulphur was considerably higher than that of bound carbon and, as with other thiono-sulphur compounds (Neal and Halpert, 1982), incubation of microsomes with ANTU resulted in a decreased activity of mixed function oxidase. The latter phenomenon also occurred in the lungs following *in vivo* treatment of rats with ANTU (Boyd and Neal, 1976).

Taken together the results from the *in vivo* and *in vitro* studies with labelled ANTU suggest that its lung toxicity results from the biotransformation of the thio-carbonyl moiety giving rise to reactive products that can covalently bind to macro-molecules in the lung. It is clear that the lungs are capable of metabolising ANTU products that bind to macromolecules and it is therefore reasonable to assume that it is metabolism *in situ* which is responsible for lung damage (Boyd, 1980a). How-ever, as pointed out by Boyd (1980a) the possibility that toxic metabolites released by the liver reach the pulmonary vascular endothelium has not been conclusively ruled out. Moreover, even if ANTU is metabolised to toxic products in the lung, the cellular sites of the biotransformation of ANTU within the lung and the reasons for the peculiar susceptibility of endothelial cells are still unknown. Both the cyto-chrome P450-dependent and the FAD-containing monoxygenase systems have been implicated in the activation of ANTU (Poulsen *et al.*, 1974, 1979; Lee *et al.*, 1980).

Two reactive metabolites have been proposed: (1) atomic sulphur released in the desulphuration of ANTU and (2) another metabolite containing the carbonyl carbon (Lee *et al.*, 1980). Approximately half the atomic sulphur bound to liver and lung microsomes appears to have reacted with cysteine of the microsomal proteins to form hydrodisulphides (Lee *et al.*, 1980). However, by virtue of its high reactivity, atomic sulphur possibly binds exclusively at the site of its production thereby only inactivating cytochrome-P450 and suggesting that it will be the less reactive metabolites that are more likely to contribute to toxicity (Neal and Halpert, 1982). Fox *et al.* (1983) have recently proposed that thiourea-induced lung injury results from OH˙ mediated oxidation of thiourea to formamidine disulphide which rapidly decomposes to yield thiourea, atomic sulphur and cyanamide. Fox and co-workers (1983) based their suggestion on the fact that OH˙ scavengers prevent the induction of oedema by thiourea and they speculated that OH˙ radicals were generated during microsomal electron transfer. They further hypothesised that cyanamide was the ultimate toxin on the basis that iv injection of high doses of cyanamide also result in lung oedema. This hypothesis seemed to be supported by the fact that singly N-substituted thioureas such as ANTU can be oxidised to cyano-containing compounds whilst the non-oedemagenic N,N'-disubstituted thioureas (Dieke *et al.*, 1947) cannot (Fox *et al.*, 1983).

Secondary mechanisms may also be critically involved in ANTU-induced oedema. Polymorphonuclear leukocytes do not seem to be crucially involved in this model of pulmonary oedema (Fantone *et al.*, 1984; Cunningham and Hurley, 1972; Meyrick and Reid, 1979) thus possibly explaining its rapid reversibility and the lack of long-term response. Platelet thrombi are a constant if not prominent feature of ANTU lung injury (Cunningham and Hurley, 1972; Meyrick *et al.*, 1972). The possible role of platelets is not easy to determine. They may be involved both in the causation and limitation of pulmonary oedema (Mais and Bosin, 1984; Fantone *et al.*, 1984). It seems possible that ANTU metabolites cause some alteration in the membrane of vascular endothelial cells. This may trigger off a 'rescue operation' by platelets which attempt to seal off gaps. The release of 5HT by aggregating platelets would cause increased vascular permeability and further recruitment of platelets. However, this phenomenon would be self limiting because of the effective sealing off of gaps by the platelets themselves. These considerations illustrate the possible sequence of events which lead to increased lung permeability via complex pathways that include direct interaction of toxins with 'permeability receptors' (possibly involving sulphydryl bonds) and the triggering off of 'second messengers' and the release of mediators (Brigham, 1978).

4-IPOMEANOL

The furan derivative, 4-ipomeanol, has been isolated from spoiled sweet potatoes infected with the common fungus *Fusarium solani* (Boyd *et al.*, 1974a). It has been reported that cattle develop pulmonary injury characterised by oedema, congestion and haemorrhage after consuming sweet potatoes contaminated with this fungus (Wilson *et al.*, 1970; Boyd and Wilson, 1972). 4-Ipomeanol is probably the most studied derivative of a number of furans which have been shown to cause acute lung injury in experimental animals (Boyd, 1980a).

Pathology

After the oral, iv or ip administration of 4-ipomeanol there can be extensive damage to the terminal airways and the development of pulmonary effusions and oedema. The pulmonary effusion is often more extensive in the mouse compared with the rat in which inter-alveolar or perivascular oedema occurs (Boyd, 1980b). If the effusion or oedema is severe enough it will cause the death of the animal. However, after dosing with minimally toxic doses of 4-ipomeanol, the lung lesion is restricted to the smaller bronchioles, with selective necrosis of the non-ciliated bronchiolar epithelial (Clara) cells (Boyd, 1977). The damage which results from the administration of higher doses of 4-ipomeanol may involve other cell types such as the alveolar type II epithelial cell or the bronchiolar ciliated cells (Newton *et al.*, 1985). In mice, the earliest damage after large doses of 4-ipomeanol is found in capillary endothelial cells (Durham *et al.*, 1985). When Clara cells, or indeed other epithelial cells in the lung, are damaged, some proliferation of the remaining Clara or alveolar type 2 cells may occur, in an attempt by the lung to restore its normal architecture. Alveolitis, a general characteristic of lung lesions induced by chemicals, is also seen.

Mechanism of toxicity

After the intraperitoneal administration of radiolabelled 4-ipomeanol the greatest amount of radioactivity is found in the liver (Boyd *et al.*, 1974b). However, when the distribution of radioactivity in the tissues is normalised to give a specific activity per weight of tissue, then the lung has the greatest amount of radioactivity (Boyd *et al.*, 1974b). This activity in the lung does not decline rapidly, since the vast majority appears to be bound to tissue macromolecules (Boyd *et al.*, 1974b). The majority of the radiolabelled ipomeanol was found to be present in the Clara cell (Boyd, 1977). Alterations of toxicity caused by modulating mixed-function oxidases *in vivo* (Boyd and Burka, 1978), as well as *in vitro* experiments (Boyd *et al.*, 1978), strongly suggested that toxicity and the binding of 4-ipomeanol-derived material resulted from the activation of 4-ipomeanol by cytochrome P-450-dependent mono-oxygenase in the lung (Boyd, 1980a). The differential activity between the lung and the liver has been studied *in vitro* where the kinetics of covalent binding of 4-ipomeanol in lung microsomes indicate that the K_m for microsomal alkylation is approximately an order of magnitude lower than that in hepatic microsomes (Boyd *et al.*, 1978). Since the cytochrome P-450 content of lung microsomes is much lower than in liver microsomes the maximum rate of alkylation in the lung must be far greater than in the liver when the results are expressed in terms of P-450 content (Boyd *et al.*, 1978).

Organ-dependent kinetic differences in the activation of chemicals are attributed not to the existence of organ-specific enzymes, but to differences in the *relative concentrations* of cytochrome P-450 isozymes having different substrate specificities (Philpot and Smith, 1984; Wolf *et al.*, 1985). Thus, the major constitutive lung cytochrome P-450s in both rat (PB$_1$ and PB$_2$) and rabbit (P-450 I and P-450 II, now known as forms 2 and 5) are isozymes which are only minor components of the liver cytochrome P-450 complement (Wolf *et al.*, 1985). Both isozymes have been shown to exhibit high rates of 4-ipomeanol activation (Wolf *et al.*, 1982). In addition to possessing a specific profile of cytochrome P-450 isozymes, the lungs are also characterised by the heterogeneous distribution of their cytochrome P450 systems.

In contrast to the liver, where mono-oxygenase activity is relatively evenly distributed throughout the tissue, the lung appears to have this activity concentrated principally in the bronchiolar nonciliated (Clara) cells, and to a lesser extent in alveolar type II epithelial cells (Boyd, 1977; Devereux *et al.*, 1979, 1981, 1982; Serabjit-Singh *et al.*, 1979; Jones *et al.*, 1983). In other words, even when pulmonary and hepatic metabolic activities towards a chemical look comparable on a tissue basis, concentrations of (toxic) metabolites must be much higher in metabolising lung cells than in hepatocytes. *The highly localised nature of xenobiotic metabolism in the lung is therefore viewed as another important determinant for some forms of chemical-induced lung toxicity*, and in particular that caused by

4-ipomeanol (Minchin and Boyd, 1983; Boyd, 1984). Accordingly, the highest rates of cytochrome P-450 metabolism of 4-ipomeanol were found in isolated Clara cells, which are the target cells for this compound *in vivo* (Boyd, 1977; Devereux *et al.*, 1982).

In conclusion, 4-ipomeanol is capable of selectively damaging the Clara cell in the terminal bronchiole (although large doses will also damage other cell types in the airway and in the lung parenchyma). The basis for this cell-selectivity appears to be the metabolism of 4-ipomeanol by isozymes of cytochrome P-450 which are specially prevalent in the Clara cells of the lung. These isozymes metabolise 4-ipomeanol to electrophilic intermediates which can bind covalently to macromolecules.

BUTYLATED HYDROXYTOLUENE

Butylated hydroxytoluene (2,6-di-tert-butyl-p-cresol, BHT) is perhaps the most widely used anti-oxidant in foods and related food products. The anti-oxidant activity of BHT inhibits free radical reactions thereby preserving the food from oxidative damage. In high doses, BHT has been shown to cause damage to the murine lung following oral and parenteral dosing. This has led to the use of BHT as a model compound for producing lung injury in mice and to investigations of its potential to cause cell injury in the lungs of other species.

It should be emphasised that BHT has been subjected to extensive safety evaluations because of its presence in food and the metabolism and toxicity of BHT to humans has recently been reviewed (Bibich, 1982).

Pathology

Marino and Mitchell (1972) first described the adverse effects of BHT in the lungs of female mice. They showed that following intraperitoneal dosing with BHT (250 mg/kg), a pulmonary lesion developed, characterised by hyperplasia and hypertrophy of the alveolar epithelial cells. There was evidence of thickening of the alveolar epithelium. This proliferation of the alveolar epithelial cells is maximal between 2 and 5 days of dosing (Witschi and Saheb, 1974). Adamson *et al.* (1977) showed that it is the alveolar type I cell which is first damaged following the administration of BHT. This damage is associated with alveolar oedema, although the type II epithelial cells and the endothelial cells remain intact (Adamson *et al.*, 1977). After 3 or 4 days the alveolar type II cells begin to proliferate, and by 9 days this returns to normal (Adamson *et al.*, 1977; Saheb and Witschi, 1975). There may also be some proliferation of endothelial cells and the development of a mild fibrosis (Adamson *et al.*, 1977). The proliferation of the alveolar type II cell is presumably to replace the damaged alveolar type I cells since type II cells eventually assume the morphologic characteristic of type I cells (Hirai *et al.*, 1977).

The effect of BHT on the murine lung can be produced after intraperitoneal, subcutaneous or oral dosing. However, it is generally accepted that BHT does not damage the rat lung.

Mechanism of toxicity

The mechanism through which BHT destroys the alveolar type I cells in the mouse lung is not known. It has been established, however (Malkinson, 1979) that the toxic effects of BHT were reduced if the mice were exposed to cedar terpenes either in the form of cedar wood shavings (used as cage bedding) or after a single injection (ip) of sesquiterpenoid compounds derived from cedar wood. The implication of these observations is that BHT activation by metabolism is involved in its mechanism of toxicity. This suggestion is further enhanced by the observation that toxicity of BHT can also be reduced by treating the mice with inhibitors of xenobiotic metabolism such as SKF 525A or piperonyl butoxide (Kehrer and Witschi, 1980). Also a high degree of covalent binding of radioactivity occurs in the lung after administration of radiolabelled BHT, and this binding can be inhibited by treating with SKF 525A, providing additional circumstantial evidence that it is a reactive metabolite of BHT that causes lung damage (Kehrer and Witschi, 1980). It is probable that cytochrome P-450 dependant mono-oxygenases are involved in the generation of the reactive metabolite (Masuda and Nakayama, 1984), but the cellular site of this process in the lung is unknown.

When labelled BHT was given to the rat (a species which is not susceptible to the lung lesion provoked by BHT) there was less binding of BHT to macromolecules in the rat lung compared with the mouse (Kehrer and Witschi, 1980). This observation may in part provide an explanation for the differential susceptibility to BHT toxicity of the mouse lung, as compared to rat lung. It also begs the question whether the human lung is more like the rat lung or the mouse lung in its ability to metabolise BHT. The answer to this question may well help to assess whether BHT has the potential to cause damage in the human lung.

PARAQUAT TOXICITY

Paraquat (1,1- dimethyl-4,4-bipyridinium) is a contact herbicide which has been marketed for over twenty years and is now available in approximately 130 countries throughout the world. Its structure was first described in 1882 by Weidel and Rosso. Its redox properties were discovered by Michaelis and Hill (1933) and since that time it has been used as a redox indicator known by the trivial name methyl viologen. Although it has proved remarkably safe in use (Howard et al. 1981; Swan, 1969) there have been several hundred human fatalities during the last two decades attributable to paraquat poisoning. The vast majority of these have been the consequence of the intentional ingestion of the concentrated commercial product (Fletcher, 1974).

Although the symptoms of poisoning depend on the amount consumed, a significant proportion of those who die from paraquat poisoning do so as the consequence of pulmonary damage which causes severe anoxia. The toxic effects of paraquat have been described in both man and experimental animals, although the most extensive studies on the effect of paraquat in the lung have been carried out in rats. This species of experimental animal provides an adequate model for the study of the lung damaging effects of paraquat in man.

Pathology

In general there are two distinct phases to the development of paraquat-induced pulmonary lesions. There is first a destructive phase in which the alveolar epithelium of the lung (type I and type II epithelial cells) are destroyed (Smith and Heath, 1974, 1976). If the destruction of the alveolar epithelium is very extensive, an alveolitis develops which involves progressive pulmonary oedema and infiltration of neutrophil polymorphs into the alveolar tissue. In rats, this acute alveolitis can be severe enough to cause death. The second phase of the lung lesion can be considered as a consequence of the epithelial cell damage and alveolitis (Smith and Heath, 1976). In this phase intra-alveolar and inter-alveolar fibrosis develops which may be so extensive and severe as to destroy alveolar architecture. Consequently, the opportunity for effective gaseous exchange is reduced and this can be severe enough to cause death from anoxia.

Mechanism of toxicity

There is no evidence that paraquat is metabolised by experimental animals (Daniel and Gage, 1966). It appears that ingested paraquat is either absorbed from the gastrointestinal tract into the bloodstream and eliminated by the kidney or it passes straight through the gastrointestinal tract and is excreted in the faeces (Daniel and Gage, 1966). The proportion of paraquat which is absorbed is largely taken into the bloodstream from the gastrointestinal tract at some point beyond the stomach (Smith et al., 1974; Bennet et al., 1976). There does not appear to be any good evidence as to the site of absorption of paraquat in man.

After the oral administration of paraquat to rats the plasma paraquat concentration remains relatively constant for approximately 30 h, during which time the concentration in the lung rises progressively to several times that in the plasma (Smith et al., 1974). This time-dependent accumulation of paraquat into the lung does not occur in any other organ studied (Rose et al., 1976). However, the kidney which is the organ responsible for the excretion of paraquat from the body does have high concentrations in comparison with other organs. This accumulation of high concentrations of paraquat in the lung, along with the high concentrations achieved in the kidney, provide a possible explanation of why these organs are selectively damaged by paraquat following oral dosing.

Using an *in vitro* system, this accumulation process in the lung was found to be energy dependent and to obey saturation kinetics (Rose et al., 1974).

The lung from various animal species, including man, has been found to have the ability to accumulate paraquat (Rose et al., 1976). Since the kinetic constants for the uptake of paraquat into the rat and human lung are similar, it appears that the rat is an acceptable model for the accumulation of paraquat into the human lung (Rose et al., 1976).

The accumulation of paraquat by lung tissue appears to result from its uptake by a transport system capable of accumulating a number of endogenous diamine and polyamine compounds such as putrescine, spermidine and spermine (Smith, 1982; Smith et al., 1982). It was the search for an explanation of the accumulation of paraquat into the lung that led to the discovery of this polyamine accumulation process (Smith, 1982). The most likely reason for the accumulation of paraquat by this system is the structural similarity of the bipyridyl to the diamine and poly-amine compounds which are the endogenous substrates for the system. The structural requirements for compounds to be accumulated into the lung have been partially characterised and it seems that the distance between the quaternary nitrogen atoms of paraquat is a critical factor in allowing the bipyridyl to be accumulated by the diamine and polyamine uptake system (Smith, 1982; Gordonsmith et al., 1983).

At present there is little published evidence that describes the cell type(s) into which paraquat and the polyamines have accumulated. However, Waddel and Marlowe (1980) demonstrated that in mice intravenously dosed with paraquat the labelled paraquat present in the lung is distributed in a manner consistent with that of the alveolar type II epithelial cells. Furthermore, in a series of unreported studies (Nemery and Dinsdale; Smith and Soames) it has been found that the distribution of paraquat and of the polyamines putrescine and spermidine was largely confined to the alveolar epithelial cells (type I and type II) with evidence of polyamines also present in the Clara cells of the lung. These data are consistent with the observation that it is the alveolar epithelial cells which are damaged by paraquat.

When paraquat is accumulated into the lung cells, it is generally accepted that the primary reaction in its mechanism of toxicity is its redox cycling from the oxidised to reduced form. Gage (1968) first reported that under anaerobic conditions the paraquat cation could be reduced by NADPH, together with a flavo-protein, to form its reduced radical. The reduced radical in turn reacts with molecular oxygen (Farrington et al., 1973) to reform the paraquat cation and concomitantly produce superoxide anion. Provided there is a continuous supply of electrons to paraquat, and oxygen is present, paraquat will continue to cycle from its oxidised to reduced form. This redox cycling has been shown to occur in microsomal preparations of lung, liver and kidney (Baldwin et al., 1975). The biochemical consequences of this redox cycling and the relationship to cell death are still unclear. There are two general hypotheses which are being put forward to explain the cause of cell damage. The first is that of Bus et al. (1974, 1975, 1976) which suggests that paraquat generates superoxide anion and this directly or indirectly leads to lipid peroxidation thereby damaging vital cell membranes. Although there is convincing evidence that paraquat increases the rate of lipid peroxidation in vitro, there is little direct evidence to demonstrate that lipid peroxidation occurs in the lungs of animals treated with paraquat. This difference between the in vitro and *in vivo* evidence may reflect the difficulty of detecting small but critical changes in the extent of lipid peroxidation within a small population of target cells of the lung. However, it is also possible that lipid peroxidation *per se* is not the cause of cell damage but is in fact a consequence of it. In a recent review Halliwell and Gutteridge (1984) recalled that it was established many years ago that damaged tissues undergo peroxidation more quickly than healthy ones.

A second hypothesis is that with the accumulation of high concentrations of paraquat within cells, redox cycling occurs to such an extent that the concentration of reducing equivalents (NADPH) falls to levels that do not allow these cells to carry out essential physiological and biochemical functions. This hypothesis was first suggested by Fisher *et al.* (1975), and later by Witschi *et al.* (1977) who demonstrated that the NADPH to $NADP^+$ ratio in the lungs of rats intravenously dosed with paraquat was decreased, a result consistent with the oxidation of the reduced nucleotide. Later Keeling and Smith (1982) demonstrated that the shift in NADPH to $NADP^+$ ratio was the result of loss of NADPH in the lung. NADPH will also be consumed in an attempt by the lung to detoxify hydrogen peroxide formed by the dismutation of superoxide anion. The hydrogen peroxide will be converted to water via the glutathione peroxidase and glutathione reductase enzyme couple. This enzyme couple requires NADPH. Thus, NADPH is consumed in the formation of hydrogen peroxide and is further consumed in its detoxification. We have attempted to summarise the possible mechanisms of paraquat toxicity in figure 1.1.

GENERAL PERSPECTIVE

What clearly emerges from the examination of the pulmonary toxicants we have discussed is the phenomenon of selective toxicity to individual cell types. As we have mentioned earlier, the selective toxicity of chemicals to the lung depends on a number of factors among which are the route of administration of the toxicant, and more importantly, the specific biochemical and physiological characteristics of individual cell types in the lung.

For toxins undergoing metabolic activation such as 4-ipomeanol, BHT or O,S,S,-trimethyl phosphorodithioate (OSSMe (O), see the chapter by Aldridge *et al.* in this volume), the specific susceptibility of the lung may be attributed to the lung's particular profile of isozymes of cytochrome P-450-dependent monooxygenases. This susceptibility may be enhanced by the heterogeneous cellular distribution of these enzymes, whereby very high levels of activation may take place in certain lung cells. These mechanisms have been well documented in the case of 4-ipomeanol, which selectively injures lung cells that are rich in the appropriate cytochrome P-450, namely Clara cells. However, for BHT and OSSMe (O), which damage the alveolar epithelial type I cells, the situation is less clear, since these cells are not considered to contain much cytochrome P-450 activity. It is not known whether these compounds are activated in type I cell or in another cell type, such as the type II cell, from where the toxic metabolite would have to diffuse to the type I cell.

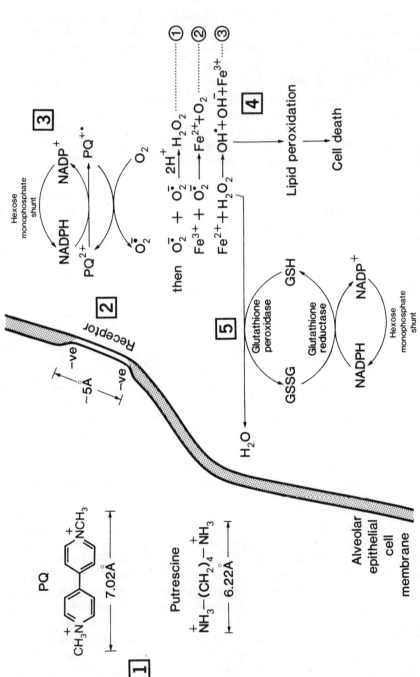

Figure 1.1 Mechanism of paraquat toxicity. [1] Structure of paraquat (PQ) and putrescine indicating the geometric standard separation of the nitrogen atoms in their structure. [2] The putative receptor for the transport of paraquat and polyamines indicating the likely minimal distance between the nitrogen atoms to allow transport. [3] Intracellular redox cycling of paraquat. [4] Generation of OH radical with possible development of lipid peroxidation. [5] Removal of H_2O_2 with loss of NADPH which also occurs at [3]

The drug-metabolising potential of the type I cell is not known. Type I cells are derived from type II cells, which are known to have appreciable drug-metabolising potential (Devereux and Fouts, 1981; Jones *et al.*, 1983), and they do possess variable amounts of endoplasmic reticulum (Kuhn, 1976). Histochemical studies (Wattenberg and Leong, 1962; Grasso *et al.*, 1971; Etherton and Conning, 1977) mention the presence of some xenobiotic-metabolising activities over the alveolar epithelium, but the sensitivity and resolving power of these histochemical methods were probably too low to either exclude or prove the presence of such enzyme activities in type I cells.

It is noteworthy that, in studies on isolated lung cells, the enzyme activities of the total lung cell suspension cannot be accounted for by the sum of the activities of Clara cells and type II cells, and this does not appear to be entirely due to losses during the isolation process (Jones *et al.*, 1983; Devereux *et al.*, 1985). A recent study has shown substantial mono-oxygenase activity in a population of cells not identifiable as either Clara or alveolar type II cells, and not corresponding to macrophages, ciliated cells, endothelial cells or polymorphonuclear leukocytes (Minchin *et al.*, 1985). Because of the very nature of type I cells, it is probably unrealistic to expect that these cells could ever be recognised morphologically, when isolated. Functional criteria (perhaps putrescine-uptake) might be more useful.

So far, this discussion has dealt exclusively with cytochrome P-450-dependent mono-oxygenases, because there is good evidence that this system is involved in the activation of BHT and OSSMe (O). Nevertheless, a possible role should also be considered for the pulmonary flavin-containing mono-oxygenase, which is present in Clara cells and alveolar type II cells (Devereux *et al.*, 1985), and for pulmonary prostaglandin synthetase, which has been shown to be capable of activating chemicals in the lung by co-oxidation with prostaglandin precursors (cf. Minchin and Boyd, 1983; Philpot and Smith, 1984).

The latter considerations may well apply to ANTU and to N-methylthiobenzamide (NMTB), a compound which causes a strikingly similar pattern of toxicity as ANTU (Cashman *et al.*, 1982). NMTB has been recently shown to be activated at least in part by the pulmonary FAD-dependent mono-oxygenase (Gottschall *et al.*, 1985; Penney *et al.*, 1985). The cellular sites of the activation of ANTU and NMTB are not known; neither is it known how activation relates to the dramatic, but short-lived alterations in endothelial permeability seen with these compounds.

In contrast to the compounds mentioned above, paraquat is not metabolised. However, it is activated by enzymes in the lung through the addition of one electron to form a paraquat radical. As stated before, this reacts with oxygen to reform the cation and produce superoxide anion. This process continues until the available reducing equivalents within the cell are exhausted or sufficient toxic radical species of oxygen are produced to cause cell damage. Similarly, the anti-tumour drug bleomycin has the ability to undergo cycling (Lown *et al.*, 1982). Bleomycin is capable of associating with the DNA of the cell and it is also capable of binding Fe^{2+}. The reduced iron is able to react with H_2O_2 to form $OH^{\cdot}$ radical at, or very close to, the DNA which is then damaged. In this process Fe^{2+} is oxidised to Fe^{3+} and this can in turn be reduced by reaction with superoxide anion. Another drug capable of causing pulmonary damage by redox cycling is nitrofurantoin. This chemical can damage the alveolar epithelium by a similar mechanism to paraquat (Boyd *et al.*, 1978; Martin, 1983). However since nitrofurantoin is not selectively accumulated into the lung from the plasma, larger doses of this drug, compared with paraquat, are required to cause lung damage.

Paraquat, bleomycin and nitrofurantoin provide three examples of free radical induced pulmonary damage. With bleomycin the redox cycling is thought to be caused by the 'trapping' of the transition metal iron in close proximity to the DNA of the cell so that toxic oxygen radicals are formed at a critical site. With paraquat and nitrofurantoin, the toxicity of these chemicals is associated with redox cycling in the cytosol of the cell. The cell-specificity of paraquat toxicity is probably attributable to its selective accumulation into alveolar epithelial cells, but the reason why the lungs are a target for nitrofurantoin and bleomycin is not clear.

Superimposed on the selective accumulation and specific metabolic activation of chemicals by individual cell types, is the possibility that various cell types may also differ in their ability to detoxify a given toxicant. It is important to realise that detoxification processes may be equally important in determining the pulmonary toxicity of chemicals. The role of reduced glutathione on the detoxification of pneumotoxic xenobiotics has been well documented for 4-ipomeanol (Boyd *et al.*, 1978; 1982) and for naphthalene, which affects Clara cells in mice (Warren *et al.*, 1982; Buckpitt *et al.*, 1984).

On a tissue basis, the lungs have 3- to 5-fold lower concentrations of GSH than the liver (Moran *et al.*, 1979; Boyd *et al.*, 1982; Buckpitt and Warren, 1983; Imamura and Hasegawa, 1984), but the *in vivo* cellular distribution of GSH in the lung is not yet known. Also, in the rat, the lungs have considerably lower activities (5- to 60-fold) of GSH-S-transferases than the liver or many other organs (Litterst *et al.*, 1975; Moran *et al.*, 1979; De Pierre and Morgenstern, 1983). Moreover, type II cells appear to have very little activity of these enzymes compared with Clara cells (Jones *et al.*, 1983).

It thus appears that *the lungs have probably much less effective defence and detoxification mechanisms towards metabolically activated xenobiotics than the liver.* This situation may be particularly true in some lung cells (e.g. type I cells).

The concept of differences in cellular susceptibility to toxic agents is well illustrated with the toxicity of oxygen to the lung. Oxygen toxicity is thought to involve the generation of toxic species of radical similar to those produced by paraquat, nitrofurantoin or bleomycin. However, it is the capillary endothelial cells which are first damaged by oxygen in comparison with the epithelial damage in the case of paraquat or bleomycin. With time, high concentrations of oxygen also damage the alveolar epithelial cells. Thus it appears that when the alveolar epithelial cells and endothelial cells are exposed to high concentrations of oxygen, the endothelial cells are more susceptible to oxygen in comparison with the epithelial cells.

The concept of individual cell susceptibility leads on naturally to consideration of species selectivity with respect to lung damaging agents. It appears that BHT does not damage the alveolar type I cells of the rat lung. It is not yet known whether this difference can be entirely accounted for by differences in the metabolic activation of BHT in the rat lung in comparison with the mouse. Similar considerations may be made about OSSMe (O) to which the rat type I cells seem to be especially susceptible, or ANTU which does not cause pulmonary oedema in humans. Paraquat on the other hand, damages the mouse, rat, monkey and human lung following a single dose, whereas the rabbit and hamster are apparently relatively resistant to paraquat induced lung damage. In part the explanation for this may reflect the inability of the lungs of those species resistant to paraquat to accumulate the chemical.

Finally, although we have discussed in some detail the ability of various chemicals to cause damage to specific cell types in the lung, it is often the case that the final morphological lesion which develops is similar. That is to say, irrespective of whether the alveolar type I, type II cell, or the endothelial cell is primarily damaged, the eventual lesion may be an alveolitis that can lead to fibrosis. It is therefore important to establish the sequence of morphological changes that take place in the lung. Even when the individual cell type which is damaged is established, it is possible that the resulting lesion (e.g. alveolitis and fibrosis) is species-dependent. This is well illustrated by the response of the rat lung to paraquat toxicity in comparison with that of the human. It is likely that in both the rat and human lung the alveolar type I and type II epithelial cells are the prime targets for paraquat toxicity. However, rats develop such a severe alveolitis that the animals usually die within a few days of dosing. In the case of the human lung, although the alveolar epithelium is damaged and pulmonary oedema and alveolitis develop, the acute phase of the pulmonary lesion rarely proves fatal to man. The patient usually survives the alveolitis but then develops a severe pulmonary fibrosis which may prove fatal. In the rat, only a small proportion of animals with severe acute alveolitis survive long enough to develop fibrosis. The problem of comparative toxicology between species is still one of the largest facing those interested in extrapolating the effects of chemicals in experimental animals to their effect in man.

REFERENCES

Adamson, I. Y. R., Bowden, D. H., Cote, M. G. and Witschi, H. P. (1977). Lung injury induced by butylated hydroxy-toluene-cytodynamic and biochemical studies in mice. *Lab. Invest.*, **36**, 26–32

Anon. (1984). Neutrophils and adult respiratory distress syndrome. *Lancet*, ii, 790–1

Autor, A. P. (ed.) (1982). *Pathology of Oxygen*, Academic Press, New York, London, p. 368

Baldwin, R. C., Pasi, A., MacGregor, J. T. and Hine, G. H. (1975). The rates of radical formation from the dipyridilium herbicides, paraquat, diquat, and morfamquat in homogenates of lung, liver and kidney: an inhibitory effect of carbon monoxide. *Toxicol. appl. Pharmacol.*, **32**, 298–304

Bennet, P. N., Davies, D. S. and Hawkesworth, G. M. (1976). *In vitro* absorption studies with paraquat and diquat in the dog. *Brit. J. Pharmacol.*, **58**, 284P

Bibich, H. (1982). Butylated hydroxytoluene (BHT): A review. *Environ. Res.*, **29**, 1–29

Block, E. R. and Stalcup, S. A. (1981). Depression of serotin uptake by cultured endothelial cells exposed to high O_2 tension. *J. appl. Physiol.*, **50**, 1212–19

Block, E. R., Patel, J. M. and Sheridan, N. P. (1985). Effect of oxygen and endotoxin on lactate dehydrogenase release, 5-hydroxytryptamine uptake, and antioxidant enzyme activities in endothelial cells. *J. Cell. Physiol.*, **122**, 240–8

Bowman, C. M., Butler, E. N. and Repine, J. E. (1983). Hyperoxia damages cultured endothelial cells causing increased neutrophil adherence. *Am. Rev. Respir. Dis.*, **128**, 469–72

Boyd, M. R. (1977). Evidence for the Clara cells as a site of cytochrome P450-dependent mixed function oxidase activity in lung. *Nature, Lond.*, **269**, 713–15

Boyd, M. R. (1980a). Biochemical mechanisms in chemical-induced lung injury: roles of metabolic activation. *CRC Crit. Rev. Toxicol.*, **7**, 103–76

Boyd, M. R. (1980b). Biochemical mechanisms in pulmonary toxicity of furan derivations. In: *Reviews in Biochemical Toxicology*, (ed. E. Hodgson, J. Bend and R. Philpot) Elsevier, North-Holland, Amsterdam, Vol. 2, pp. 71–101

Boyd, M. R. (1984). Metabolic activation and lung toxicity: a basis for cell-selective pulmonary damage by foreign chemicals. *Environ. Health Perspect.*, **55**, 47–51

Boyd, M. R. and Burka, L. T. (1978). *In vivo* studies in the relationship between target organ alkylation and the pulmonary toxicity of a chemically reactive metabolite of 4-ipomeanol. *J. Pharmacol. exptl. Ther.*, **207**, 687–97

Boyd, M. R., Burka, L. T., Harris, T. M. and Wilson, B. J. (1974a). Lung toxic furanoterpenoids produced by sweet potatoes (*Ipomea batatas*) following microbial infection. *Biochem. Biophys. Acta*, **337**, 184–95

Boyd, M. R., Burka, L. T., Wilson, B. J. and Sastry, B. V. R. (1974b). Distribution and excretion of radioactivity in the rat after intraperitoneal administration of the lung-edemagenic toxin [^{14}C] 4-Ipomeanol. *Toxicol. appl. Pharmacol.*, **29**, 132

Boyd, M. R., Burka, L. T., Wilson, B. J. and Sasame, H. A. (1978). *In vitro* studies on the metabolic activation of the pulmonary toxin 4-ipomeanol by rat lung and liver microsomes. *J. Pharmacol. exptl Ther.*, **207**, 677–86

Boyd, M. R. and Neal, R. A. (1976). Studies of the mechanism of toxicity and development of tolerance to the pulmonary toxin: α-naphthylthiourea (ANTU). *Drug. Metab. Dispos.*, **4**, 314–22

Boyd, M. R., Stiko, A., Statham, C. N. and Jones, R. B. (1982). Protective role of endogenous glutathione and other sulfhydryl compounds against lung damage by alkylating agents. Investigations with 4-ipomeanol in the rat. *Biochem. Pharmacol.*, **31**, 1579–83

Boyd, M. R. and Wilson, B. J. (1972). Isolation and characterisation of 4-ipomeanol, a lung toxic furanoterpenoid produced by sweet potatoes. *J. Agric. Food Chem.*, **20**, 428–30

Braude, S., Krausz, T., Apperley, J., Goldman, J. M. and Royston, D. (1985). Adult respiratory distress syndrome after allogenic bone marrow transplantation: evidence for a neutrophil-independent mechanism. *Lancet*, **i**, 1239–42

Brigham, K. L. (1978). Lung oedema due to increased vascular permeability. In: *Lung Water and Solute Exchange (Lung biology in health and disease; Vol. 7)*, (ed. N. C. Staub), M. Dekker, New York, Basel, pp. 235–73

Brigham, K. L. (1982). Mechanisms of lung injury. *Clin. Chest. Med.*, **3**, 9–24

Buckpitt, A. R. and Warren, D. L. (1983). Evidence for hepatic formation, export and covalent binding of reactive naphthalene metabolites in extrahepatic tissues *in vivo*. *J. Pharmacol. exptl. Ther.*, **225**, 8–16

Buckpitt, A. R., Bahnson, L. S. and Franklin, R. B. (1984). Hepatic and pulmonary microsomal metabolism of naphthalene to glutathione adducts: factors affecting the relative rates of conjugative formation. *J. Pharmacol. exptl. Ther.*, **231**, 291–300

Bus, J. S., Aust, S. D. and Gibson, J. E. (1974). Superoxide and singlet oxygen-catalysed lipid peroxidation as a possible mechanism for paraquat (methyl viologen) toxicity. *Biochem. Biophys. Res. Commun.*, **58**, 749–55

Bus, J. S., Aust, S. D. and Gibson, J. E. (1975). Lipid peroxidation: a possible mechanism for paraquat toxicity. *Res. Commun. Chem. Pathol. Pharmacol.*, **11**, 31–8

Bus, J. S., Cagen, S. Z., Olgaard, M. and Gibson, J. E. (1976). A mechanism of paraquat toxicity in mice and rats. *Toxicol. appl. Pharmacol.*, **35**, 501–13

Cashman, J. R., Traiger, G. J. and Hanzlik, R. P. (1982). Pneumotoxic effects of thiobenzamide derivatives. *Toxicology*, **23**, 85–93

Christman, J. W., Rinaldo, J. E., Henson, J. E., Moore, S. A. and Dauber, J. H. (1985). Modification by hyperoxia *in vivo* of endotoxin-induced neutrophil alveolitis in rats. Production of chemotactic factors by alveolar macrophages and ultrastructure. *Am. Rev. Respir. Dis.*, **132**, 152–8

Clark, J. M. and Lambertsen, C. J. (1971). Pulmonary oxygen toxicity: a review. *Pharmacol. Rev.*, **23**, 37–133

Crapo, J. D., Peters-Golden, M., Marsh-Salin, J. and Shelburne, J. S. (1978). Pathologic changes in the lungs of oxygen adapted rats. A morphometric analysis. *Lab. Invest.*, **39**, 640–53

Crapo, J. D., Barry, B. E., Foscue, H. A. and Shelburne, J. (1980). Structural and biochemical changes in rat lungs occurring during exposure to lethal and adaptive doses of oxygen. *Am. Rev. Respir. Dis.*, **122**, 123–43

Cunningham, A. and Hurley, J. (1972). Alpha-naphthyl thiourea-induced pulmonary edema in the rat: a topographical and electronmicroscope study. *J. Pathol.*, **106**, 25–35

Daniel, J. W. and Gage, J. C. (1966). Absorption and excretion of diquat and paraquat in rats. *Brit. J. ind. Med.*, **23**, 133–6

Davis, W. B., Rennard, S. I., Bitterman, P. B. and Crystal, R. G. (1983). Pulmonary oxygen toxicity. Early reversible changes in human alveolar structures induced by hyperoxia. *N. Engl. J. Med.*, **309**, 878–83

Deneke, S. M., Gershoff, S. N. and Fanburg, B. L. (1983). Potentiation of oxygen toxicity in rats by dietary protein or amino acid deficiency. *J. appl. Physiol.*, **54**, 147–51

De Pierre, J. W. and Morgenstern, R. (1983). Comparison of the distribution of microsomal and cytosolic glutathione S-transferase activities in different organs of the rat. *Biochem. Pharmacol.*, **32**, 721–3

Devereux, T. R. and Fouts, J. R. (1981). Xenobiotic metabolism by alveolar type 11 cells isolated from rabbit lung. *Biochem. Pharmacol.*, **30**, 1231–7

Devereux, T. T., Hook, G. and Fouts, J. R. (1979). Foreign compound metabolism by isolated cells from rabbit lung. *Drug Metab. Dispos.*, **7**, 70–5

Devereux, T. R., Serabjit-Singh, C. J., Slaughter, S. R., Wolf, C. R., Philpot, R. M. and Fouts, J. R. (1981). Identification of pulmonary cytochrome P-450 isozymes, in nonciliated bronchiolar epithelial (Clara) and alveolar type 11 cells isolated from rabbit lung. *Exp. Lung Res.*, **2**, 221–30

Devereux, T. R., Jones, K. G., Bend, J. R., Fouts, J. R., Statham, C. N. and Boyd, M. R. (1982). *In vitro* metabolic activation of the pulmonary toxin, 4-ipomeanol, in nonciliated bronchiolar epithelial (Clara) and alveolar type 11 cells isolated from rabbit lung. *J. Pharmacol. exptl. Ther.*, **220**, 223–7

Devereux, T. R., Diliberto, J. J. and Fouts, J. R. (1985). Cytochrome P-450 monooxygenase, epoxide hydrolase and flavin monooxygenase activities in Clara cells and alveolar type 11 cells isolated from rabbit. *Cell Biol. Toxicol.*, **1**, 57–65

Dieke, S. H., Allen, G. S. and Richter, C. P. (1947). The acute toxicity of thioureas and related compounds to wild and domestic Norway rats. *J. Pharmacol. exptl. Ther.*, **90**, 260–70

Durham, S. K., Boyd, M. R. and Castleman, W. L. (1985). Pulmonary endothelial and bronchiolar epithelial lesions induced by 4-ipomeanol in mice. *Am. J. Pathol.*, **118**, 66–75

Eiermann, G. J., Dickey, B. F. and Thrall, R. S. (1983). Polymorphonuclear leukocyte participation in acute oleic-acid-induced lung injury. *Am. Rev. Respir. Dis.*, **128**, 845–50

Etherton, J. E. and Conning, D. M. (1977). Enzyme histochemistry of the lung. In: *Metabolic Function of the Lung* (*Lung biology in health and disease*; Vol. 4) (ed. Y. S. Bakhle and J. R. Vane), Marcel Dekker, New York, Basel, pp. 233–58

Fantone, J. C., Kunkel, R. G. and Kinnes, D. A. (1984). Potentiation of α-naphthyl-thiourea-induced lung injury by prostaglandin E, and platelet depletion. *Lab. Invest.*, **50**, 703–10

Farrington, J. A., Ebert, M., Land, E. J. and Fletcher, K. (1973). Bipyridilium quaternary salts and related compounds V. Pulse radiolysis studies on the reaction of paraquat radicals with oxygen, implications for the mode of action of bipyridilium herbicides. *Biochim. Biophys. Acta*, **314**, 372–81

Fisher, A. B., Forman, H. J. and Glass, M. (1984). Mechanisms of pulmonary oxygen toxicity. *Lung*, **162**, 255–9

Fisher, H. K., Clements, J. A., Tierney, D. F. and Wright, R. R. (1975). Pulmonary effects of paraquat in the first day after injection. *Am. J. Physiol.*, **228**, 1217–23

Fletcher, K. (1974). Paraquat poisoning. In *Forensic Toxicology* (ed. B. Ballantyne), John Wright and Sons, Birmingham, pp. 86–98

Fox, R. B., Hoidal, J. R., Brown, D. M. and Repine, J. E. (1981). Pulmonary inflammation due to oxygen toxicity: involvement of chemotactic factors and polymorphonuclear leukocytes. *Am. Rev. Respir. Dis.*, **123**, 521–3

Fox, R. B., Harada, R. N., Tate, R. M. and Repine, J. E. (1983). Prevention of thiourea-induced pulmonary edema by hydroxyl-radical scavengers. *J. appl. Physiol.*, **55**, 1456–9

Frank, L. (1983). Superoxide dismutase and lung toxicity. *Trends Pharmacol. Sci.*, **4**, 124–8

Frank, L., Bucher, J. R. and Roberts, R. J. (1978). Oxygen toxicity in neonatal and adult animals of various species. *J. appl. Physiol.*, **45**, 699–708

Freeman, B. A. and Crapo, J. D. (1982). Biology of disease. Free radicals and tissue injury. *Lab. Invest.*, **47**, 412–26

Gage, J. C. (1968). The action of paraquat and diquat on the respiration of liver cell fractions. *Biochem. J.*, **109**, 757–61

Glauser, F. L. and Fairman, R. P. (1985). The uncertain role of neutrophil in increased permeability of pulmonary oedema. *Chest*, **88**, 601–7

Gordonsmith, R. H., Brooke-Taylor, S., Smith, L. L. and Cohen, G. M. (1983). Structural requirements of compounds to inhibit pulmonary diamine accumulation. *Biochem. Pharmacol.*, **32**, 3701–9

Gosselin, R. E., Smith, R. P., Hodge, M. C. and Braddock, J. E. (eds) (1984). *Clinical Toxicology of Commercial Products* (5th edn), Williams and Wilkins, Baltimore, London, Vol. 111, pp. 40–111.

Gottschall, D. W., Penney, D. A., Traiger, G. J. and Hanzlik, R. P. (1985). Oxidation of N-methylthiobenzamide and N-methylthiobenzamide S-oxide by liver and lung microsomes. *Toxicol. appl. Pharmacol.*, **78**, 332–41

Grasso, P., Williams, M., Hodgson, R., Wright, M. G. and Gangolli, S. D. (1971). The histochemical distribution of aniline hydroxylase in rat tissues. *Histochem. J.*, **3**, 117–26

Halliwell, B. and Gutteridge, J. M. C. (1984). Lipid peroxidation, oxygen free radicals, cell damage and antioxidant therapy. *Lancet*, **23**, 1396–7

Hill, N. S., O'Brien, R. F. and Rounds, S. (1984). Repeated lung injury due to α-naphthylthiourea causes right ventricular hypertrophy in rats. *J. appl. Physiol.*, **56**, 388–96

Hirai, K., Witschi, H. P. and Cote, M. G. (1977). Electron microscopy of butylated hydroxytoluene induced lung damage in mice. *Exp. Mol. Pathol.*, **27**, 295–308

Housset, B., Ody, C., Rubin, D., Elemer, G. and Junod, A. F. (1983). Oxygen toxicity in cultured aortic endothelium: Selenium-induced partial protective effects. *J. appl. Physiol.*, **55**, 343–52

Howard, J. K., Sabopathy, N. N. and Whitehead, P. A. (1981). Study of the health of Malaysian plantation workers with particular reference to paraquat spraymen. *Brit. J. ind. Med.*, **38**, 110–16

Imamura, T. and Hasegawa, L. (1984). Role of metabolic activation, covalent binding and glutathione depletion in pulmonary toxicity produced by an impurity of malathion. *Toxicol. appl. Pharmacol.*, **72**, 476–83

Jones, K. G., Holland, J. F., Foureman, G. L., Bend, J. R. and Fouts, J. R. (1983). Xenobiotic metabolism in Clara cells and alveolar type 11 cells isolated from lungs of rats treated with β-naphthoflavone. *J. Pharmacol. exptl. Ther.*, **225**, 316–19

Kapanci, Y., Weibel, E. R., Kaplan, H. P. and Robinson, F. R. (1969). Pathogenesis and reversibility of the pulmonary lesions of oxygen toxicity in monkeys. 11. Ultrastructural and Morphometric studies. *Lab. Invest.*, **20**, 101–18

Keeling, P. L. and Smith, L. L. (1982). Relevance of NADPH depletion and mixed disulphide formation in rat lung to the mechanism of cell damage following paraquat administration. *Biochem. Pharmacol.*, **31**, 3243–9

Kehrer, J. P. and Witschi, H. P. (1980). Effects of drug metabolism inhibitors on butylated hydroxytoluene-induced pulmonary toxicity in mice. *Toxicol. appl. Pharmacol.*, **53**, 333–43

Kistler, G. S., Caldwell, P. R. B. and Weibel, E. R. (1967). Development of fine ultrastructural damage to alveolar and capillary lining cells in oxygen-poisoned rat lungs. *J. Cell Biol.*, **32**, 605–28

Krieger, B. P., Loomis, W. H., Czer, G. T. and Spragg, R. G. (1985). Mechanisms of interaction between oxygen and granulocytes in hyperoxic lung injury. *J. appl. Physiol.*, **58**, 1326–30

Kuhn, C. (1976). The cells of the lung and their organelles. In: *The Biochemical Basis of Pulmonary Function* (*Lung biology in health and disease*: Vol. 2) (ed. R. G. Crystal), Marcel Dekker, New York, Basel, pp. 3–48

Lee, P. W., Arran, T. and Neal, R. A. (1980). Metabolism of α-naphthylthiourea by rat liver and lung microsomes. *Toxicol. appl. Pharmacol.*, **53**, 164–73

Litterst, C. L., Mimnaugh, E. G., Reagan, R. L. and Gram, T. E. (1975). Comparison of *in vitro* drug metabolised by lung, liver and kidney of several common laboratory species. *Drug Metab. Dispos.*, **3**, 259–65

Lown, J. W., Joshua, A. V. and Chen, H. H. (1982). Reactive oxygen species leading to lipid peroxidation and DNA lesions implicated in the cytotoxic action of certain antitumour antibiotics. In: *Free Radicals, Lipid Peroxidation and Cancer* (ed. D. C. H. McBrien and T. F. Slater), Academic Press, London, pp. 305–28

Machado, D. C., Bohm, G. M. and Padovan, P. A. (1977). Comparative study of the ultrastructural alterations in the pulmonary vessels of rats treated with alpha-naphthylthiourea (ANTU) and ammonium sulphate. *J. Pathol.*, **121**, 205–11

Mais, D. E. and Bosin, T. R. (1984). A role for serotonin in α-naphthylthiourea-induced pulmonary edema. *Toxicol. appl. Pharmacol.*, **74**, 185–94

Malkinson, A. M. (1979). Prevention of butylated hydroxytoluene-induced lung damage in mice by Cedar terpene administration. *Toxicol. appl. Pharmacol.*, **49**, 551–60

Marino, A. A. and Mitchell, J. T. (1972). Lung damage in mice following intraperitoneal injection of butylated hydroxytoluene. *Proc. Soc. exptl. Biol. Med.*, **140**, 122–5

Martin, W. J., II (1983). Nitrofurantoin: evidence for the oxidant injury of lung parenchymal cells. *Am. Rev. Respir. Dis.*, **127**, 482–6

Martin, W. J., II, Gadek, J. E., Hunninghahe, G. W. and Crystal, R. G. (1981). Oxidant injury of lung parenchymal cells. *J. Clin. Invest.*, **68**, 1277–88

Masuda, Y. and Nakayama, N. (1984). Prevention of butylated hydroxy toluene-induced lung damage by diethyldithiocarbamate and carbon disulfide in mice. *Toxicol. appl. Pharmacol.*, **75**, 81–90

Meyrick, B., Miller, J. and Reid, L. (1972). Pulmonary oedema induced by ANTU or by high or low oxygen concentrations in rat – an electron microscopic study. *Brit. J. exp. Pathol.*, **53**, 347–58

Meyrick, B. and Reid, L. (1979). Development of pulmonary artery arterial changes in rats fed Crotalania Spectabilis. *Am. J. Pathol.*, **94**, 37–50

Michaelis, L. and Hill, E. S. (1933). Potentiometric studies on semiquinones. *J. Am. chem. Soc.*, **55**, 1481–94

Minchin, R. F. and Boyd, M. R. (1983). Localisation of metabolic activation and deactivation systems in the lung: Significance to the pulmonary toxicity of xenobiotics. *Ann. Rev. Pharmacol. Toxicol.*, **23**, 217–38

Minchin, R. F., McManus, M. E., Thorgeirsson, S. S., Schwarts, D. and Boyd, M. R. (1985). Metabolism of 2-acetylaminofluorene in isolated rabbit pulmonary cells. Evidence for the heterogeneous distribution of monoxygenase activity in lung tissue. *Drug Metab. Dispos.*, **13**, 406–11

Moran, M. S., DePierre, J. W. and Mannervik, B. (1979). Levels of glutathione, glutathione reductase and glutathione S-transferase activities in rat lung and liver. *Biochim. Biophys. Acta*, **582**, 67–78

Murphy, S. D. (1980). Pesticides. In: *Casarett and Doull's Toxicology: the basic science of poisons* 2nd edn, (ed. J. Doull, C. D. Klaassen and M. O. Amdur), Macmillan, New York, pp. 357–407

Mustafa, M. G. and Tierney, D. F. (1978). Biochemical and metabolic changes in the lung with oxygen, ozone and nitrogen dioxide toxicity. *Am. Rev. Resp. Dis.*, **118**, 1061–88

Neal, R. A. and Halpert, J. (1982). Toxicology of thiono-sulphur compounds. *Ann. Rev. Pharmacol. Toxicol.*, **22**, 321–39

Newman, J. E., Lloyd, J. E., English, D. K., Ogletree, M. L., Fulkerson, W. J. and Brigham, K. L. (1983). Effects of 100% oxygen on lung vascular function in awake sheep. *J. appl. Physiol.*, **54**, 1379–86

Newton, P. E., Latendresse, J. R., II, Mattie, D. R. and Pfledderer, C. (1985). Alterations in alveolar clearance after 4-ipomeanol induced necrosis of Clara and ciliated cells in the terminal bronchioles of the rat. *Toxicol. appl. Pharmacol.*, **80**, 534–41

Parke, D. V. (1982). Unifying mechanisms of toxicity. *Regul. Toxicol. Pharmacol.*, **2**, 267–86

Penney, D. A., Gottschall, D. W., Hanzlik, R. P. and Traiger, G. J. (1985). The role of metabolism in N-methylthio-benzamide induced pneumotoxicity. *Toxicol. appl. Pharmacol.*, **78**, 323–31

Philpot, R. M. and Smith, B. R. (1984). Role of cytochrome P-450 and related enzymes in the pulmonary metabolism of xenobiotics. *Environ. Health. Perspect.*, **55**, 359–367

Poulsen, L. L., Hyslop, R. M. and Ziegler, D. M. (1974). S-oxidation of thioureylenes catalysed by a microsomal flavoprotein mixed-function oxidase. *Biochem. Pharmacol.*, **23**, 3431–40

Poulsen, L. L., Hyslop, R. M. and Ziegler, D. M. (1979). S-oxidation of N-substituted thioureas catalysed by the pig liver microsomal FAD-containing mono-oxygenase. *Arch. Biochem. Biophys.*, **198**, 78–88

Pryor, W. A. (1982). Free radical biology: xenobiotics, cancer and aging. *Ann. N.Y. Acad. Sci.*, **393**, 1–22

Raj, J. V., Hazinski, T. A. and Bland, R. D. (1985). Oxygen-induced lung micro-vascular injury in neutropenic rabbits and lambs. *J. appl. Physiol.*, **58**, 921–7

Rinaldo, J. E. and Borovetz, H. (1985). Deterioration of oxygenation and abnormal lung microvascular permeability during resolution of leukopenia in patients with diffuse lung injury. *Am. Rev. Respir. Dis.* **131**, 579–83

Rose, M. S., Lock, E. A., Smith, L. L. and Wyatt, I. (1976). Paraquat accumulation: tissue and species specificity. *Biochem. Pharmacol.*, **25**, 419–23

Rose, M. S., Smith, L. L. and Wyatt, I. (1974). Evidence for energy-dependent accumulation of paraquat into rat lung. *Nature, Lond.*, **252**, 314–15

Roszkowski, A. P. (1967). Comparative toxicity of rodenticides. *Fed. Proc.*, **26**, 1082–8

Rutili, G., Kvietys, P., Martin, D., Parker, J. C. and Taylor, A. E. (1982). Increased pulmonary microvascular permeability induced by α-naphthylthiourea. *J. appl. Physiol.*, **52**, 1316–23

Saheb, W. and Witschi, H. P. (1975). Lung growth in mice after one single dose of butylated hydroxytoluene. *Toxicol. appl. Pharmacol.*, **33**, 309–19

Serabjit-Singh, C. J., Wolf, C. R. and Philpot, R. M. (1979). The rabbit pulmonary monooxygenase system: immunochemical and biochemical characterization of enzyme components. *J. Biol. Chem.*, **254**, 9901–7

Shasby, D. M., Fox, R. B., Haranda, R. N. and Repine, J. E. (1982). Reduction of the oedema of acute hyperoxic lung injury by granulocyte depletion. *J. appl. Physiol.*, **52**, 1237–44

Smith, L. L. (1982). The identification of an accumulation system for diamines and polyamines into the lung and its relevance to paraquat toxicity. *Arch. Toxicol. Suppl.*, **5**, 1–14

Smith, L. L., Wright, A. F., Wyatt, I. and Rose, M. S. (1974). Effective treatment for paraquat poisoning in rats and its relevance to the treatment of poisoning in man. *Br. med. J.*, **4**, 569–71

Smith, L. L., Wyatt, I. and Cohen, G. M. (1982). The accumulation of diamines and polyamines into rat lung slices. *Biochem. Pharmacol.*, **31**, 3029–33

Smith, P. and Heath, D. (1974). The ultrastructure and time sequence of the early stages of paraquat lung in rats. *J. Path.*, **114**, 177–84

Smith, P. and Heath, D. (1976). Paraquat. *CRC. Crit. Rev. Toxicol.*, **4**, 411–45

Sorokin, S. P. (1970). The cells of the lungs. In: *Conference on Morphology of Experimental Respiratory Carcinogenesis* (ed. P. Nettesheim, M. G. Hanna and J. W. Deatherage), Atomic Energy Commission, USA, pp. 3–43

Staub, N. C. (1974). Pathogenesis of pulmonary oedema. *Am. Rev. Respir. Dis.*, **109**, 358–72

Staub, N. C., Nagano, H. and Pearce, M. C. (1967). Pulmonary oedema in dogs, especially the sequence of fluid accumulation in lungs. *J. appl. Physiol.*, **22**, 227–40

Suttorp, N. and Simon, L. M. (1982). Lung cell oxidant injury. Enhancement of polymorphonuclear leukocyte-mediated cytotoxicity in lung cells exposed to sustained *in vitro* hyperoxia. *J. Clin. Invest.*, **70**, 342–50

Suttorp, N. and Simon, L. M. (1983). Decreased bactericidal function and impaired respiratory burst in lung macrophages after sustained *in vitro* hyperoxia. *Am. Rev. Respir. Dis.*, **128**, 486–90

Swan, A. A. B. (1969). Exposure of spray operators to paraquat, *Brit. J. ind. Med.*, **26**, 322–9

Tate, R. M. and Repine, J. E. (1983). Neutrophils and the adult respiratory distress syndrome. *Am. Rev. Respir. Dis.*, **128**, 552–9

Van den Brenk, H. A. S., Kelly, H. and Stone, M. G. (1976). Innate and drug-induced resistance to acute lung damage caused in rats by alpha-naphthylthiourea (ANTU) and related compounds. *Brit. J. exptl. Pathol.*, **57**, 621–36

Waddell, W. J. and Marlowe, C. (1980). Tissue and cellular disposition of paraquat in mice. *Toxicol. appl. Pharmacol.*, **56**, 127–40

Warren, D. L., Brown, D. L. and Buckpitt, A. R. (1982). Evidence for cytochrome P-450 mediated metabolism in bronchiolar damage by naphthalene. *Chem. Biol. Interact.*, **40**, 287–303

Wattenberg, L. W. and Leong, J. L. (1962). Histochemical demonstration of reduced pyridine nucleotide dependent polycyclic hydrocarbon metabolizing systems. *J. Histochem. Cytochem.*, **10**, 412–20

Weibel, E. R. and Bachofen, H. (1979). Structural design of the alveolar septum and fluid exchange. In: *Pulmonary Oedema* (ed. A. P. Fishman and E. M. Renkin), American Physiological Society, Bethesda, pp. 1–20

Weidel, M. and Rosso, M. (1882). Studien uber das pyridin. *Monatsh. Chem.*, **3**, 850–85

Wilson, B. J., Yang, D. T. C. and Boyd, M. R. (1970). Toxicity of mold damaged sweet potatoes (*Ipomea batatas*). *Nature, Lond.*, **227**, 521–2

Witschi, H., Kacew, S., Hirai, K. and Cote, M. (1977). *In vivo* oxidation of reduced nicotinamide-adenine dinucleotide phosphate by paraquat and diquat in rat lung. *Chem. Biol. Interact.*, **19**, 143–60

Witschi, H. P. and Saheb, W. (1974). Stimulation of DNA synthesis in mouse lung following intraperitoneal injection of butylated hydroxytoluene. *Proc. Soc. exptl. Biol. Med.*, **147**, 690–3

Wolf, C. R., Statham, C. N., McMenamin, M. G., Bend, J. R., Boyd, M. R. and Philpot, R. M. (1982). The relationship between the catalytic activities of rabbit pulmonary cytochrome P-450 isozymes and the lung-specific toxicity of the furan derivative, 4-ipomeanol. *Mol. Pharmacol.*, **22**, 738–44

Wolf, C. R., Hartmann, R., Oesch, F. and Adams, D. J. (1985). Regulation and multiplicity of drug metabolizing enzymes in tissues and cells. In: *Drug Metabolism. Molecular Approaches and Pharmacological Implications* (ed. G. Siest), Pergamon Press, Oxford, pp. 121–30

2

Organophosphate-induced Delayed Neuropathy: Anomalous Data Lead to Advances in Understanding

M. K. Johnson

INTRODUCTION

The main purpose of this contribution is not to provide a comprehensive review of the topic. This has been done several times with emphasis on either biochemical mechanisms (Davis and Richardson, 1980; Johnson, 1975a, 1982) or pathology (Cavanagh, 1964, 1973). I wish to present a scientific detective story. The theme is the dictum cited in the title and frequently invoked by Norman Aldridge, in whose honour this volume is prepared, and the style is historical, personal and reflective.

I had the privilege of learning by close contact with Norman over 27 years. His habit of treating data which 'did not fit' with interest and, indeed, with enthusiasm is, to me, his most notable characteristic and contrasts with the habit of lesser mortals to find such data irritating discrepancies which we wished did not exist. The benefit of taking anomalous data seriously is well illustrated in the story of the progress in understanding of organophosphate-induced delayed neuropathy (OPIDN) from the total ignorance at the beginning of the Ginger Jake episode in 1930 to our present state of knowledge which is being applied, albeit slowly, in both basic science and in safety evaluation procedures.

Prior to 1930 peripheral neuropathy was known to occur occasionally in tuberculosis patients being treated with phosphocreosote, an uncharacterised mixture of esters derived from phosphoric acid and coal tar phenols. The neuropathic potential of this medicament was not realised, however, until a massive outbreak of poisoning involving more than 10 000 persons occurred in the United States. The toxic agent in 'Ginger Jake' paralysis was a mixture of cresyl phosphates used to extract ginger. The extract was either drunk neat or used to flavour illicit distilled liquors. Extensive descriptions of the syndrome and its production in animals were published.

27

Cresyl and related phosphates have physical properties suited for use as hydraulic fluids, lubricants and plasticisers. They also impart flame resistance to fabrics. Since the early investigations showed that, among the symmetrical cresyl phosphates, only the ortho-isomer produced a toxic effect, it became customary for mixed phosphate esters to be prepared from coal-tar stock containing various alkyl phenols but with less than a specified low amount of ortho-cresol. However, further outbreaks of poisoning occurred from time to time in spite of this precaution. In a major outbreak in Morocco the origin was traced to adulterated cooking oil. Several studies have been published in which the toxicity of phosphate esters of individual phenols present in coal-tar fractions was assessed (summarised by Johnson, 1975b). These showed that a large number of triaryl phosphates possessed neuropathic potential; although limited correlations could be made between structure and activity there were many exceptions.

In 1953 cases of neuropathy were reported in two workers engaged in laboratory synthesis of a prospective OP pesticide, mipafox (N,N'-diisopropylphosphoramido-fluoridate) (Bidstrup et al., 1953). Laboratory studies established that there was no essential difference in the neuropathic effect produced by mipafox and some other alkyl phosphoryl esters and by the triaryl phosphates (Barnes and Denz, 1953). However, whereas the triaryl phosphates had been regarded as rather inert chemicals, the newly found neuropathic agents were all known to be acutely toxic and included some but not all of the so-called nerve agents. Anticholinesterase activity ranges from high to negligible among the large number of neuropathic OP esters which are now known.

There are degrees of species sensitivity although many species are susceptible to a single dose. It is difficult to produce clinical OPIDN in rodents even by repeated dosing and hens have become the species of choice in laboratory tests.

Delayed neuropathy testing in hens is now normal practice during safety evaluation of OP esters for use as plasticisers, hydraulic fluids and insecticides. It is, therefore, not surprising that only a few cases of neuropathy have been associated with their manufacture or use in recent years. However, a few cases of neuropathy associated with misuse of certain OP pesticides are known (Johnson, 1982).

CHARACTERISTICS OF OPIDN IN MAN AND ANIMALS

Neuropathic effects are not seen until 8–14 days after ingestion of the toxic agent, although most anticholinesterase effects occur within 1–3 days. The lag period is not shortened in experimental animals by repeated doses. Mild cases in man may not develop fully until the third or fourth week after poisoning. After initial sensory disorders (sense of cramp and tingling), weakness and ataxia develop in the lower limbs, progressing to paralysis, which in severe cases affects the upper limbs also. Children and young animals are less severely affected than adults in whom recovery is slow and seldom complete: it seems that clinical features change in the period of 6–24 months after intoxication as peripheral nerves repair to some degree and spinal defects become more obvious. In a 47-year follow up of 11 survivors of

Ginger Jake paralysis, spasticity and abnormal reflexes of upper motor neuron syndrome were very apparent (Morgan and Penovich, 1978).

In man, all the cases due to single exposure to a neuropathic pesticide have involved early cholinergic crises with profound inhibition of acetylcholinesterase (AChE) so that some inhibition of erythrocyte AChE may persist until neuropathy develops. Some, but not all, of the neuropathic triaryl phosphates inhibit plasma butyrylcholinesterase so that neuropathy caused by these agents has not always been associated with detected changes in blood enzymes. Moreover, resynthesis of the plasma enzyme may be comparatively rapid and the concentration may be restored before samples are taken from an affected patient. The possibility of a more specific blood marker for the initiating event is discussed later. Electrophysiological examinations during the early stages of a neuropathy are valuable aids for diagnosis since OPIDN has the almost unique feature that conduction velocities are unimpaired although the amplitude of signals is reduced due to loss of some conducting fibres. This aspect is discussed in detail by LeQuesne (1975) and exemplified in the case reported by Hierons and Johnson (1978). However, several months after onset of peripheral neuropathy, reinnervation can occur and the newer finer fibres conduct considerably more slowly, thereby changing the overall pattern of conduction velocities.

Histological examinations led originally to the mistaken conclusion that the lesions were essentially due to loss of the myelin sheath surrounding long nerve axons and names such as Organophosphate Demyelinating Disease were widely used. Later work showed, however, that the nerve axon itself was primarily affected and damage to myelin was secondary. 'Demyelination' is, therefore, a misleading description. A number of light- and electron-microscopic studies of the degenerative process in various species have been published and critically reviewed (listed by Davis and Richardson, 1980). Recent work by Bouldin and Cavanagh (1979a,b) has clarified the details of early stages of the degeneration. It is necessary to sample in a way that takes into account the intricate structure of the nervous system and the manner in which the nervous system both degenerates and responds to degeneration; axon samples need to be taken at various distances from the cell body. Moreover, some popular methods (such as the Marchi stain) that were used in early studies of organophosphate neuropathy are unsuited to reveal anything except severe damage: they may overlook quite extensive degeneration that is revealed by haemotoxylin and eosin or by silver staining.

CHEMISTRY AND BIOCHEMISTRY OF TOXIC OP ESTERS

The general chemistry and biochemistry of OP esters is covered in many textbooks and Davis and Richardson (1980) give a useful summary. For the present review, the ability of OP esters to react with esterases is their most important biochemical property. A number of esterases, including the cholinesterases, can be inhibited in a time-dependent reaction with some OP esters at low concentrations. Figure 2.1 shows the several reactions which are now known to occur in the progressive inhi-

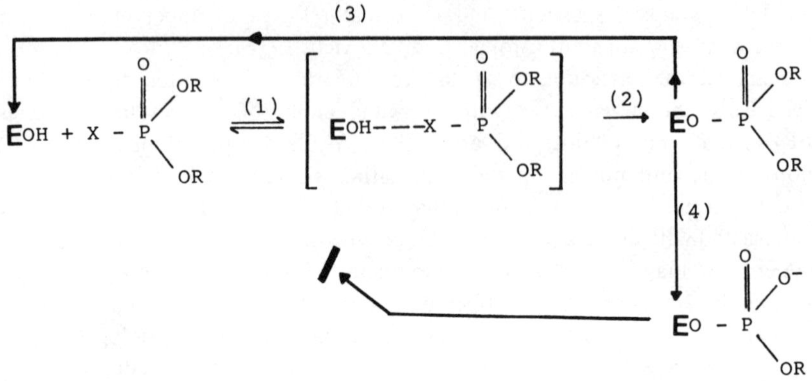

Figure 2.1 Steps in the interaction of an esterase with an organophosphorus inhibitor: (1) formation of Michaelis complex; (2) phosphorylation of enzyme; (3) reactivation (spontaneous or forced by oximes or KF); (4) ageing to a form which cannot be reactivated as in (3)

bition of AChE and it seems likely that each of the steps illustrated can occur with other OP-sensitive esterases (a detailed discussion is given by Aldridge and Reiner (1972)). It should be noted that reactions (1)-(3) of inhibition are strictly analogous to substrate hydrolysis except that reaction (3) is rapid (milliseconds) for substrates and slow (minutes to weeks) for inhibitors; inhibition by carbamates and by sulphonyl fluorides operates in the same fashion. Reaction (3) (reactivation) may occur spontaneously and may, in some cases, be catalysed by agents such as fluoride salts and some nucleophilic oximes. After inhibition by organophosphates (for chemical structure of these and following inhibitors, cf. Fig. 2.6), phosphonates or phosphoramidates an alternative reaction is (4), which involves cleavage of an R–O–P or R–NH–P bond and generation of a negatively charged substituent on the enzyme. This reaction has been most studied with the cholinesterases. For these enzymes it is clear that once reaction (4) occurs, reactivation in the manner of (3) is no longer feasible. The enzyme is said to have aged (i.e. it has lost its responsiveness to reactivators) as a result of a time-dependent group loss. For esterases inhibited by phosphinates, sulphonyl fluorides or carbamates, ageing is precluded since no suitable hydrolysable bond exists in the molecule; this is an important factor in OPIDN.

THE DETECTIVE STORY WITH FOCUS ON ANOMALOUS DATA

1. The range of species sensitivity

The earliest studies with suspect samples of adulterated ginger used an acute and lethal neurological response in rabbits as a toxicity screen (Smith et al., 1930b). These workers found that dogs and monkeys were unresponsive but that a delayed neuropathic effect similar to that seen in man was elicited from calves dosed with the samples identified as toxic in the rabbit test. They produced some evidence of the presence of cresyl phosphates in such samples. Smith *et al.* (1930a) subsequently reported that typical delayed neuropathy was caused by a single dose of tri-ortho-cresyl phosphate (TOCP) to calves or adult hens but the effect was not seen in a number of other species. It was proposed that variability in absorption might underlie species differences; this is now known to be incorrect for at least some species. The reasons for the apparent resistance of certain species will be considered later. The studies discussed hereafter have all been performed in adult hens unless it is specifically stated otherwise.

2. Structure/activity anomalies

Having established a positive model of OPIDN with a single oral dose of TOCP in the adult hen, Smith *et al.* (1932) demonstrated that esters of ortho-cresol with acetic, benzoic or phthalic acids were not neuropathic and neither were the tri-meta- or tri-para-cresyl phosphates. This clear picture became confused when Bondy *et al.* (1960) showed an inverse relationship for the ortho- and para-ethyl-phenyl phosphates (see figure 2.2). More and more compounds were found to cause delayed neuropathy in the 1950s and 1960s but no sound structural basis for predicting delayed neuropathic potential emerged (Davies, 1963). However the availability of a large variety of compounds with diverse structures was a great asset for the testing of the various hypotheses which were proposed concerning the mechanism of initiation of OPIDN.

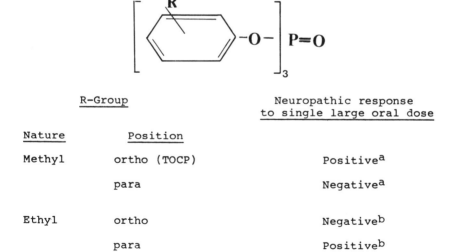

R-Group		Neuropathic response to single large oral dose
Nature	Position	
Methyl	ortho (TOCP)	Positive[a]
	para	Negative[a]
Ethyl	ortho	Negative[b]
	para	Positive[b]

Figure 2.2 The effect on neuropathic potency of the position of alkyl substitution in the atomic rings of symmetrical tri-alkylphenyl phosphates. [a]From Smith *et al.*, (1932). [b]From Bondy *et al.* (1960)

3. Proposed involvement of the cholinesterases

By the early 1940s it was known that two distinct enzymes capable of hydrolysing the neurotransmitter acetylcholine were present in blood and brain of most mammals and birds. The human erythrocyte enzyme hydrolysed acetylcholine in preference to butyrylcholine and, was referred to as 'True' ChE, while the plasma enzyme, referred to as 'Pseudo' ChE, was less specific but with a preference for butyrylcholine. Inhibition of 'True' ChE of nervous tissue was known to be associated with the cholinergic poisoning caused by the early organophosphate chemical warfare nerve agents although the exact mechanism of inhibition was not clear. No obvious function was apparent for 'Pseudo' ChE.

Hottinger and Bloch (1943) first reported that TOCP inhibited 'Pseudo' ChE of human serum and brain *in vitro* and soon afterwards Mendel and Rudney (1944) reported on results of dosing rats with TOCP: *in vivo* the 'Pseudo' ChE of rat blood was inhibited but not the 'True' ChE. Even though rat was a 'non-sensitive' species, the implication was that inhibition of 'Pseudo' ChE was causally related to OPIDN. However this hypothesis appears not to have been stated very clearly until 1952 when several lines of evidence were collated. Earl and Thompson (1952a) reported comparative studies *in vitro* of the effect of TOCP on both enzymes from sensitive and insensitive species. They found that (a) for hen the 'Pseudo' ChE was more sensitive to inhibition than 'True' ChE; and (b) 'Pseudo' ChE of hen and man (both sensitive species) were more easily inhibited than the same enzyme from the rat (an insensitive species). Moving to *in vivo* studies, Earl and Thompson (1952b) confirmed that the 'Pseudo' ChE of hen nervous tissue (brain) was much more sensitive to a dose of TOCP than was the 'True' ChE.

The combination of the above studies with results of work as yet unpublished by Barnes, Denz and Aldridge seemed to provide strong support for the specific involvement of 'Pseudo' ChE in the aetiology of OPIDN. However work being carried out by Norman Aldridge in the early 1950s on the detailed mechanism of the process of inhibition of esterases by OP esters gradually turned up anomalies which undermined this hypothesis. Aldridge (1953a) reported fully on the studies cited already by Earl and Thompson which showed a wide range of selectivity of OP esters as inhibitors of 'Pseudo' ChE. Table 2.1 shows the ratio of pI_{50}s for inhibition of 'Pseudo' and 'True' ChEs of horse blood by the 4 compounds cited by Earl and Thompson: these were 270 and 4000 respectively for the two known neuropathic nerve agents while for the non-neuropathic paraoxon and its isopropyl analogue the ratios were only 3–10. However by 1953 two other non-neuropathic esters had also been tested. Tetra-isopropyl pyrophosphate (TIPP) and tetra-isopropyl pyrophosphoramide (IsoOMPA) were also highly selective inhibitors of horse blood 'Pseudo' ChE (table 2.1), although Barnes and Denz (1953) had shown them to be not neuropathic in adult hens. The discrepancy was shown to be slightly less striking when Alan Davison (1953) working under Aldridge's supervision, retested five of these compounds along with others against the ChEs of hen brain rather than horse blood. Table 2.1 shows that Mipafox stood out as highly selective for 'Pseudo' ChE and DFP, the other neuropathic compound, was the next most selective although only two-fold more so than TIPP. The hypothesis was finally

Table 2.1   Ratio of Inhibitory Power against 'Pseudo' ChE over that against 'True' ChE of Horse Blood and Hen Brain

Inhibitor	Tissue	
	Horse blood[a]	Hen brain[b]
Paraoxon	3	—
Isopropyl-paraoxon	10	5
DFP	270	80
Mipafox	4000	30 000
Tetraiso-propyl pyrophosphate	520	41
Tetraiso-propyl pyrophosphoramide	9400	18

Data drawn from Aldridge (1953a)[a] and Davison (1953)[b]

disproved by the observation (Aldridge and Barnes, 1961) of substantial anomalies among the responses of brain 'Pseudo' ChE to administration of a range of tri-aryl phosphates *in vivo*. The availability of a large number of structural variants of active compounds was essential for testing the hypothesis of involvement of 'Pseudo' ChE in the aetiology of OPIDN and the many careful studies involved helped to pave the way for further propositions to be investigated. This account illustrates how the survival of a hypothesis depends less on the collection of supporting evidence than on its robustness in the face of challenge.

4. The anomaly of inhibition *in vitro* by TOCP

The mechanism of interaction of OP esters with esterases outlined in figure 2.1 was not elucidated until the 1950s. The demonstration that the inhibition process is a covalent phosphorylation was a seminal finding of fundamental significance (Aldridge, 1953b; Aldridge and Davison, 1953). During these studies evidence had emerged that various samples of OP esters being studied were impure and that the inhibitory power lay in highly inhibitory impurities present in low concentration. With this information and the understanding of the phosphorylative nature of inhibition, Aldridge began to suspect that the available samples of TOCP might also be contaminated, since TOCP was only a very weak phosphorylating agent, as judged by its stability to mild alkaline hydrolysis. He then showed (Aldridge, 1954) that, after recrystallisation, samples of TOCP lost their *in vitro* inhibitory power but were still active *in vivo*. Moreover when such purified TOCP was incubated with rat liver slices *in vitro* a highly active anti-esterase metabolite was obtained. The nature of this metabolite was elucidated later by Casida *et al.* (1961) and a pure specimen was shown to be not only active against several esterases *in vitro* but to be neuropathic at only 6 mg/kg *in vivo* compared with the dose of 500 mg/kg for TOCP. The structure of o-cresyl saligenin cyclic phosphate (the main toxic metabolite of TOCP) is shown in figure 2.3 (structure II). A number of analogues were shown to be neuropathic at low doses and were also direct inhibitors of some esterases (Casida *et al.*, 1963).

I

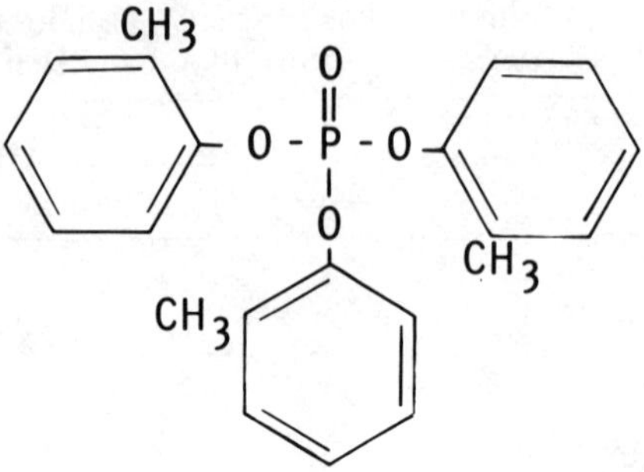

II

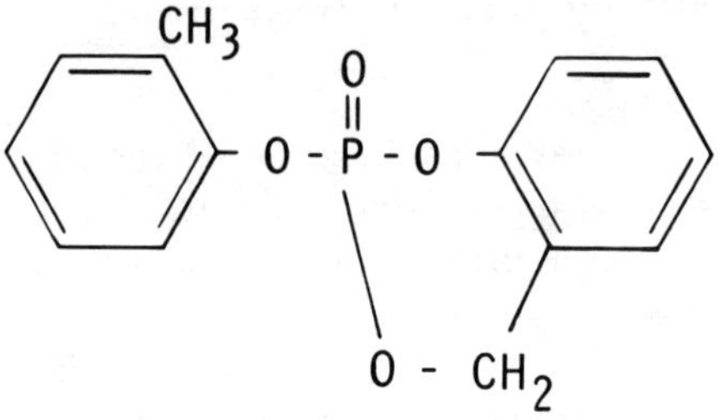

III

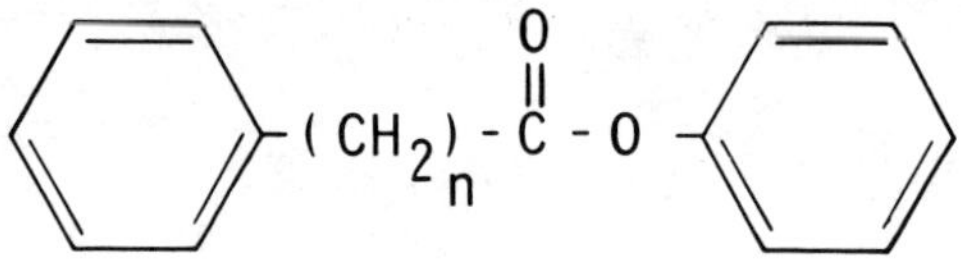

IV

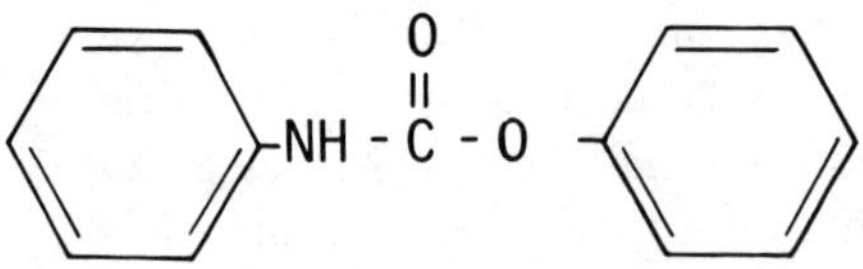

V

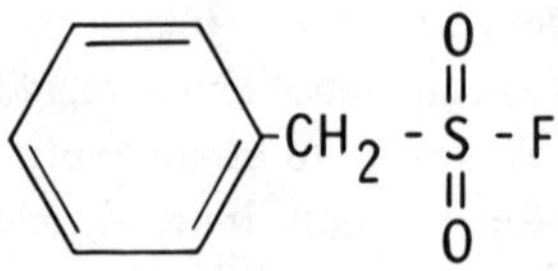

Figure 2.3 Esters (III–V) having a structural resemblance to the principal toxic metabolite (II) of TOCP (I)

5. A new hypothesis based on the 1950–61 understanding: the search for a target esterase

Aldridge was stimulated by the identification of the TOCP metabolite and considered how such a compound might act to initiate neuropathy. As already pointed out, he had demonstrated that the acutely toxic OP esters acted as partial substrates for True ChE now normally named acetylcholinesterase (AChE). He had also pointed out (Aldridge, 1954) that every OP ester known to cause delayed neuropathy was either a direct inhibitor of esterases or was metabolised to such an inhibitor *in vivo*. After the discovery of the neuropathic cyclic saligenin phosphates with their demonstrable anti-esterase activity, Aldridge proposed that these compounds initiated neuropathy by progressive phosphorylative inhibition of an, as yet unidentified, esterase in nervous tissue. He also argued that the potency of the simplest aromatic analogue, phenyl saligenin cyclic phosphate (PSP), was, at least partially, a function of the 'fit' of the PSP molecule at the active site of the target enzyme. Furthermore high-affinity hydrolysable ester substrates for this enzyme would be likely to contain the same essential structural elements as good inhibitors, albeit around a quadrivalent carboxylic ester bond rather than the pentavalent phosphate. Figure 2.3 shows a homologous series of putative substrates (III; n = 0–3) proposed, synthesised in his own laboratory and subsequently tested. It is worth recording that Ted Lock, Scientific Secretary of the British Toxicology Society and co-organiser of the Canterbury Symposium in honour of Norman Aldridge, was, at that time, the technician working under Aldridge's supervision and it was he who actually prepared some of these compounds.

Experiments *in vitro* soon revealed two distinct enzymes in hen brain which rapidly hydrolysed the analogues where n = 1 or 2, respectively (Poulsen and Aldridge, 1964). These enzymes were distinguished by their preference for hydrolysing phenyl phenylacetate (PPA) or phenyl phenylpropionate, respectively. As an exercise in theoretical enzymology the prediction and discovery of these two enzymes is remarkable. However the expectation that one or other would prove to be the neuropathy target was soon dashed by Aldridge's careful challenging of his own hypothesis using a range of the available OP esters. Just as previously shown for 'Pseudo' ChE it was soon apparent that these newly-identified enzymes were more sensitive to the non-neuropathic compounds, TEPP and Paraoxon than to DFP or Mipafox (Poulsen and Aldridge, 1964). Moreover, Aldridge and Barnes (1966) extended their screening to effects on these enzymes *in vivo* of a yet wider range of compounds and found several more which did not fit the hypothesis.

This brilliant piece of detective work had uncovered hitherto unknown enzymes but had entered an apparent dead-end as regards the mechanism of OPIDN. Several years were to pass with investigations proceeding along different lines before these apparently fruitless studies were found, after all, to have some value in the elucidation of mechanism.

6. Yet another hypothesis based on understanding: the search for a specific DFP-binding site

There are two general manners in which an approach can be made to elucidation of the mode of action of a toxic substance at the molecular level. The first approach consists of examination of reasonable guesses about the nature of the target. These guesses are built upon whatever knowledge is available about tissues or metabolic processes which may have been affected. Such knowledge may come from examination of the intoxicated whole animal, or by pharmacological screening tests of anaesthetised intoxicated animals or by morphological or biochemical screening of tissue taken post-mortem. On this basis not only inhibition of esterases had been screened in connection with OPIDN, but also protein and lipid metabolism of nervous tissue though with no convincing leads being established (see Johnson, 1975a).

Some time after the demise of the phenyl phenylacetate esterase hypothesis I was encouraged by Barnes and Aldridge to take what I call 'the second approach' to elucidation of a mechanism of toxicity. This second method seeks to pursue the toxic agent to its target and it is based on the assumption that a 'binding' reaction will take place at the target: it requires that any binding of the agent at sites which are irrelevant to the particular toxic process being studied should be recognised and distinguished from binding at the target.

It has already been pointed out that Aldridge's major work on mechanism of inhibition of esterases by OP esters was to prove beyond doubt that the process was a time-dependent progressive phosphorylation. Since $[^{32}P]$-labelled DFP was available commercially and DFP is a direct-acting inhibitor of esterases and known to be neuropathic, it was hoped $[^{32}P]$-DFP would react progressively and covalently with the unknown neuropathy target and that processes might be worked out to distinguish such a reaction from covalent reaction with the ChEs and the numerous other DFP-sensitive enzymes of nervous tissue (including the two phenyl phenylacetate esterases of Poulsen and Aldridge).

Preliminary experiments *in vitro* (Johnson, 1969a) in which $[^{32}P]$-DFP was incubated with hen brain homogenate for 30 min at 25° and pH 8.0 revealed that the measured quantity of DFP-binding sites increased by a factor of about 1.6x for every four-fold increase of concentration of DFP and there was no sign of saturation at the highest concentration tested. Simple chemical analysis showed that the binding sites were associated with protein rather than with lipid or nucleic acids. Many unpublished attempts were made to obtain the binding sites in soluble form by extraction of hen brain with organic solvents or detergents. These were unsuccessful although post-extraction of $[^{32}P]$-DFP-labelled brain microsomes with sodium deoxycholate was successful in producing a clarified extract. My attempts to fractionate this extract failed at that time when protein chromatographic and electrophoretic separation techniques were relatively naive.

Dissection of the bulk of DFP-labelling sites

I was able to dissect the bulk of labelling sites by again taking advantage of the large variety of inhibitory OP esters available to us. It was interesting to find that pre-incubation of the homogenates with a wide variety of inhibitors produced an equally wide variety of reductions in the subsequent labelling by DFP, and some of the non-neuropathic compounds (such as TEPP or Paraoxon) were more effective than the neuropathic agent, mipafox (table 2.2). It was difficult to decide the significance of this observation. It might signify that the target was accessible *in vitro* to the non-neuropathic compounds although not so *in vivo*. However Paraoxon, for instance, clearly penetrates the brain to reach its AChE in cases of intoxication so that a

Table 2.2 Effect of Preincubation with Various Esterase Inhibitors on Subsequent Binding of [^{32}P]-DFP to Hen Brain Homogenate *in vitro*

Preincubation inhibitor conc. (μM)		Decrease in bound label (%) compared with buffer control
TEPP	4	77
	32	76
Paraoxon	4	60
	32	70
Mipafox	4	25
	32	37
Phenyl saligenin cyclic phosphate	4	83
	32	75
Physostigmine	32	40

Data from two previously unpublished experiments. Preincubation was for 30 min at 25°, pH 8.0 followed by labelling with DFP (8 μM) for 6 min. Note that DFP concentration was lower than that used in later work (Johnson, 1969a)

proposal that the neuropathy target was inaccessible seemed unlikely. Failure to cause neuropathy seemed more likely to be due to a specificity at the molecular level of the target. A laborious process followed in which I explored the effect on the labelling step of preincubation of the tissue with many OP esters, not only singly but in combination and at a wide range of concentrations and times. It appeared that, in most cases, a near-maximum effect was reached as concentration × time was increased, indicating that the residual sites were relatively insensitive to the particular inhibitor being studied. However these residual amounts were often sensitive to some other OP inhibitors.

In order to choose appropriate concentrations of DFP for further study *in vitro* it was necessary to administer neuropathic doses of [^{32}P]-DFP to 2 hens and remove and analyse the brains and spinal cords about 4 h later. This somewhat hazardous experiment showed that about 730 pmoles of DFP were bound covalently per g brain at that time: this quantity could reasonably be considered about the peak since DFP was known to be degraded rapidly *in vivo*. Storage of the carcasses in isolation on our laboratory roof was a memorable event since biological decay was faster than radiochemical decay! Experiments *in vitro* were continued under conditions which gave a similar total quantity of binding to that found *in vivo*. I then found (figure 2.4) that about 20% of total sites were relatively insensitive to pre-incubation with TEPP or Paraoxon at concentrations in the 10–200 μM range and that about one quarter of these TEPP-resistant sites were sensitive to mipafox. Crude titration of the mipafox-sensitive sites with a range of concentrations suggested that the quantity behaved fairly homogeneously in this reaction, that there was a near-maximum effect at 128 μM, and, assuming first-order kinetics, the I_{50} was about 16 μM for 30 min preincubation at 25°. These procedures *in vitro* had revealed the presence of a sub-set, amounting to about 5%, of all the DFP-binding sites which had characteristics appropriate to the putative OPIDN target, namely sensitivity to the neuropathic compounds, DFP and mipafox, at realistic concentrations and relative insensitivity to two potent anti-esterase compounds which were not neuropathic, namely TEPP and Paraoxon.

Similar tests were then performed *in vitro* on brains removed from hens killed at various times after administration of test OP compounds of a wide variety of

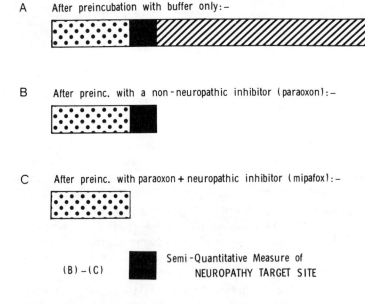

Figure 2.4 Dissection of [^{32}P]-DFP binding sites in homogenates of hen brain to reveal the OPIDN target site (not to scale; the black square represents about 5% of total sites measured in procedure A). Note that in the earliest experiments (Johnson, 1969a) the non-neuropathic ester was TEPP rather than paraoxon. (From Johnson (1984a) with permission)

Table 2.3 Measurement *in vitro* of Presumed Neuropathy Target Site in Homogenate of Brain Taken from Hens Dosed with a Variety of Neuropathic and Non-neuropathic OP Compounds *in vivo*

Nature of administered compounds	Number of different compounds	Quantity of site remaining (mean % of control (range))
Neuropathic	7	10 (5–27)
Non-neuropathic	5	67 (38–116)

Data from Johnson (1969a)

structures and all known to be active anti-esterases. Table 2.3 shows that all the neuropathic compounds were very effective at eliminating this sub-set of sites: total binding was affected much less uniformly (data not shown). The effect of non-neuropathic compounds on the sub-set was less marked and also less uniform. The results for 2 out of the 5 non-neuropathic compounds were nearer the 50% mark and presented an opportunity to pursue the thesis that data which don't fit are particularly interesting. One compound was tri-2-ethylphenyl phosphate (figure 2.2) which had always been regarded as non-neuropathic by the currently applied test criteria. However after 4 doses of this compound given at 2-day intervals the quantity of proposed target site remaining in the brain was only 13% of control and pair-dosed birds developed clear neuropathy 10 days later. The successful prediction and demonstration of this compound's neuropathic potency arising from the initial biochemical test provided strong support for the view that the target site had indeed been identified. A similar result was obtained after 2 doses of the other compound which gave an intermediate response in the single-dose test.

It should be emphasised that the biochemical response was measured only 4–24 h after doses which gave clinical expression some 10–14 days later. It is well known that this delay period is not shortened by increasing the dose so that the organophosphorylation of the target must be regarded as an event which initiates an unknown number of disturbed biochemical and physiological processes leading to axonal degeneration and clinical OPIDN. Moreover it was clear right from the earliest report (Johnson, 1969a) that simple replacement of the site by substantial resynthesis during the delay period was of no apparent value in preventing the neuropathic development. Also it was known that oximes which were highly effective in therapy of the acute poisoning by OP esters had no effect on the onset of OPIDN and such treatment did not prevent the organophosphorylation of the target site by [^{32}P]-DFP (Johnson, 1969a).

Investigation of the nature of the chemistry of the proteinaceous target proceeded very slowly in the 10 years following its identification although a great many enzymological studies were performed (see below). Since some of the later advances in the protein chemistry are not directly relevant to the thesis of this article it is noted here only in passing that analysis of the DFP-binding sites of brain by SDS–PAGE and other techniques have resolved the 5% apparently homogeneous sub-set into one principal protein of sub-unit MW 155–168K and a minor component whose importance to OPIDN was eliminated by various criteria (Williams and Johnson, 1981; Williams, 1983).

7. Identification of the neuropathy target protein as an esterase

This work again built upon the foundation of knowledge built up by Aldridge and others about the mechanism of inhibition of esterases and the conclusion (Aldridge, 1954) that all neuropathic OP esters were capable of inhibiting esterases. I, therefore, considered it likely that the recently identified organophosphorylation target was the active site of an OP-sensitive esterase. Now figure 2.1 shows that the first step in inhibition by OP esters is formation of a reversible Michaelis complex. Also it is clear that the further irreversible covalent phosphorylation (step 2) can be prevented by adding an alternative compound of higher affinity (say a good substrate with low K_m) which effectively discharges the OP-enzyme complex. Therefore I proposed that labelling of the site by $[^{32}P]$-DFP would be halted or markedly slowed in the presence of an appropriate substrate. Initially about 30 esters, amides, glycerides and peptides available on the shelves of our laboratories were chosen on the basis of the diversity of their chemical structure and were tested. Many other compounds have been tested since but only one compound was effective and, to our great surprise, this was the phenyl ester of phenylacetic acid (Johnson, 1969b). It will be recalled that this compound (PPA, $n = 1$; figure 2.3) was a substrate for the esterases discovered by Poulsen and Aldridge and then excluded from being implicated in OPIDN. Yet another anomaly had emerged! I recollect that, just for once, Dr Aldridge was not immediately excited by this anomaly and he suggested that the effect was unspecific, pointing out, for analogy, that phenyl acetate can be used as a non-specific substrate for AChE. However, it seemed wise to re-examine the capability of brain homogenate to hydrolyse PPA. The earlier work had measured substrate hydrolysis in CO_2/bicarbonate buffer in a Warburg apparatus under conditions where some non-enzymic hydrolysis occurred and the 'noise' level was significant. I adopted a direct colorimetric method for measurement of phenol and modified reaction conditions (lower substrate concentration, different buffer, etc.) to obtain a low non-enzymic blank and then re-examined the effect of a wide range of both TEPP and Paraoxon on the tissue-catalysed hydrolysis; furthermore I increased the amount of tissue in those experiments where the bulk of enzyme activity was inhibited. Using the range of conditions applied in detecting the target site, I found (Johnson, 1969b) that about 10% of the total PPA-hydrolase was relatively insensitive to TEPP or Paraoxon at concentrations up to 250 μM, although the I_{50}s for the 90% which was sensitive were 100–400× lower than this. Of this 10% which was insensitive to Paraoxon, about one fifth was sensitive to mipafox in a homogeneous fashion showing an I_{50} of 17 μM indistinguishable from the I_{50} previously found for the labelling site. Many further tests *in vitro* and *in vivo* followed which established a close correlation (see, for instance, figure 2.5, besides much later work) between the sensitivity to inhibitor of the DFP-labelling target site and the esterase which, initially, was called 'neurotoxic esterase' but is now, less confusingly, called neuropathy target esterase (NTE).

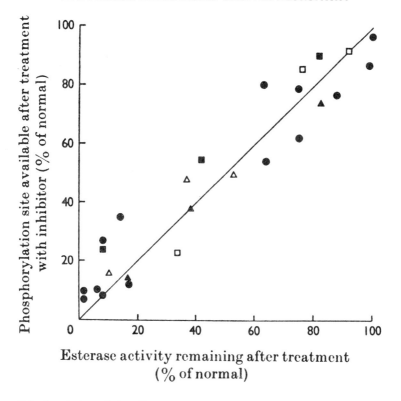

Figure 2.5   Correlation of the effects of various organophosphorus, carbamate or sulphonyl fluoride inhibitors applied either *in vivo* or *in vitro* on the 'neurotoxic site' (measured *in vitro* with [^{32}P]-DFP as indicated in figure 2.4) and the 'neurotoxic esterase' (measured *in vitro* by the differential assay with phenyl phenylacetate as substrate) (from Johnson (1970))

The correlations of inhibition of NTE *in vivo* with initiation of neuropathy has been substantiated for more than 100 test compounds and by a variety of independent workers, too many to be listed here. However, one or two interesting anomalies have emerged along the way. Each, when pursued, has led to a further degree of understanding and will be discussed below. However, none of these anomalies has undermined the status of NTE as the identified target for initiation of OPIDN. It should be recognised that the basis for identifying NTE lay in the screening of *all* available DFP-binding sites. The process of identifying NTE could then be described in terms of the traditional search for a needle in a haystack: there is no basis for suggesting that the needle is anywhere else than in the stack. By way of contrast, we have no basis to believe that *all* the esterases of nervous tissue have been screened so that a sceptic may still propose that an esterase other than NTE is the true target and that the blocking of the labelling site by PPA and the mass of supportive correlations is fortuitous. Such an argument has been advanced at intervals when apparent anomalies have appeared but it forgets the basic identification of the site by radiolabelling and, moreover, the 'other esterase' progressively lost its raison d'etre as the interesting anomalies were tackled and led to new understanding.

The element of serendipity in these advances should not be overlooked: (i) it is unlikely that a bottle of PPA rested on a shelf in any other laboratory in the world awaiting the day when it would be used in random screening of compounds to block the labelling of the neuropathy site; (ii) phenyl valerate has, subsequently, been identified as a more sensitive and selective substrate for NTE (Johnson, 1975c, 1977): choice of this structure for a substrate followed rationally after structure-related screening of many carbamate inhibitors of NTE (see later). However, phenyl valerate might well have been missed in a search using the site-blocking test both because its K_m is rather high and also because it is hydrolysed so rapidly that an adequate concentration would not have persisted throughout that test. Thus PPA, designed and discarded years before, was essential to the discovery of NTE.

8. Identification of neuropathy target esterase has produced diverse benefits

Since the main purpose of this article is to highlight the benefits of the study of anomalous data, I shall mention only briefly the beneficial application of the understanding which has emerged. However reference will also be made to a more extensive treatment of this aspect in other publications.

(A) In assessment of delayed neuropathic hazard of new chemicals (Johnson, 1975b, 1980, 1982, 1984b; OECD, 1983; WHO, 1986)

   (i) By contrast with the dose-and-watch tests lasting at least 6 weeks, with time for histopathological examination thereafter, the biochemical test assesses initiation rather than endpoint and can be completed within 2 days after dosing.
  (ii) In such tests the response is gradeable and is particularly useful in distinguishing truly non-neuropathic compounds from others which were not quite positive in a prescribed dose schedule.
 (iii) A clear rationalisation of structure/activity relations has been established. Based on *in vitro* studies of responses of both NTE and AChE (Johnson 1975b,c, 1982; Lotti and Johnson, 1978) the salient structural features which favour attack on NTE and which favour selectivity for NTE rather than for AChE are known.
  (iv) Using the $I_{50}^{AChE}/I_{50}^{NTE}$ ratio as a guideline, predictions of neuropathic potential in relation to pesticidal activity can be made with milligram quantities of compound at an early stage of product development and without the necessity to dose animals.
   (v) Comparisons *in vitro* of the sensitivities of AChE and NTE of hen and human tissue have been made (Lotti and Johnson, 1978, 1980a). Differences are comparatively small and it is possible to review more closely the effects of selected compounds using human autopsy material *in vitro*.

(vi) Monitoring of NTE responses to multi-dose schedules has revealed that there is an equilibrium between inhibition and resynthesis and that there are dose-levels where the effect on NTE is not cumulative although cumulative inhibition may occur at higher doses (Lotti and Johnson, 1980b). Moreover, prolonged low-level inhibition of NTE for many weeks appears to have no clinical correlate whereas a brief high-point of inhibition followed by comparatively rapid restoration of NTE level by resynthesis does precipitate neuropathy (Lotti and Johnson (1980b), and see further discussion by Johnson (1982)). The implication of this observation for the biology of the axon is intriguing and worthy of further exploration.

(B) In other safety considerations

Understanding the initiation process has enabled rational attempts to be made in:

(i) Therapy by suitably tailored oximes. This has been unfruitful since it soon appeared that ageing of inhibited NTE to a oxime-unresponsive form was usually rapid (see later).

(ii) Development of non-neuropathic blocking agents of the target (see below) for prophylaxis. This has been highly successful and these agents might be used prophylactically in situations where it was desired to use an OP ester which had very desirable therapeutic or pesticidal properties but which carried significant neuropathic hazard.

(C) Potential applications in neurobiology and enzymology

NTE-orientated probes (fluorescent or radiolabelled) are being designed to be far more specific than DFP so that the purification of the protein and, also, its tissue and sub-cellular location may be followed more easily. In addition, the studies which have been reviewed above have shown what an exquisitely effective set of dissecting tools is to hand for the enzymologist with a large variety of structurally related covalent inhibitors. NTE represents less than 5% of the DFP-binding sites and about 2% of PPA esterase and there are, undoubtedly, at least 5 other PPA esterases, yet patient dissection has not brought them to light. There is no reason to believe that similar procedures are not applicable for study of other classes of enzymes.

9. A new anomaly: the functional significance of the neuropathy target site

The initiation of OPIDN had been shown convincingly to start with organophosphorylation of a sub-set of DFP-sensitive sites and compelling evidence had been obtained that this site is the catalytic centre of one identifiable esterase (NTE). The simplest interpretation for these findings might perhaps be that the neuropathic effect is the direct outcome of either the loss of products normally provided by NTE activity or of the accumulation of untransformed substrate to toxic levels. The observations described below led, however, to a radical rethinking about the site, in terms more acceptable to a pharmacologist than to a biochemist, as different biological responses were found to be elicited by different chemicals, even though they all reacted with the same site.

It was of obvious practical and theoretical interest to test whether other acylating agents, besides some OP esters, might be inhibitors of NTE and neuropathic agents. My interest in this question grew from my training as an organic chemist and, at first, I synthesised a variety of carbamate esters. Several (such as phenyl N-phenyl-carbamate, Structure IV in figure 2.3) were found to be capable of inhibiting NTE without affecting AChE (Johnson and Lauwerys, 1969). However the inhibited enzyme is unstable and *in vivo* activity returns to normal within 1–60 h (Johnson and Lauwerys, 1969; Johnson, 1970). The effect on NTE measured by PPA hydro-lysis correlated closely with the effect on the radiochemically identified target protein in these and subsequent experiments with other inhibitors. Predosing hens with these short-acting inhibitors of NTE protected them against the clinical neuropathic effects of challenge doses of DFP which normally causes prolonged inhibition. Protective effects were only seen if the challenge was given while more than 30% of the NTE was carbamylated and unavailable to DFP. This was strong confirmation of the relevance of NTE to OPIDN. Thereafter it was found that some sulphonyl fluorides produce stable sulphonylated NTE. The rate of return of activity *in vivo* was similar to that after injection of DFP, but, surprisingly, these compounds were not neuropathic and even repeated doses of phenylmethane-sulphonyl fluoride (PMSF; structure V in figure 2.3) did not cause neuropathy (Johnson, 1970). From a biochemical viewpoint this was a striking anomaly and might be thought to indicate, despite all the positive correlations, that the target protein and its esterase activity were, after all, not relevant to OPIDN. This is not so, for we found that every compound capable of inhibiting NTE *in vivo* produced a biological response pertinent to OPIDN but that the response differed according to chemical structure; none were without effect. Thus, while the target remained sulphonylated by PMSF *in vivo*, challenge doses of DFP or other neuropathic esters did not cause any delayed neuropathic effect and table 2.4 shows that this protec-tion was effective provided that the challenge was not delayed more than 4–6 days, whereas carbamate protection lasted only for a few hours. It was noticeable that cholinergic effects were not prevented by PMSF so that protection could not be ascribed to some non-specific effect on distribution of DFP. In every case the duration of protection was controlled by the time taken for 70–80% of normal NTE levels to be restored. Table 2.4 shows also that the protective effect of PMSF (days) could in turn be 'protected against' by prior administration of short-acting phenyl benzylcarbamate so that when DFP was given after the other two, the overall duration of protection against neuropathy was hours (due to carbamate injected first) rather than days due to PMSF (injected second). We were forced to the conclusion that initiation does not depend simply on loss of the esterase activity of NTE although that loss is a convenient indicator of covalent binding. Rather, the initiation must involve a further step in response to the binding of the 'covalent agonist' to NTE. PMSF was the first protective ('covalent antagonist') compound

Table 2.4 Protective Action of some Inhibitors of NTE

Compound	Mean time (days) for NTE activity to return to 70% of normal after 80–100% inhibition *in vivo*	Duration (days) of protection due to single highly inhibitory dose
PMSF	8	6–7
Carbamates	0.1–0.5	0.1–0.5
Phenyl benzylcarbamate followed 1 h later by PMSF	0.5	$> 0.1; < 1$

At intervals after dosing groups of hens, one bird was killed and NTE activity was assayed. At the time of killing, further birds in the group received a challenge neuropathic dose of DFP and protection was assessed 2–3 weeks later
From Johnson and Lauwerys (1969) and Johnson (1974)

found to inhibit NTE for as long a period as DFP. Since this compound left only one alkyl chain attached to NTE through its sulphur atom rather than the two chains typically attached through DFP or other OP esters it seemed possible at that time that the crucial difference between neuropathic and protective compounds might lie in the number of these attached side-chains. To test this proposal various organophosphinate esters were designed as inhibitors of NTE: these have 2 side-chains like the organophosphates but differ in that both chains are connected to the phosphorus atom through rather stable unhydrolysable bonds (figure 2.6). All organophosphinates which have been shown to inhibit NTE *in vivo* were found to act as protective agents (Johnson 1974, 1982; Meredith 1986). According to biological response, inhibitors of NTE are now classified in two groups (see figure 2.6). Those in Group A (phosphates, phosphonates or phosphoramidates, are neuropathic, whereas those in Group B (carbamates, sulphonyl fluorides and phosphinates) are not only non-neuropathic, but prior administration of any such Group B inhibitor to hens protects the animals from the neuropathic effects of subsequent challenge doses of Group A compounds. The characteristic common to all the protective compounds is that, like the phosphinate depicted in Box 2b of figure 2.7, they produce inhibited NTE with no residual bonds suitable for further transformation to a charged species. This left for consideration only one hypothesis about the nature of step (2). This is depicted in Box 2a of figure 2.7 which shows conversion of inhibited NTE to a modified form bearing an ionised acidic group on the phosphorus atom (cf. Ageing: reaction (4) in figure 2.1). Although the ageing proposal (Johnson, 1974, 1976) seemed the only rational explanation of the cumulated data on protection it was hard for biochemists to accept that an active enzyme such as NTE (catalytic centre activity is $> 10^5$) could be inhibited for prolonged periods, for example by repeated injections of some of the protective compounds, without any ill effect. Moreover no precise result of the generation of this protein-bound negative charge could be stated although it was realised that charged inorganic phosphate groups on some proteins could exert

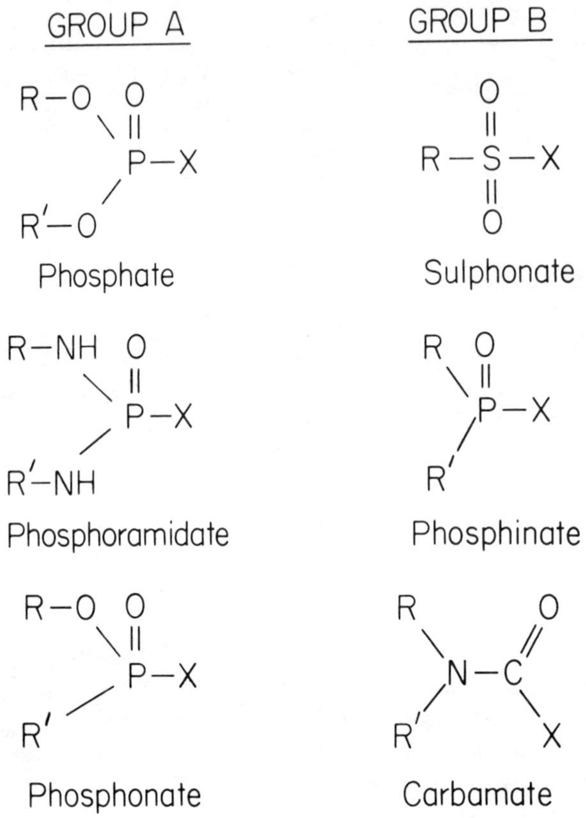

Figure 2.6   Comparison of structures of inhibitors of NTE which (A) cause neuropathy or (B) protect against neuropathy

dramatic control effects on physiological functions. A further problem was that my attempts to demonstrate the proposed ageing process of inhibited NTE failed during several years. However this failure, in itself, led ultimately to a new comprehension of the process of ageing of OP-inhibited esterases.

10. Anomalies in the radiochemical versus the enzymological studies of ageing of inhibited NTE

It can be seen from figure 2.1 that the process of 'ageing' as usually understood, involves cleavage of a bond linking one of the two 'R' groups to the phosphorus, while the phosphorus is itself bound to the active site of the enzyme. Studies, principally on the cholinesterases and summarised by Aldridge and Reiner (1972), have confirmed that there is a hydrolytic action, which may be S_N1 or S_N2 according to the structure of inhibitors involved, and that any radioactivity used to label the cleaved group is liberated into the medium. Thus for uniformly labelled

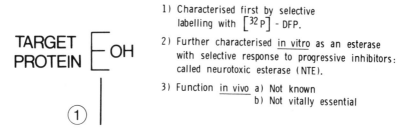

TARGET PROTEIN ⊢OH

1) Characterised first by selective labelling with $[^{32}P]$ - DFP.

2) Further characterised in vitro as an esterase with selective response to progressive inhibitors: called neurotoxic esterase (NTE).

3) Function in vivo a) Not known
b) Not vitally essential

①

IN VIVO ORGANOPHOSPHORYLATION (or PHOSPHINYLATION, etc) OF ACTIVE SITE OF THE TARGET INHIBITS NTE ACTIVITY.

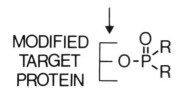

MODIFIED TARGET PROTEIN

BIOLOGICAL RESPONSES IN VIVO DEPEND ON THE NEXT CHEMICAL CHANGE

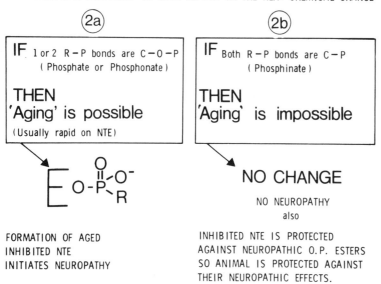

②a

IF 1 or 2 R−P bonds are C−O−P
(Phosphate or Phosphonate)

THEN
'Aging' is possible
(Usually rapid on NTE)

②b

IF Both R−P bonds are C−P
(Phosphinate)

THEN
'Aging' is impossible

NO CHANGE

NO NEUROPATHY
also

FORMATION OF AGED
INHIBITED NTE
INITIATES NEUROPATHY

INHIBITED NTE IS PROTECTED
AGAINST NEUROPATHIC O.P. ESTERS
SO ANIMAL IS PROTECTED AGAINST
THEIR NEUROPATHIC EFFECTS.

Figure 2.7   The respective consequences of alternative further chemical modifications (2a and 2b) of the OPIDN target protein after it has been modified by covalent binding of certain organophosphorus inhibitors of esterases. (From Johnson (1982) with permission)

[^{14}C]-DFP half the radioactivity is liberated while half remains in the mono-isopropyl phosphoryl group still bound to protein (Berends *et al.*, 1959). I could detect no similar reaction for NTE even when the tests were applied at intervals up to several hours after a labelling period of only 1 min (Johnson, unpublished): tests with mixtures of [^{32}P] and tritium-labelled DFP showed that inhibition of NTE had been completed within the minute. It could be argued that ageing was so very fast that it was finished completely within that first minute but it seemed worth-while to re-examine the assumptions on which these tests were based. The original definition of ageing of OP-inhibited esterases derives from studies by Hobbiger (1956) using nucleophilic reactivators to restore activity to the inhibited enzyme (reaction 3 of figure 2.1). In those studies 'ageing' was detected as a time-dependent loss in responsiveness of the inhibited AChE to certain nucleophiles. Bruce Clothier and I therefore attempted to reactivate some inhibited species of NTE by treatment with hydroxylamine which is a known reactivator for several esterases inhibited by OP compounds (see Aldridge and Reiner, 1972). Since it is a small molecule, hydroxylamine seemed unlikely to be hindered in its access to the active site of NTE. We were unsuccessful so that Clothier went back to a simpler system to re-examine the processes of reactivation and ageing: he investigated a range of nucleo-philes as reactivators of phosphinylated enzymes. By stages he showed (Clothier, 1979) that:

(i) A phosphinylated AChE could be reactivated by some nucleophiles.
(ii) More vigorous conditions were needed to reactivate phosphinylated than phosphorylated AChE.
(iii) KF had certain practical advantages as a reactivator.
(iv) KF would reactivate both dialkylphosphinylated and dialkylphosphorylated AChE but not the latter after an appropriate 'ageing' period had elapsed.
(v) KF would reactivate several dialkylphosphinyl NTEs;
(vi) KF would not reactivate NTE after inhibition by several organophosphates or phosphonates.

This extensive exploratory work with phosphinylated enzymes (a new field at that time) presented us with a perfect example of anomalous observations. On the one hand, failure to reactivate various species of inhibited NTE with KF suggested that the 'ageing' had occurred but, on the other hand, no label was liberated from [^{3}H]-DFP-inhibited NTE as expected for a typical ageing process. We decided to regard the radiochemical evidence against 'ageing' of inhibited NTE as possibly anomalous and to consider further whether our failures to reactivate organophos-phorylated NTE did, after all, indicate that our samples had 'aged' (perhaps very rapidly). In our investigations so far, inhibition and removal of enzyme from excess inhibitor had taken at least an hour. We revised conditions to achieve substantial inhibition with higher concentrations of inhibitor for 1–2 min, slowed inhibition by a massive dilution and treated with KF immediately or after a further 5 min. The technical procedure was very difficult but we found that it was now possible to reactivate the inhibited NTE species immediately after inhibition and that ageing was very rapid indeed ($t\frac{1}{2}$ = 1-4 min for several dialkyl phosphoryl NTEs) (Clothier, 1979; Clothier and Johnson, 1979, 1980).

11. Ageing of inhibited NTE — a unique molecular mechanism revealed

The extensive study described above showed that inhibited NTE did indeed 'age', in the operational sense, very rapidly: there was a time-dependent loss of the responsiveness to nucleophilic reactivation. For 'aged' inhibited AChE this loss of responsiveness had been understood in terms of reaction (4) of figure 2.1 with the phosphoryl-enzyme bond in aged inhibited enzyme being stabilised against attack by a reactivating anion because of the presence of the neighbouring negative charge.

We had shown that no label was released from radiolabelled DFP-inhibited enzyme after inhibition. Moreover using mixtures of [^{32}P] and [^{3}H]-labelled reagent, we confirmed that the ratio of label found bound to NTE remained the same as in the reagent. By contrast, this ratio changed with time when we tested similarly labelled hen brain AChE: tritium was released as expected (Clothier and Johnson, 1979). We therefore resorted to physico-chemical analyses of the nature of the labelled molecule at different times after inhibition and showed that, initially, all label was present in a diisopropyl phosphoryl group but that a change occurred with the same time course as the loss of ability to undergo reactivation. Ten minutes after labelling, the label remained bound to protein but it was shown to be present in groupings which could be released separately by alkaline hydrolysis to yield respectively monoisopropyl phosphoric acid (all the [^{32}P] and half [^{3}H], all involatile) and a moderately volatile compound containing the other half of the tritium. The nature of the volatile molecule has not been established but we presume it is likely to be either propan-2-ol or, possibly, propan-2-thiol. This transformation of the bound group appears to provide the molecular basis for the ageing of inhibited NTE and it is probably an intramolecular rather than intermolecular transfer (Clothier and Johnson, 1979; Williams and Johnson, 1981).

Williams (1983) has shown that NTE appears to be the only DFP-sensitive protein in several different tissues which ages by a process of rapid intramolecular group transfer. We have only demonstrated the reaction by direct radiochemical means for 2 inhibitors. However, since in both cases the time-course was indistinguishable from that for loss of ability to be reactivated, we have considered it reasonable to use the latter property as an indicator of the molecular change in a large variety of cases (Clothier and Johnson, 1980; Johnson et al., 1985; Johnson et al., 1986).

The hypothesis put forward in 1974 that 'ageing' of inhibited NTE is an essential second step in the initiation of OPIDN appeared the only rational explanation of the protective effects of unageable inhibitors. It took much effort to demonstrate for a range of neuropathic compounds that ageing does indeed occur. The contrast in mechanistic terms between ageing of inhibited AChE and NTE is shown in figure 2.8.

CONTRASTS IN AGING OF DiPF - INHIBITED ESTERASES

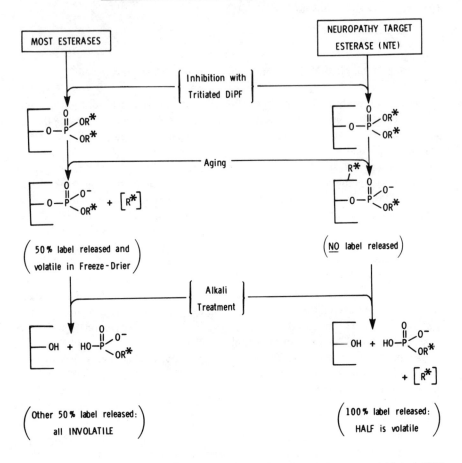

Figure 2.8 Contrasting fates of tritiated alkyl group during ageing of DFP-inhibited NTE versus other esterases. From (Johnson (1984a) with permission)

12. Which feature of ageing of inhibited NTE initiates neuropathy?

I proposed that nerve degeneration ultimately occurs because of the formation of the charged group attached to the NTE molecule and that this charge upsets a normal physiological process of the neurone (Johnson, 1974). However, the possibility must now also be considered that the group transferred to a secondary site during ageing may be the initiating agent.

As noted above it was found that, during the ageing of NTE which had been inhibited by either tritiated DFP or di-n-pentyl 2,2-dichlorovinyl phosphate, the label associated with the alkoxy groups which were removed from phosphorus was not liberated into solution but became attached to another macromolecular site. This was in contrast to the liberation of small molecular-weight products into solution during ageing of inhibited brain cholinesterases. Without a complete range of radiolabelled neuropathic esters it is impossible to show whether this efficient transfer occurs when every variety of chemical group takes part in the ageing reaction. On chemical grounds this seems unlikely for phosphoramidates or for phenoxy substituents, but many unexpected reactions can occur in special environments such as may be provided by an enzyme active centre. Figure 2.9 illustrates

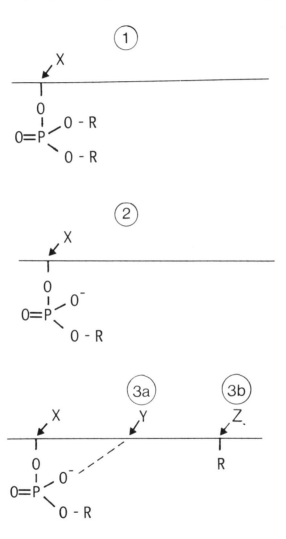

Figure 2.9 The proven steps (1 and 2) of initiation of OPIDN with proposed alternative (3a or 3b) consequences. (1) organophosphorylation occurs at X causing inhibition of catalytic activity of NTE; (2) cleavage of one R-O-P bond to form a negatively charged group with concomitant ageing of inhibited NTE; (3a) negative charge at X disrupts normal (unknown) function of another site, Y, *or* (3b) transfer of R to a site, Z, during ageing disrupts the normal (unknown) function of Z (from Johnson (1982) with permission)

the proposal that, if such a transfer does occur when NTE is inhibited by any neuropathic ester, then modification of the receiving site (labelled Z) could be the event that precipitates neuropathy, with formation of the charged group on the aged enzyme having no direct consequence.

Two approaches have been made to try to obtain evidence in favour of either of these two alternative mechanisms (3a or 3b of figure 2.9). The first was to synthesise an inhibitor that could age but that would liberate a group intrinsically unsuited to attachment at Z: fluoride seemed such a group. Several compounds were synthesised and phenylmethanephosphonodifluoridate $(C_6H_5.CH_2.P.O.F_2)$ was found to inhibit NTE at easily tolerable doses *in vivo*. It must be assumed that one fluoride atom was lost during inhibition leaving the other P–F bond as the only bond available for cleavage during ageing. However, although P–F bonds are not intrinsically very stable, very little ageing was detected in inhibited NTE of brains removed from hens two days after dosing and considerable spontaneous reactivation had occurred. It seems possible that unless site Z has some ability to 'pull' the relevant group off phosphorus and onto itself, ageing of NTE is no longer facile. During the 2–3 days necessary for NTE activity to return to 80% normal the hens were resistant to challenge doses of DFP just the same as if the target had been covered by a compound that could not age instead of by one that could but didn't (Johnson, 1982).

These observations confirm the absolute necessity of step (2) for initiation but fail to show whether an effect at site Y or site Z is the key to OPIDN. The second approach has been to attempt to block site Z directly instead of by transfer from phosphorus attached to X. Several chloromethyl ketones or N-substituted haloacetamides have been synthesised to resemble phenyl phenylcarbamate or phenyl benzylcarbamate, both acylating inhibitors of NTE. Thus far the ketones inhibit NTE *in vitro* but are too reactive and corrosive to be used *in vivo*, whereas the amides are surprisingly uninhibitory. It has also been shown that 4-bromophenylacetylurea, a neuropathic compound with some formal similarity to phenyl phenylcarbamate, appears not to modify site Z *in vivo* because predosing with this compound does not alter the ability of rat brain NTE inhibited by DFP to undergo the ageing reaction (Johnson, 1982).

Although both the above rational approaches have failed to resolve the problem, some recent studies have shown that modification of the target site *in vivo* by attachment of a phosphoromonoamidate in which the $-NH_2$ group is unsubstituted has unusual effects — possibly the negativity of the charged oxygen is moderated in some way and a part-protected state is brought about. Further studies with related model compounds are under way.

13. More recent anomalies and growing understanding

This article has traced the historical growth of understanding of the initiation of OPIDN to the point where the mechanism seems established beyond all reasonable doubt. Some of the benefits of the characterisation of NTE have been listed already. However the firmness of the foundation also enables us to explore several problematic areas and to choose between alternative hypotheses. Space does not permit development of this theme in detail but the following brief comments provide some illustration.

The species anomaly

For a long time it has been difficult to explain why rats appear to be resistant to OPIDN. Demonstration of the presence in rat brain of NTE and of its ability to age has stimulated further research in rats. As a result, it has been shown recently that typical morphological damage to spinal cord is caused in rats by single doses of TOCP or of mipafox, that the dose/effects correlate with inhibition of NTE, and that prior dosing of rats with PMSF protects against the lesions produced by a challenge dose of mipafox (Padilla and Veronesi, 1985; Veronesi and Padilla, 1985). The 'anomaly' therefore appears to lie in the realm of anatomy and the question is now why the clinical walking behaviour of rats does not reflect their neuronal damage.

Regional effects

OPIDN is a clinical expression of damage to neurones in both peripheral nerve and regions of the medulla and spinal cord. However local delivery of neuropathic or protective compounds with concomitant specific regional inhibition of NTE has revealed separate clinical expressions of damage to spinal or peripheral neurones (Lotti *et al.*, 1985).

Repeated low doses

The surprising fact that neurones can survive a substantial persistent inhibition for quite long periods provided the insult of NTE inhibition does not exceed the threshold of about 50% has been mentioned in section 8(A). The implication of this observation for the biology of the axon is intriguing and worthy of further exploration.

Toxicology of chiral OP esters

It was shown for many organophosphates which inhibit NTE that the subsequent ageing reaction was very fast (Clothier and Johnson, 1980). More recently, studies *in vitro* with resolved isomers of phosphonate inhibitors have shown that some will inhibit NTE but that subsequent ageing is slow for one or another isomer (Johnson *et al.*, 1985; Johnson *et al.*, 1986). The slow-ageing isomers are now turning out to act as protective agents in challenge experiments with hens (Johnson and Read, 1987 and unpublished work). Clearly it is important to know whether metabolism in man will deliver a predominance of the neuropathic or of the protective isomer to NTE and this may not be easily predicted from tests in other species or with trace levels of the agent in man.

The physiological significance of the whole NTE protein

This is a continuing mystery which is, perhaps, exacerbated by the fact that NTE is present in non-neural as well as neural tissue (Dudek and Richardson, 1982; Williams, 1983).

CONCLUSION

In the realm of OPIDN, exploration of anomalies in existing views or data has, indeed, led to advances in understanding. This understanding has, in turn, provided a basis for improvements in procedures for hazard evaluation and for more efficient design of safer OP esters for defined uses. A target is known and a set of probes are available to explore a protein intimately involved in the health of long axons. It is hoped that, with this basis, rational advances can be made in the study of the normal processes which maintain axons and, also, of the mechanisms of other clinical neuropathies with, as yet, undefined aetiology.

Norman Aldridge shared many brain-storming sessions with me as some of the anomalies encountered during studies on OPIDN seemed quite unresolvable. I gladly acknowledge his pioneer work on enzyme mechanisms, enthusiasm for raw data and his encouragement to persist in formulating testable hypotheses.

SUMMARY

Two major toxic effects of OP esters are known. These are the acute (cholinergic) toxicity initiated by covalent organophosphylation of the active centre of acetyl-cholinesterase and the delayed neuropathy which is now known to be initiated by a similar reaction at the active site of neuropathy target esterase (NTE, formerly called 'neurotoxic esterase'). 'Ageing' of inhibited NTE is an essential second step which precipitates an unknown sequence of events culminating in distal degeneration of some long axons of spinal and peripheral nerve with associated clinical polyneuropathy.

Progress in understanding the mechanism of OP neuropathy has hinged on observations that did not fit current hypotheses about mechanism. Some of the crucial 'anomalies' seen and subsequently resolved were: (1) irregularities in structure/activity relationships; (2) differences in inhibitory power *in vitro* between pure and impure OP esters; (3) apparent correlations implicating brain pseudo-cholinesterase or other named enzymes as the target; (4) selectivity of OP esters in their attack on sites susceptible to labelling by [^{32}P]-DFP (di-isopropyl phosphorofluoridate, a rather general OP inhibitor and a neuropathic agent); (5) selective affinity for the apparent target of phenyl phenylacetate which had already been excluded from the list of likely target site substrates; (6) blocking of the target site by non-neuropathic phenylmethanesulphonyl fluoride (PMSF) and some phosphinates; (7) apparent necessity for ageing of inhibited NTE in spite of radiochemical studies which showed no apparent ageing; (8) enzymological and toxicological differences when chiral isomers are bound to the active site of NTE, and (9) different clinical effects when DFP is administered systemically or locally. Resolution of each of the above anomalies led to advances in understanding such that the initiation site for OPIDN has been identified and the 2 initial reactions have been characterised extensively. Benefits of the understanding have accrued in the realms of toxicity testing and hazard evaluation, prophylaxis and therapy and also in neurobiology and enzymology. Some unresolved anomalies have been presented and it is hoped that close attention to these will, in time, yield further advances in understanding.

REFERENCES

Aldridge, W. N. (1953a). The differentiation of true and pseudo cholinesterase by organophosphorus compounds. *Biochem. J.*, **51**, 62–7

Aldridge, W. N. (1953b). The inhibition of erythrocyte cholinesterase by tri-esters of phosphoric acid. 3. The nature of the inhibitory process. *Biochem. J.*, **54**, 442–8

Aldridge, W. N. (1954). Tri-cresyl phosphates and cholinesterase. *Biochem. J.*, **56**, 185–9

Aldridge, W. N. and Barnes, J. M. (1961). Neurotoxic and biochemical properties of some triaryl phosphates. *Biochem. Pharmacol.*, **6**, 177–88

Aldridge, W. N. and Barnes, J. M (1966). Further observations on the neurotoxicity of organophosphorus compounds. Esterases and neurotoxicity of some organophosphorus compounds. *Biochem. Pharmacol.*, **15**, 541–8 and 549–54

Aldridge, W. N. and Davison, A. N. (1953). The mechanism of inhibition of cholinesterases by organophosphorus compounds. *Biochem. J.*, **55**, 763–6

Aldridge, W. N. and Reiner, E. (1972). *Enzyme Inhibitors as Substrates,* North-Holland, Amsterdam

Barnes, J. M. and Denz, F. A. (1953). Experimental demyelination with organophosphorus compounds. *J. Path. Bact.*, **65**, 597–605

Berends, F., Posthumus, C. H., Van den Sluys, I. and Deierkauf, F. A. (1959). The chemical basis of the "aging process' of DFP-inhibited pseudocholinesterase. *Biochim. Biophys. Acta*, **34**, 576–8

Bidstrup, P. L., Bonnell, J. A. and Beckett, A. G. (1953). Paralysis following poisoning by a new organic phosphorus insecticide. *Brit. Med. J.*, **I**, 1068–72

Bondy, H. F., Field, E. J., Worden, A. N. and Hughes, J. P. W. (1960). A study on the acute toxicity of the triaryl phosphates used as plasticisers. *Brit. J. Indust. Med.*, **17**, 190–200

Bouldin, T. W. and Cavanagh, J. B. (1979a). Organophosphorus neuropathy; I. A teased-fibre study of the spatio-temporal spread of axonal degeneration. *Am. J. Pathol.*, **94**, 241–52

Bouldin, T. W. and Cavanagh, J. B. (1979b). Organophosphorus neuropathy; II. A fine-structural study of the early stages of axonal degeneration. *Am. J. Pathol.*, **94**, 253–70

Casida, J. E., Eto, M. and Baron, R. L. (1961). Biological activity of a tri-*o*-cresyl phosphate metabolite. *Nature, Lond.*, **191**, 1396–7

Casida, J. E., Baron, R. L., Eto, M. and Engel, J. L. (1963). Potentiation and neurotoxicity induced by certain organophosphates. *Biochem. Pharmacol.*, **12**, 73–83

Cavanagh, J. B. (1964). The significance of the "dying-back" process in experimental and human neurological disease. *Int. Rev. exp. Path.*, **3**, 219–67

Cavanagh, J. B. (1973). Peripheral neuropathy caused by toxic agents. *Crit. Rev. Toxicol.*, **2**, 365–417

Clothier, B. C. (1979). Reactivation and aging of esterases. M.Phil. thesis, UK Council for National Academic Awards

Clothier, B. and Johnson, M. K. (1979). Rapid aging of neurotoxic esterase after inhibition by di-isopropyl phosphorofluoridate. *Biochem. J.*, **177**, 549–58

Clothier, B. and Johnson, M. K. (1980). Reactivation and aging of neurotoxic esterase inhibited by a variety of organophosphorus esters. *Biochem. J.* **185**, 739–47

Davies, D. R. (1963). Neurotoxicity of organophosphorus compounds. In: *Handbuch der Experimentellen Pharmakologie*, Vol XV (ed. G. D. Koelle), Erganzungswerk, Springer, Berlin-Heidelberg-New York, pp. 860–82

Davis, C. S. and Richardson, R. J. (1980). Organophosphorus compounds. In: *Clinical and Experimental Neurotoxicology*, (ed. P. S. Spencer and H. Schaumberg), Williams & Wilkins, Baltimore, pp. 527–44

Davison, A. N. (1953). Some observations on the cholinesterases of the central nervous system after the administration of organophosphorus compounds. *Brit. J. Pharmacol.*, **8**, 212–16

Dudek, B. R. and Richardson, R. J. (1982). Evidence for the existence of neurotoxic esterase in neural and lymphatic tissue of the adult hen. *Biochem. Pharmacol.*, **31**, 1117–21

Earl, C. J. and Thompson, R. H. S. (1952a). The inhibitory action of tri-*ortho*-cresyl phosphate on cholinesterases. *Brit. J. Pharmacol.*, **7**, 261–9

Earl, C. J. and Thompson, R. H. S. (1952b). Cholinesterase levels in the nervous system in tri-*ortho*-cresyl phosphate poisoning. *Brit. J. Pharmacol.*, **7**, 685–94

Hierons, R. and Johnson, M. K. (1978). Clinical and toxicological investigations of a case of delayed neuropathy in man after acute poisoning by an organophosphorus pesticide. *Arch. Toxicol.*, **40**, 279–84

Hobbiger, F. (1956). Chemical reactivation of phosphorylated human and bovine true cholinesterase. *Brit. J. Pharmacol.*, **11**, 295–303

Hottinger, A. and Bloch, H. (1943). Uber die spezifitat der cholinesterase-hemmung durch tri-*o*-kresyl-phosphat. *Helv. Chim. Acta*, **26**, 142–55

Johnson, M. K. (1969a). A phosphorylation site in brain and the delayed neurotoxic effect of some organophosphorus compounds. *Biochem. J.*, **111**, 487–95

Johnson, M. K. (1969b). The delayed neurotoxic effect of some organophosphorus compounds. Identification of the phosphorylation site as an esterase. *Biochem. J.*, **114**, 711–17

Johnson, M. K. (1970). Organophosphorus and other inhibitors of brain "neurotoxic esterase" and the development of delayed neurotoxicity in hens. *Biochem. J.*, **120**, 523–31

Johnson, M. K. (1974). The primary biochemical lesion leading to the delayed neurotoxic effects of some organophosphorus esters. *J. Neurochem.*, **23**, 785–9

Johnson, M. K. (1975a). The delayed neuropathy caused by some organophosphorus esters: Mechanism and challenge. *Crit. Rev. Toxicol.*, **3**, 289–316

Johnson, M. K. (1975b). Organophosphorus esters causing delayed neurotoxic effects: Mechanism of action and structure/activity studies. *Arch. Toxicol.*, **34**, 259–88

Johnson, M. K. (1975c). Structure–activity relationships for substrates and inhibitors of hen brain neurotoxic esterase. *Biochem. Pharmacol.*, **24**, 797–805

Johnson, M. K. (1976). Mechanism of protection against the delayed neurotoxic effects of organophosphorus esters. *Fed. Proc.*, **35**, 73–4

Johnson, M. K. (1977). Improved assay of neurotoxic esterase for screening organo-phosphates for delayed neurotoxicity potential. *Arch. Toxicol.*, **37**, 113–15

Johnson, M. K. (1980). Delayed neurotoxicity induced by organophosphorus compounds – areas of understanding and ignorance. In: *Mechanisms of Toxicity and Hazards Evaluation* (ed. B. Holmstedt, R. Lauwerys, M. Mercier and M. Roberfroid), Elsevier, North Holland, Amsterdam, pp. 27–38

Johnson, M. K. (1982). The target for initiation of delayed neurotoxicity by organophosphorus esters: biochemical studies and toxicological applications. *Rev. Biochem. Toxicol.*, **4**, 141–212

Johnson, M. K. (1984a). The aging reaction of inhibited neuropathy target esterase – fundamental studies and toxicological significance. In: *Cholinesterases: Fundamental and Applied Aspects* (ed. M. Brzin, E. A. Barnard and D. Sket), W. de Gruyter, Berlin, pp. 463–82

Johnson, M. K. (1984b). Delayed neurotoxicity tests of organophosphorus esters: A proposed protocol integrating Neuropathy Target Esterase (NTE) assays with behaviour and histopathology tests to obtain more information more quickly from fewer animals. In: *Proc. Int. Conf. on Environmental Hazards of Agrochemicals in Developing Countries*, Alexandria, Egypt 8–12 Nov. 1983 (ed. A. H. El-Sebae, University of Alexandria, pp. 474–93

Johnson, M. K. and Lauwerys, R. (1969). Protection by some carbamates against the delayed neurotoxic effects of di-isopropyl phosphorofluoridate. *Nature,. Lond.*, **222**, 1066–7

Johnson, M. K. and Read, D. J. (1987). The influence of chirality on the delayed neuropathic potential of some organophosphorus esters: Neuropathic and protective effects of stereoisomeric esters of ethylphenylphosphonic acid (EPN oxon and EPN) correlate with quantities of aged and unaged neuropathy target esterase *in vivo. Toxicol. appl. Pharmacol.* (in press)

Johnson, M. K., Read, D. J. and Benschop, H. P. (1985). Interaction of the four stereoisomers of soman with acetylcholinesterase and neuropathy target esterase of hen brain. *Biochem. Pharmacol.*, **34**, 1945–51

Johnson, M. K., Read, D. J. and Yoshikawa, H. (1986). The effect of steric factors on the interaction of some phenylphosphonates with acetylcholinesterase and neuropathy target esterase of hen brain. *Pest. Biochem. Physiol.*, **25**, 133–42

Le Quesne, P. M. (1975). Neurotoxic substances. In: *Modern Trends in Neurology* (ed. D. Williams), Butterworths, London, pp. 83–97

Lotti, M. L. and Johnson, M. K. (1978). Neurotoxicity of organophosphorus pesticides: Predictions can be based on in vitro studies with hen and human enzymes. *Arch. Toxicol.*, **41**, 215–21

Lotti, M. L. and Johnson, M. K. (1980a). Neurotoxic esterase in human nervous tissue. *J. Neurochem.*, **34**, 747–9

Lotti, M. L. and Johnson, M. K. (1980b). Repeated small doses of a neurotoxic organophosphate. Monitoring of neurotoxic esterase in brain and spinal cord. *Arch. Toxicol.*, **48**, 263–71

Lotti, M., Caroldi, S., Moretto, A., Johnson, M. K., Fish, C., Gopinath, G. and Roberts, N. L. (1987). Central–peripheral delayed neuropathy caused by di-isopropyl phosphorofluoridate (DFP): Segregation of peripheral nerve and spinal cord effects using biochemical, clinical and morphological criteria. *Toxicol. appl. Pharmacol.* (in press)

Mendel, B. and Rudney, H. (1944). The cholinesterases in the light of recent findings. *Science, N.Y.*, **100**, 499–500

Meredith, C. (1986). Biochemical studies on neuropathy target esterase and its role in the initiation of delayed neuropathy by some organophosphorus esters. PhD thesis UK Council for National Academic Awards

Morgan, J. P. and Penovich, P. (1978). Jamaica ginger paralysis. 47-year follow-up. *Arch. Neurol.*, **35**, 530–2

OECD (1983). Acute delayed neurotoxicity of organophosphorus substances; subchronic delayed neurotoxicity of organophosphorus substances: 90-day study. OECD Guidelines for the Testing of Chemicals, Nos. 418 and 419

Padilla, S. and Veronesi, B. (1985). The relationship between neurological damage and neurotoxic esterase inhibition in rats acutely exposed to tri-*ortho*-cresyl phosphate. *Toxicol. appl. Pharmacol.*, **78**, 78–87

Poulsen, E. and Aldridge, W. N. (1964). Studies on esterases in the chicken central nervous system. *Biochem. J.*, **90**, 182–9

Smith, M. I., Elvove, E. and Frazier, W. H. (1930a). The pharmacological action of certain phenol esters with special reference to the etiology of so-called ginger paralysis. *U.S. Publ. Hlth Rep.*, **45**, 2509–24

Smith, M. I., Elvove, E., Valaer, P. J., Frazier, W. H. and Mallory, G. E. (1930b). Pharmacological and chemical studies of the cause of so-called ginger paralysis. *U.S. Publ. Hlth Rep.*, **45**, 1703–16

Smith, M. I., Engel, E. W. and Stohlman, E. F. (1932). Further studies on the pharmacology of certain phenol esters with special reference to the relation of chemical constitution and physiologic action. *Nat. Inst. Hlth Bull.*, **160**, 1–53

Veronesi, B. and Padilla, S. (1985). Phenylmethylsulfonyl fluoride protects rats from mipafox-induced delayed neuropathy. *Toxicol. appl. Pharmacol.*, **81**, 258–64

WHO (1986). Environmental health criteria for organophosphorus pesticides. A general introduction. *Wld Hlth Org. E.H.C.* No. 63, Geneva

Williams, D. G. (1983) Intramolecular group transfer is a characteristic of neurotoxic esterase and is independent of the tissue source of the enzyme. *Biochem. J.*, **209**, 817–29

Williams, D. G. and Johnson, M. K. (1981). Gel electrophoretic identification of hen brain neurotoxic esterase, labelled with tritiated diisopropyl phosphorofluoridate. *Biochem. J.*, **199**, 323–33

3

The Nephrotoxicity of Haloalkane and Haloalkene Glutathione Conjugates

Edward A. Lock

INTRODUCTION

The kidneys are susceptible to the toxicity of a large number of chemicals, although the precise mechanisms of renal injury are not well understood (Maher, 1976; Kluwe, 1981; Hook et al., 1979; Lock, 1982; Rush et al., 1984). This chapter will discuss the mechanism(s) whereby a small number of halogenated chemicals undergo metabolism to form glutathione conjugates. Glutathione conjugates are frequently less toxic than their parent compounds and are eliminated in the bile or after bio-transformation to mercapturic acids, in the urine. However, glutathione conju-gation has been also implicated in the formation of reactive intermediates. In the kidney, at least two different mechanisms have been reported for glutathione dependent generation of reactive intermediates. The first mechanism involves the conjugation of 1,2-dihaloethanes with glutathione. The S-(2-haloethyl)glutathione formed may then rearrange to give a highly reactive ethylene-S-glutathionyl episul-phonium ion (Livesey and Anders, 1979; Van Bladeren et al., 1980; Hill et al., 1978) or undergo degradation to S-(2-haloethyl)-L-cysteine prior to rearranging to give the episulphonium ion (Schasteen and Reed, 1983; Elfarra et al., 1985). This reactive episulphonium ion can then react with nucleophilic groups in various macromolecules to produce toxicity. The second mechanism of glutathione depen-dent metabolic activation involves the formation of stable glutathione conjugates in the liver which are degraded to their cysteine conjugates, concentrated in renal cells and activated by the renal enzyme cysteine conjugate β-lyase (Lock and Green, 1984). The glutathione conjugates of chlorotrifluoroethylene (Dohn and Anders, 1982a; Hassall et al., 1984); hexachloro-1,3-butadiene (Wolf et al., 1984; Nash et al., 1984); tetrafluoroethylene (Odum and Green, 1984), and 2-bromohydroquinone (Monks *et al.*, 1983, 1984) produce their nephrotoxicity via such a mechanism.

The chapter has been divided into three parts; (1) a brief discussion on the structure and physiological functions of the kidney with particular reference to heterogeneity and toxicity; (2) the enzyme systems present in the liver and kidney involved in glutathione conjugate formation and activation and (3) some examples of chemicals that are thought to undergo conjugation and metabolic activation to their proximate nephrotoxins by these mechanisms.

The kidney as a target organ for chemical injury

Because of their structure and physiological functions, the kidneys may be exposed to higher concentrations of chemicals than other organs. The two kidneys comprise about 1% of the body weight, but receive about 25% of the cardiac output (Valtin, 1973).

The kidney is composed of a cortex and medulla, the cortex contains the glomeruli, proximal and distal tubules. Within the proximal tubules there are morphologically and functionally discrete cell types occurring along the nephron which have been designated the S1, S2 and S3 segments (Maunsbach, 1966; Jacobsen and Jorgensen, 1973; Tisher, 1976). The cortex has a high oxygen consumption and is particularly susceptible to agents that produce cellular anoxia, especially in the S3 segment (Glaumann and Trump, 1975; Venkatchalam *et al.*, 1978).

Foreign chemicals present in the blood stream can be delivered to the kidneys in large quantities, especially the renal cortex, which receives about 80% of the total renal blood flow. This, together with the ability of the kidney to concentrate tubular fluid, may enhance the toxicity to proximal tubular cells, by generating high concentrations of foreign compounds in the tubular lumen. In addition, there are other ways in which high concentrations of foreign compounds can accumulate in proximal tubular cells. Solutes which have been filtered at the glomerulus and reabsorbed by passive or active mechanisms can pass through and concentrate in tubular cells. Many organic chemicals undergo active secretion into the tubular lumen via the organic anion transport system, thereby exposing those cells to high concentrations. Organic anion transport occurs in all three segments of the proximal tubule, although considerable variations exist from segment to segment depending on the species (Tune *et al.*, 1969; Roch-Ramel and Weiner, 1980; Roch-Ramel *et al.*, 1980). In the rat, organic anion transport occurs to an equal extent in both the S2 and S3 segments.

The renal medulla receives a much lower blood flow than the cortex, is more anaerobic in its metabolism and is the site of the counter current mechanism which is responsible for concentrating the urine. This counter current mechanism leads to compounds becoming concentrated in the medulla and papilla many times more than in the plasma (Duggin and Mudge, 1976; Mudge *et al.*, 1978).

Once a chemical has become concentrated in a kidney cell it may act directly or require further intrarenal metabolism to produce a toxic response. A direct acting chemical presumably acts by interfering with an important metabolic event, such as inhibiting mitochondrial function leading to anoxia, or by impairing other key functional renal enzymes (Cater and Peters, 1961; Ganote et al., 1974). Alternatively the chemical may be metabolised to a reactive intermediate that may bind covalently to protein, or initiate lipid peroxidation, resulting in cellular damage. In the latter case, the chemical may have already undergone glutathione conjugation by extrarenal enzymes, to give a stable metabolite which can enter the kidney via the systemic circulation.

Most of the common enzymes involved in the metabolism of foreign compounds, e.g. cytochrome P-450 mixed function oxidases and glutathione S-transferases are present in the kidney although the specific activities of these enzymes are generally lower than that found in the liver (Litterst et al., 1975, 1977; Fry et al., 1978). However, in the kidney there are marked regional differences in the relative amounts of certain enzymes due to the cellular heterogeneity of the nephron (Wachsmuth, 1985; Trump et al., 1985). Thus the use of whole kidney as opposed to renal cortex or papilla can grossly underestimate the metabolic activity of certain regions of the kidney. Frequently the intrarenal site of necrosis represents the site of accumulation of the chemical, and the location of the activation enzymes which are responsible for producing the reactive moiety. For example the nephrotoxic chemicals chloroform and 4-ipomeanol concentrate in the proximal tubule, where they are believed to be activated by cytochrome P-450 mixed function oxidases (Ilett et al., 1973; Smith and Hook, 1984; Branchflower et al., 1984; Boyd and Dutcher, 1981) which are also concentrated in that part of the nephron (Fowler et al., 1977; Zenser et al., 1978; Dees et al., 1982).

Glutathione conjugation and degradation enzymes in the liver and kidney

Glutathione conjugate formation is catalysed by cytosolic, microsomal and mitochondrial glutathione-S-transferases present in several tissues (Chasseaud, 1979; Jakoby and Habig, 1980). Of recent interest are reports that the hepatic microsomal enzymes are more effective than the cytosolic enzymes in catalysing the addition reaction of glutathione with chlorotrifluoroethylene or tetrafluoroethylene (Dohn and Anders, 1982a; Odum and Green, 1984), as well as the substitution reaction of glutathione with hexachloro-1,3-butadiene (Wolf et al., 1984; Oesch and Wolf, 1986). Glutathione S-transferase activity in the kidney is much lower than in the liver (Chasseaud, 1979), however with a marked heterogeneity along the nephron, glutathione S-transferase activity in specific cell types could be higher than in hepatocytes. In fact renal glutathione S-transferases and glutathione itself are localised to a significant extent in the cells of the proximal tubule (Ross and Guder, 1982), the site of necrosis caused by chemicals which undergo glutathione conjugation.

Glutathione conjugates can undergo elimination from the liver, via the bile, into the gastrointestinal tract. Biliary derived glutathione conjugates usually undergo rapid hydrolysis to their cysteine conjugates by enzymes present in bile canaliculi, pancreatic secretion and intestinal microflora (Rafter et al., 1983; Grafstrom et al., 1979; Nash et al., 1984). While cysteine conjugates reabsorbed from the gastrointestinal tract can undergo N-acetylation in the liver (Inoue *et al.*, 1982) followed by secretion into the blood stream. The activities of the enzymes that catalyse mercapturic acid formation, γ-glutamyltransferase, cysteinyl glycinase and cysteine conjugate N-acetyltransferase are higher in the kidney than in the liver (Tate, 1980; Jakoby *et al.*, 1984). The renal selectivity of the toxic glutathione conjugates may be attributable to filtration at the glomerulus followed by stepwise processing by γ-glutamyltransferase and cysteinyl glycinase to their cysteine conjugates (figure 3.1). These peptidases are located in the brush border of the proximal renal tubule

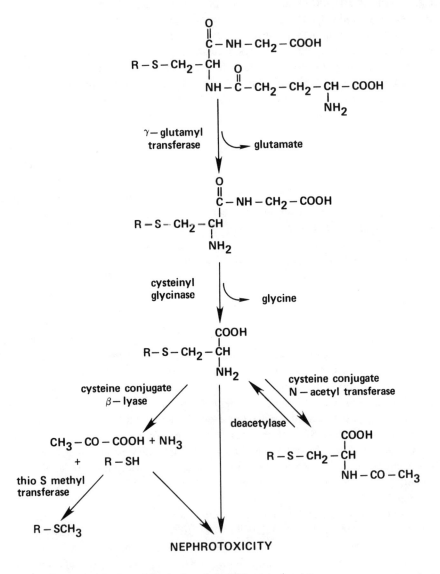

Figure 3.1   The metabolism of S-substituted glutathione conjugates

in high concentrations (Kozak and Tate, 1982; McIntyre and Curthoys, 1982; Ross and Guder, 1982). The cysteine conjugate is then reabsorbed from the lumen into the proximal tubule cells, prior to N-acetylation (figure 3.2).

Alternatively, glutathione and glutathione-derived chemical conjugates may leave the liver via the blood stream and undergo transport across the renal basal-lateral membrane (figure 3.2). A significant amount of glutathione is removed from the circulation by the kidney via a non-filtration mechanism (McIntyre and Curthoys, 1982), which involves transport into renal cells across the basal-lateral membrane

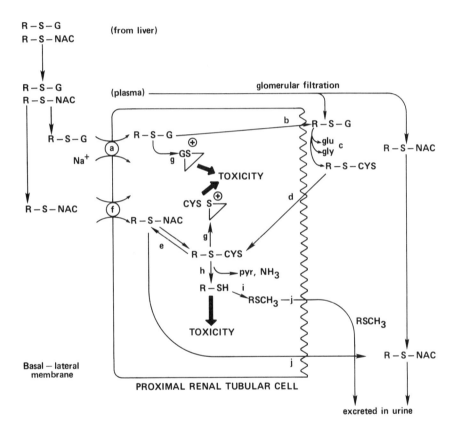

Figure 3.2 The renal metabolism and transport of S-substituted glutathione (R-S-G) and N-acetylcysteine conjugates (R-S-NAC). (a: R-S-G/Na$^+$ co-transport across the basal-lateral membrane; b: efflux of R-S-G from the cell across the brush border membrane; c: removal of glutamate and glycine by γ-glutamyltransferase and cysteinyl glycinase, respectively; d: reabsorption of the cysteine conjugate (R-S-CYS); e: N-acetylation by cysteine conjugate N-acetyltransferase; f: transport of R-S-NAC across the basal-lateral membrane; g: formation of episulphonium ion; h: cleavage of the cysteine conjugate by cysteine conjugate β-lyase; i: methylation via thiol S-methyltransferase; j: efflux of the mercapturate and thiomethyl conjugate from the cell across the brush border membrane.) (Modified from Lash and Jones (1985))

(Rankin and Curthoys, 1982; Lash and Jones, 1983, 1984). The transport of glutathione by renal basal-lateral membrane vesicles, is electrogenic, Na^+-coupled and the transport can be blocked by probenecid (Lash and Jones, 1983, 1984). Lash and Jones have recently extended these findings by showing that the glutathione conjugate, S-(1,2-dichlorovinyl)glutathione, is also transported by this system in renal basal-lateral membranes and isolated kidney cells (Lash and Jones, 1985). This basal-lateral membrane transport system may be important in determining the selective nephrotoxicity of glutathione conjugates. It also suggests that the renal clearance of glutathione conjugates includes transport from the blood through renal cells into the tubular lumen as well as direct filtration through the glomerulus. The fate of the accumulated glutathione conjugates is not clear. In order for it to be excreted as a mercapturate it must come into contact with the luminal facing enzymes γ-glutamyltransferase and cysteinyl glycinase. Whether it is sequestered inside cells or transported across the tubular epithelium is not known.

N-acetylcysteine conjugates undergo transport into renal cells (figure 3.2), both *in vitro* and *in vivo* across the basal-lateral membrane, by a probenecid-sensitive transport system (Inoue *et al.*, 1981, 1984; Smith and Francis, 1983; Lock and Ishmael, 1985; Lock *et al.*, 1986). This system appears to be distinct from the glutathione transport system, as the latter requires the presence of a γ-glutamyl moiety (Lash and Jones, 1984, 1985). N-acetylated cysteine conjugates are not substrates for β-lyase (Bhattacharya and Schultze, 1967; Lock and Green, 1984), but renal deacetylase activity can lead to recycling of the mercapturic acid back to the non-acetylated form (Duffel and Jakoby, 1982; Pratt *et al.*, 1986) (figure 3.1). Cysteine conjugates formed in the tubular lumen are reabsorbed into cells where they have two alternative fates; either they can be N-acetylated by the microsomal cysteine S-conjugate N-acetyltransferase (Green and Elce, 1975; Jakoby *et al.*, 1984) or be cleaved by the enzyme cysteine conjugate β-lyase (figure 3.1, Stevens and Jakoby, 1983; Stevens, 1985a).

Thus proximal tubular cells can receive glutathione conjugates by filtration at the glomerulus and these conjugates can then undergo degradation in the brush border to the cysteine conjugates followed by reabsorption from the lumen (figure 3.2). In addition, two distinct transport systems have been identified on the basal-lateral membrane for the transport of glutathione and mercapturates into renal cells (figure 3.2). The handling of glutathione conjugates of foreign chemicals thus involves considerable metabolic co-operation between the liver, gastrointestinal tract and kidney.

Several cysteine conjugates are metabolised by cysteine conjugate β-lyase to produce pyruvate, ammonia and thiols (Bhattacharya and Schultze, 1967). The thiols can then undergo methylation by the enzyme thiol S-methyltransferase (Weisiger and Jakoby, 1980), which may account for the *in vivo* formation of methyl thiol derivatives of several xenobiotics (Jakoby *et al.*, 1984). Cysteine conjugate β-lyase is a pyridoxal phosphate-dependent enzyme which shares a common reaction mechanism with several related enzymes (Stevens and Jakoby, 1983). The enzyme has been isolated and purified from bovine, turkey and rat kidney, from bovine and rat liver and from intestinal microflora (Anderson and

Schultze, 1965; Bhattacharya and Schultze, 1967; Tateishi *et al.*, 1978; Stevens and Jakoby, 1983; Larsen *et al.*, 1983; Tomisawa *et al.*, 1984; Green and Odum, 1985). Liver cytosolic cysteine conjugate β-lyase can utilise either kynurenine or 3-hydroxykynurenine as substrates, and the enzymes β-lyase and kynureninase have recently been isolated and shown to be identical (Stevens, 1985a). The nature of the renal enzyme has not been studied in detail, but it appears to be localised in cytosol and mitochondria (Stonard and Parker 1971b; Dohn and Anders, 1982b; Stevens, 1985b). It is possible that renal cysteine conjugate β-lyase is not attributable to a single enzyme, but is a composite of activities of several enzymes (Stevens and Jakoby, 1983; Stevens, 1985a,b). Future studies should clarify the identity and nature of renal cysteine conjugate β-lyase activity.

NEPHROTOXIC GLUTATHIONE OR CYSTEINE CONJUGATES THAT ARE DIRECT ACTING

Both 1,2-dibromoethane and 1,2-dichloroethane have been shown to produce kidney damage, in addition to damaging other organs such as the liver in experimental animals (Spencer *et al.*, 1951; Rowe *et al.*, 1952) and man (Olmstead, 1960). Very few studies have dealt specifically with the question of renal conjugation and activation of dihaloethanes and its relevance to nephrotoxicity. However, hepatic conjugation has been extensively studied and may be important in determining the extent of renal injury. 1,2-Dichloroethane lowers hepatic glutathione in the rat (Johnson, 1965) while 1,2-dibromoethane lowers both hepatic and renal glutathione content (Nachtomi *et al.*, 1968; Kluwe *et al.*, 1981). Subsequent work showed that 1,2-dibromoethane is excreted primarily in urine as 2-hydroxyethylmercapturic acid (figure 3.3), which is formed by further metabolism of the glutathione conjugate (Nachtomi *et al.*, 1966; Van Bladeren *et al.*, 1980). The involvement of glutathione in hepatic and renal metabolism was investigated by Nachtomi (1970) who identified S-(2-hydroxyethyl)glutathione and S,S'-ethylenebisglutathione, the conjugation products of 1,2-dibromoethane with one and two molecules of glutathione respectively, in hepatic and renal tissues of rats dosed with 1,2-dibromoethane.

Rannug *et al.* (1978) have implicated hepatic glutathione and cytosolic glutathione S-transferases in the activation of 1,2-dichloro- and 1,2-dibromoethane to metabolites, presumably S-(2-haloethyl)glutathione derivatives, which were mutagenic to *Salmonella typhimurium* TA1535 (table 3.1). The hepatic subcellular distribution, cofactor requirements and the effect of various inhibitors suggests that the enzymes involved in reactive intermediate formation are glutathione S-transferase(s) (Rannug *et al.*, 1978; Hill *et al.*, 1978; Livesey and Anders, 1979; Van Bladeren *et al.*, 1980; Guengerich *et al.*, 1980). Studies with purified cytosolic glutathione S-transferase(s) confirmed the formation of reactive intermediates from 1,2-dichloro- and 1,2-dibromoethane with the isoenzyme Ya Yc (or B) being the most active (Rannug *et al.*, 1978; Inskeep and Guengerich, 1984). There is some indication that a microsomal glutathione S-transferase may also catalyse the forma-

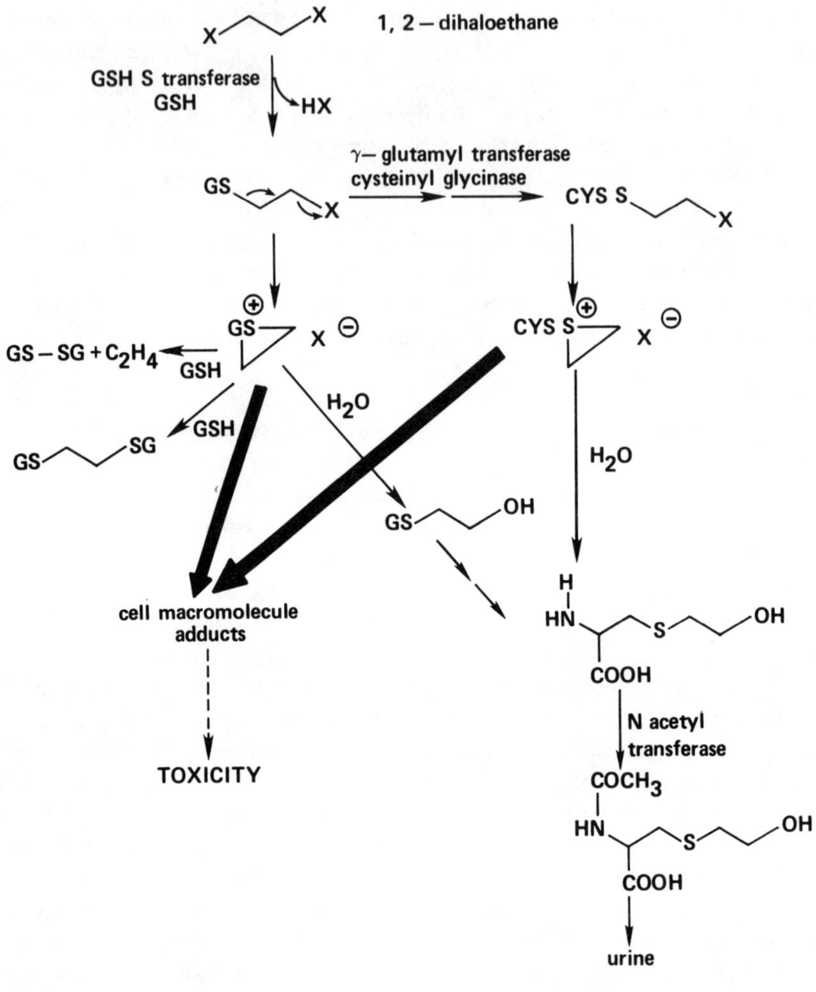

Figure 3.3   Postulated metabolism of 1,2-dihaloethanes which gives rise to toxic glutathione-derived intermediates. (Modified from Van Bladeren *et al.* (1980) and Elfarra *et al.* (1985)

Table 3.1 Cysteine S-Conjugates of Halogenated Hydrocarbons that are Nephrotoxic and Mutagenic

Cysteine conjugate R = Cysteine	Nephrotoxic	Mutagenic	Reference
1. $H-\underset{\underset{Cl}{\vert}}{\overset{\overset{H}{\vert}}{C}}-\underset{\underset{H}{\vert}}{\overset{\overset{H}{\vert}}{C}}-R$	+	+	Elfarra et al., 1985 Rannug et al., 1978 Van Bladeren et al., 1980
2. $H-\underset{\underset{F}{\vert}}{\overset{\overset{Cl}{\vert}}{C}}-\underset{\underset{F}{\vert}}{\overset{\overset{F}{\vert}}{C}}-R$	+[a]	ND	Bonhaus and Gandolfi, 1981 Gandolfi et al., 1981 Elfarra and Anders, 1984
3. $H-\underset{\underset{F}{\vert}}{\overset{\overset{F}{\vert}}{C}}-\underset{\underset{F}{\vert}}{\overset{\overset{F}{\vert}}{C}}-R$	+	–	Odum and Green, 1984 Green and Odum, 1985
4. $H-\underset{\underset{F}{\vert}}{\overset{\overset{F}{\vert}}{C}}-\underset{\underset{F}{\vert}}{\overset{\overset{F}{\vert}}{C}}-\underset{\underset{F}{\vert}}{\overset{\overset{F}{\vert}}{C}}-R$	+[b]	–	Green and Odum, 1985
5. $\underset{Cl}{\overset{H}{}}{>}C{=}C{<}\underset{R}{\overset{Cl}{}}$	+	+	Terracini and Parker, 1965 Schultze et al., 1962 Green and Odum, 1985
6. $\underset{Cl}{\overset{Cl}{}}{>}C{=}C{<}\underset{R}{\overset{Cl}{}}$	+[b]	+	Green and Odum, 1985
7. $\underset{Cl}{\overset{Cl}{}}{>}C{=}C{<}\underset{\underset{Cl}{}}{\overset{Cl}{}}C{=}C{<}\underset{R}{\overset{Cl}{}}$	+	+	Jaffe et al., 1983 Lock et al., 1984 Green and Odum, 1985
8. $F-\underset{\underset{F}{\vert}}{\overset{\overset{F}{\vert}}{C}}-C{=}C{<}\underset{R}{\overset{F}{}}$	+[b]	–	Green and Odum, 1985
9. Br-[aromatic ring with HO, R, OH]	+	ND	Monks et al., 1984

[a] Gandolfi and coworkers originally identified this conjugate as the haloalkene, it now seems likely it was the haloalkane.
[b] Nephrotoxicity was assessed *in vitro* in renal cortical slices.
ND = not determined.

tion of reactive intermediates from 1,2-dichloroethane (Guengerich *et al.*, 1980). Both glutathione-S-transferase and its endogenous substrate glutathione are localised to a significant extent in the proximal tubule (Ross and Guder, 1982), the site of necrosis caused by these chemicals.

S-(2-haloethyl)glutathione conjugates are thought to form electrophilic episulphonium ions by internal displacement of the second halogen atom by the sulphur atom (figure 3.3). The episulphonium ion can then react with biological macromolecules (Rannug *et al.*, 1978; Van Bladeren *et al.*, 1980). An interesting finding was the preferential alkylation of nucleic acids versus proteins by 1,2-dihaloethanes (Hill *et al.*, 1978; Bannerjee and Van Durren, 1979; Shih and Hill, 1981; Guengerich *et al.*, 1980). This binding was dependent on cytosolic enzymes and glutathione, but not on microsomal protein (Shih and Hill, 1981; Sundheimer *et al.*, 1982). Irreversible binding to DNA of a 1,2-dibromoethane–glutathione adduct formed by a glutathione S-transferase catalysed reaction has been reported (Ozawa and Guengerich, 1983; Inskeep and Guengerich, 1984). In this case, equimolar amounts of [^{35}S]-glutathione and 1,2-dibromo[1,2^{14}C]ethane were bound to DNA in the presence of glutathione S-transferase or isolated hepatocytes. An S-[2-(N^7-guanyl)-ethyl]glutathione adduct was identified after enzymatic degradation of the DNA (Ozawa and Guengerich, 1983). Vadi *et al.* (1985) have reported a marked difference in the reactivity of S-(2-chloroethyl)cysteine and S-(2-chloroethyl)glutathione in their interaction with supercoiled plasmid DNA *in vitro*. Extensive binding of ^{35}S from labelled S-(2-chloro or bromoethyl) cysteine was found in DNA whereas ^{35}S from S-(2-chloroethyl)glutathione did not bind, suggesting a major difference in reactivity of the corresponding episulphonium ions of the conjugates.

Hepatic glutathione dependent metabolism of 1,2-dihaloethanes may account for some of the 1,2-dihaloethane-induced nephrotoxicity. *In vivo*, the half sulphur mustard formed subsequent to glutathione conjugation could leave the hepatocyte and enter the bile in sufficient quantity to be reabsorbed from the intestine and enter the kidney. There it could be degraded to the cysteine conjugate and then form a reactive episulphonium ion (figure 3.3, Elfarra *et al.*, 1985). Evidence for such a route is supported by the demonstration of mutagenicity of rat bile, produced by perfused livers, when 1,2-dibromoethane is included in the perfusion medium (Rannug and Beije, 1979). In addition, Schasteen and Reed (1983) have suggested that S-(2-chloroethyl)glutathione may have a significantly longer half-life than S-(2-chloroethyl)cysteine. Thus S-(2-chloroethyl)glutathione formed in the liver may be transported to the kidney.

Renal protein, RNA and DNA exhibited the highest concentration of covalently bound radioactivity in comparison to other organs studied 24 h after administration of 1,2-dibromo[1,2^{14}C]ethane (Hill *et al.*, 1978), suggesting that direct conjugation with glutathione in the kidney is also significant. The rat kidney contains a high glutathione S-transferase activity with 1,2-dibromoethane as substrate (Hill *et al.*, 1978). It is therefore likely that reactive episulphonium ions can be generated within renal cells and thereby alkylate protein and DNA and cause necrosis and carcinogenesis, respectively. S-(2-chloroethyl)cysteine (1, Table 3.1), a putative metabolite of 1,2-dichloroethane formed via glutathione conjugation, is nephrotoxic to the rat, where it produces an elevation in blood urea and urinary glucose concentrations which are associated with proximal tubular necrosis (Elfarra *et al.*, 1985). However, analogues of S-(2-chloroethyl)cysteine in which the chlorine atom is replaced by a hydrogen atom, a hydroxy group or a chloromethylene group were not nephrotoxic (Elfarra *et al.*, 1985). These findings strongly implicate episulphonium ion formation in S-(2-chloroethyl)cysteine-induced nephrotoxicity.

The renal necrosis produced by S-(2-haloethyl)cysteine or glutathione (derived conjugates) may be related to selective accumulation of these chemicals by renal cells via a probenecid-sensitive transport system Elfarra *et al.* (1985) have shown that probenecid administration can partially protect against the nephrotoxicity produced by S-(2-chloroethyl)cysteine in the rat (figure 3.4).

S-(2-chloroethyl)cysteine is not a substrate for the hepatic or renal enzyme cysteine conjugate β-lyase (Stevens and Jakoby, 1983; Elfarra *et al.*, 1985), and thus does not produce a reactive metabolite by this mechanism.

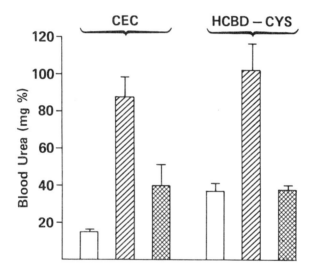

Figure 3.4 The effect of probenecid on S-(2-chloroethyl)cysteine and S-(1,2,3,4,4-pentachloro-1,3-butadienyl)cysteine induced increases in blood urea in the rat

Rats were given S-(2-chloroethyl)cysteine (CEC) at 100 mg/kg ip or S-(1,2,3,4,4-pentachloro-1,3-butadienyl)cysteine (HCBD-CYS) at 12.5 mg/kg ip, alone or 30 min after probenecid. Animals were killed 36 h (CEC) or 24 h (HCBD-CYS) after dosing. Results are mean ± SEM. Control (open bars); treated, (single cross-hatching); treated plus probenecid (double cross-hatching). (Modified from Elfarra *et al.* (1985) and Lock and Ishmael (1985)

NEPHROTOXIC CYSTEINE CONJUGATES THAT ARE SUBSTRATES FOR CYSTEINE CONJUGATE β-LYASE

A number of haloalkenes, hexachloro-1,3-butadiene (HCBD) (Gradiski *et al.*, 1975; Kociba *et al.*, 1977a; Harleman and Seinen, 1979; Lock and Ishmael, 1979; Berndt and Mehendale, 1979); chlorotrifluoroethylene (CTFE) (Walther *et al.*, 1969; Dilley *et al.*, 1974; Clayton, 1977; Potter *et al.*, 1981; Buckley *et al.*, 1982); hexafluoropropene (HFP) (Dilley *et al.*, 1974; Clayton, 1977; Potter *et al.*, 1981); difluorodichloroethylene (CDFE) (Sakharova and Tolgskaya, 1977) and tetrafluoroethylene (TFE) (Walther *et al.*, 1969; Dilley *et al.*, 1974; Odum and Green, 1984) produce marked nephrotoxicity with minimal liver injury. These compounds probably all undergo metabolism via glutathione conjugation. Reports have shown that hepatic microsomal glutathione S-transferases are more effective than the cytosolic enzymes in catalysing the addition reaction of CTFE (Dohn and Anders, 1982a) or TFE (Odum and Green, 1984) and glutathione, as well as the substitution reaction of glutathione and HCBD (Wolf *et al.*, 1984; Oesch and Wolf, 1986). Evidence has been presented showing that these glutathione conjugates, as well as their corresponding cysteine conjugates are nephrotoxic (Elfarra and Anders, 1984; table 3.1) The glutathione and cysteine conjugates of 2,3,7 and 9 (table 3.1) are known metabolites of the nephrotoxins HCBD (Nash *et al.*, 1984; Reichert *et al.*, 1985), CTFE (Bonhaus and Gandolfi, 1981; Dohn and Anders, 1982a), TFE (Odum and Green, 1984) and 2-bromohydroquinone, a metabolite of bromobenzene (Monks *et al.*, 1983, 1984), respectively. The cysteine conjugate S-(1,2-dichlorovinyl)-L-cysteine (DCVC) (5, table 3.1) was identified as the toxic factor causing aplastic anaemia in cattle fed soya bean meal, that had been extracted with trichloroethylene (McKinney *et al.*, 1959; Schultze *et al.*, 1959). In a number of laboratory species only renal damage was found after giving DCVC, while, in the calf, recovery from renal injury is followed by the onset of aplastic anaemia (Terracini and Parker, 1965). The cysteine conjugate S-(1,2,2-trichlorovinyl)-L-cysteine (6, table 3.1) is the postulated conjugate formed by the substitution reaction of glutathione and perchloroethylene, which has not been reported *in vivo* as cytochrome P-450 appears to be the predominant route of metabolism. Finally S-(1,1,2,2,3,3-hexafluoropropyl)-L-cysteine and S-(1,2,3,3,3-pentafluoropropen-1-yl)-L-cysteine (4 and 8, table 3.1) could arise following addition and substitution reactions of glutathione with HFP. Thus a number of nephrotoxic cysteine conjugates derived from glutathione conjugation have been identified.

Hexachloro-1,3-butadiene is probably the best established example of glutathione conjugation followed by renal processing and its activation by cysteine conjugate β-lyase and will be used to illustrate this type of nephrotoxicity. Where appropriate other examples will also be used to illustrate certain points.

Following either oral or intraperitoneal administration of a nephrotoxic dose of radiolabelled HCBD, radioactivity appears primarily in the faeces (Davis *et al.*, 1980; Nash *et al.*, 1984; Reichert *et al.*, 1985). Twenty-four hours after dosing the highest concentration of radioactivity from HCBD is found in the kidneys, while autoradiographic studies show accumulation in the outer stripe of the outer medulla, the site of necrosis, suggesting that retention or binding of radiolabel and toxicity are related events (Nash *et al.*, 1984; Lock and Green, 1984). Administration of HCBD to adult male rats produced a depletion of hepatic, but not renal, non-protein sulphydryl (glutathione) content (Lock and Ishmael, 1981; Kluwe *et al.*, 1981; Hook *et al.*, 1983). Analysis of bile from HCBD-treated rats showed the major metabolite was S-(1,2,3,4,4-pentachloro-1,3-butadienyl) glutathione (Nash *et al.*, 1984), while *in vitro* studies with rat liver microsomes or cytosol (Wolf *et al.*, 1984) or isolated hepatocytes (Gerdes *et al.*, 1985) have confirmed the formation of both mono- and di-glutathionyl conjugates of HCBD. The relevance to nephrotoxicity of the di-glutathionyl conjugate of HCBD formed in the presence of rat liver cytosol, is currently not understood. Cannulation of the bile duct of HCBD-treated rats prevented the nephrotoxicity, while administration of lyophilised bile, collected from HCBD-treated rats, to naive rats produced renal necrosis analogous to that seen with the parent compound (figure 3.5). These findings are in agreement with the idea that a glutathione-derived conjugate of HCBD is involved in the nephrotoxicity (Nash *et al.*, 1984) an interpretation also strongly supported by studies with chemically synthesised glutathione, cysteine and mercapturic acid conjugates of HCBD, which cause renal necrosis identical to that produced by HCBD itself (Jaffe *et al.*, 1983; Nash *et al.*, 1984; Lock *et al.*, 1984; Lock and

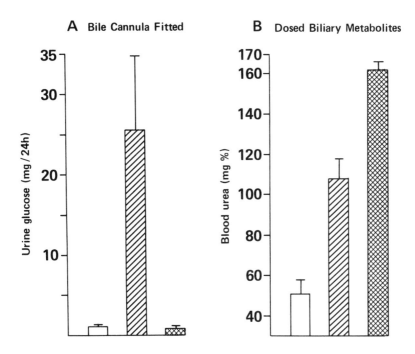

Figure 3.5 The effect of biliary cannulation on the nephrotoxicity of hexachloro-1,3-butadiene (HCBD) in the rat. (A) Rats were biliary cannulated and given a single oral dose of HCBD, 200 mg/kg (double cross-hatching), controls were cannulated but given vehicle alone (open bars), while a third group were not cannulated but given HCBD (single cross-hatching). Urine was collected for 24 h and analysed for glucose. (B) Rats were dosed orally with ^{14}[C]-bile (equivalent to 107 mg/kg HCBD) collected from rats dosed orally with ^{14}[C]-HCBD, 200 mg/kg, (double cross-hatching), controls were dosed with an equivalent amount of control bile (open bars) or with HCBD, 200 mg/kg alone (single cross-hatching). Animals were killed 24 h after dosing and plasma analysed for urea. Results are mean ± SEM. (Modified from Nash *et al.* (1984))

Ishmael, 1985). The cysteinylglycine conjugate of HCBD has also been identified in bile (Nash *et al.*, 1984). Rapid hydrolysis of biliary derived glutathione conjugates to their corresponding cysteine conjugates would be anticipated within the intestine (Grafstrom *et al.*, 1979; Hirata and Takahashi, 1981). Reabsorption of these conjugates, from the gastrointestinal tract, will allow them to reach the kidney in significant amounts, where they may accumulate in proximal tubular cells by a number of mechanisms (figure 3.2).

The role of γ-glutamyltransferase in the nephrotoxicity of glutathione conjugates has been studied using the inhibitor AT-125 (L-(αS, 5S)α-amino-3-chloro-4,5-dihydro-5-isoazoleacetic acid). Treatment of rats with AT-125 inhibits renal γ-glutamyltransferase and produces glutathionuria (Reed and Ellis, 1981). Prior treatment of rats with AT-125 before S-(1,2-dichlorovinyl)glutathione afforded some protection against the nephrotoxicity as assessed by blood urea and urinary glucose excretion (Elfarra and Anders, 1984). AT-125 treatment also gave some protection against 2-bromohydroquinone-induced increases in blood urea concentrations (Monks *et al.*, 1984). However AT-125 does not afford complete protection against the nephrotoxicity of S-(1,2-dichlorovinyl)glutathione or 2-bromohydroquinone and gave no protection against HCBD-induced nephrotoxicity (Davis, 1984). Treatment of isolated renal cells with AT-125 greatly increased the renal accumulation of S-(1,2-dichlorovinyl)glutathione (Lash and Jones, 1985) but reduced the extent of nephrotoxicity as measured by organic anion and cation accumulation (Hassall *et al.*, 1984). These results suggest that AT-125 does not completely stop the renal processing of glutathione conjugates to cysteine derivatives, while it also facilitates their accumulation via the glutathione conjugate transport system.

The selectivity of the kidney for HCBD-induced toxicity is related to the kidney's ability to accumulate organic anions (Lock and Ishmael, 1985). Radiolabel from [^{14}C] HCBD-N-acetylcysteine conjugate is readily accumulated by the kidney, presumably within the proximal tubule, where it can reach concentrations in the cortex many times that in the plasma (Lock and Ishmael, 1985). This accumulation can be prevented by the organic anion transport inhibitor probenecid, which gives protection against the nephrotoxicity of HCBD and its glutathione-derived conjugates (figure 3.4, Lock and Ishmael, 1985). Studies with renal cortical slices have demonstrated an energy-dependent accumulation of radioactivity from [^{14}C]-HCBD-N-acetylcysteine, which shows competitive inhibition with organic anions, but not cations (Lock *et al.*, 1986). The transport process has an apparent K_m of 5.6 μM and a V_{max} of 234 nmol/g kidney/h with a K_i for probenecid of 14 μM (Lock *et al.*, 1986). The N-acetylcysteine conjugate of HCBD undergoes rapid deacetylation in the presence of rat kidney cytosol to yield the cysteine conjugate and also results in the covalent binding of radioactivity from HCBD to renal protein (Pratt *et al.*, 1986). Aminooxyacetic acid, an inhibitor of pyridoxal phosphate-dependent enzymes (Wallach, 1961) inhibits renal cysteine conjugate β-lyase (Elfarra and Anders, 1984; Lock, unpublished observation) and prevents the covalent binding of radioactivity from HCBD-N-acetylcysteine conjugate to renal protein (Pratt *et al.*, 1986). Radioactivity from HCBD-N-acetylcysteine conjugate also becomes covalently bound to renal protein *in vivo*, in a dose related manner, which can be prevented by probenecid (Lock and Ishmael, 1985). These findings indicate that further metabolism and activation of the cysteine conjugate of HCBD in renal proximal tubular cells is necessary to produce toxicity.

S-(1,2-dichlorovinyl)-L-cysteine (DCVC) has been reported to undergo activation *via* the renal enzyme cysteine conjugate β-lyase, which cleaves the C–S bond generating 1 mole of pyruvate, 1 mole of ammonia, 2 moles of chloride ion and a reactive mercaptan moiety which can combine with proteins and glutathione (Bhattacharya and Schultze, 1967). The substrate specificity of the renal enzyme was examined using a wide range of sulphur and non-sulphur containing amino acids. Significant pyruvate production was only detected with L-DCVC and L-DCVC sulphoxide (Bhattacharya and Schultze, 1967). The mercapturate N-acetyl-DCVC, the D-isomer of DCVC and L-DVCX methyl ester were not substrates for the enzyme. Recently Elfarra and Anders (1984) have synthesised S-(1,2-dichlorovinyl)-DL-α-methylcysteine, which cannot be cleaved by cysteine conjugate β-lyase and shown that *in vivo* it does not produce nephrotoxicity. These workers have also shown that aminooxyacetic acid inhibits renal cysteine conjugate β-lyase *in vitro* and *in vivo* and protects against DCVC-induced nephrotoxicity (Elfarra and Anders, 1984). All these findings clearly implicate cysteine conjugate β-lyase in DCVC mediated nephrotoxicity.

HCBD-cysteine, but not N-acetylcysteine-HCBD or HCBD-glutathione, is a substrate for renal cysteine conjugate β-lyase where it generates 1 mole of pyruvate, 1 mole of ammonia and a reactive moiety which inhibits the transport of organic anions and cations into renal cortical slices (Lock and Green, 1985; Green and Odum, 1985). These studies have also shown that the nephrotoxins S-(1,1,2,2-tetrafluoroethyl)-L-cysteine (3, table 3.1), S-(1,2,2-trichlorovinyl) L-cysteine (6, table 3.1), S-(1,1,2,2,3,3-hexafluoropropyl)-L-cysteine (4, table 3.1) and S-(1,2,3,3,3-pentafluoropropene-1-yl)-L-cysteine (8, table 3.1) are also substrates for renal cysteine conjugate β-lyase (Green and Odum, 1985; Lock and Green, 1985), and generate a reactive moiety which inhibits the transport of organic anions and cations into renal cortical slices.

2-Bromohydroquinone-cysteine (9, table 3.1), but not 2-bromohydroquinone-N-acetyl cysteine is also a substrate for cysteine conjugate β-lyase (Monks *et al.*, 1984). The toxicity of a number of these haloalkene cysteine conjugates to isolated renal tubular fragments or cells has been demonstrated using organic anion and cation accumulation as a sensitive marker of toxicity (Jaffe *et al.*, 1983; Hassall *et al.*, 1983, 1984; Earl *et al.*, 1984).

Following β-lyase cleavage of HCBD-cysteine, the presumed chlorobutadienyl-thiol moiety will then react with one of the following targets: (1) glutathione, a reaction which may account for the decrease in renal glutathione seen under some conditions (Kluwe *et al.*, 1981; Hook *et al.*, 1983; Lock *et al.*, 1984): (2) protein, where it binds covalently (Lock and Ishmael, 1985; Reichert *et al.*, 1985) possibly to cysteine residues or across disulphide bridges in proteins. The inhibition of the enzyme glutathione reductase (Lock, unpublished observation), which contains a disulphide bond at the active site (Massey and Williams, 1965) may be relevant in this respect. Finally (3) DNA, accounting for its mutagenic properties in the Ames Salmonella bacterial assay, using rat kidney S9 fraction (Green and Odum, 1985; Lock and Green, 1984). This is in agreement with the increased incidence of renal tubular adenomas and adenocarcinoma (Kociba *et al.*, 1977b) which have been reported after chronic administration of HCBD to rats. No binding to DNA could be detected following the *in vitro* incubation of HCBD, glutathione S-transferase, [35][S] glutathione and DNA, whereas 1,2-dibromoethane showed extensive binding under these conditions (Inskeep and Guengerich, 1984). This indicates that HCBD does not produce its toxicity by forming a reactive episulphonium ion as is the case with 1,2-dibromoethane.

Two other chloroalkene cysteine conjugates, S-(1,2-dichlorovinyl)-L-cysteine and S-(1,2,2-trichlorovinyl)-L-cysteine (5 and 6, table 3.1) were both mutagenic in the Ames Salmonella bacterial assay, either in the presence or absence of rat kidney S9 fraction (Green and Odum, 1985) possibly suggesting activation by bacterial cysteine conjugate β-lyase (Saari and Schultze, 1965). The reactive metabolite formed *in vitro* from the cleavage of DCVC will combine with nucleic acids (Bhattacharya and Schultze, 1972), proteins and glutathione (Anderson and Schultze, 1965). Chronic administration of DCVC to mice (Jaffe *et al.*, 1984) or rats (Terracini and Parker, 1965) for 37 and 47 weeks respectively, produced severe renal injury but no evidence of renal tumours. However, both the parent haloalkenes have been reported to produce a small increase in the incidence of renal tumours in male rats in a two year bioassay (Kluwe *et al.*, 1984). Interestingly the fluorine containing cysteine conjugates (3,4 and 8, table 3.1) are all negative in a number of Salmonella Ames tests, in the presence and absence of renal S9 fraction (Green and Odum, 1985). The difference between the fluorine and chlorine containing conjugates presumably lies in the nature or reactivity of the species generated by the β-lyase enzyme. The chlorinated conjugates (5, 6 and 7, table 3.1) are able to undergo tautomerism to produce an acylating agent capable of reacting with DNA, while the fluorinated alkane conjugates (3 and 4, table 3.1) are not (Green and Odum, 1985). It appears that pentafluoropropenylcysteine (8, table 3.1) generates a thiol that does not tautomerise to produce an acylating agent, perhaps due to the greater stability of the C–F bond. Thus neither cysteine conjugate of HFP is mutagenic.

Three metabolites have so far been identified in rat urine from HCBD-treated animals, namely S-(1,2,3,4,4-pentachloro-1,3-butadienyl)sulphenic acid (Nash *et al.*, 1984), pentachloro-1-methyl-thio-1,3-butadiene and pentachloro-carboxymethylthio-1,3-butadiene (Reichert *et al.*, 1985). Two of these metabolites support the *in vitro* data indicating that C–S bond cleavage has occurred followed by subsequent methylation or oxidation. A summary of the pathways of HCBD metabolism is shown in figure 3.6.

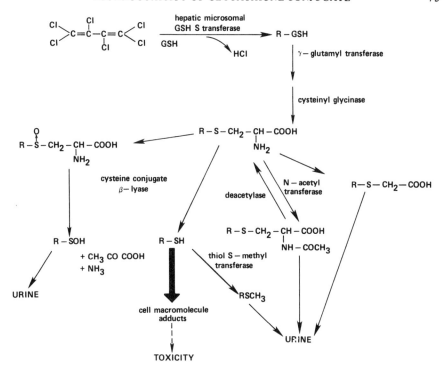

Figure 3.6 Postulated metabolism of hexachloro-1,3-butadiene which gives rise to toxic glutathione-derived intermediates. (Modified from Nash *et al.* (1984) and Reichert *et al.* (1985)

CONCLUDING REMARKS

The data summarised in this chapter show that cysteine conjugates derived from glutathione conjugation with halogenated chemicals are nephrotoxic. The target organ selectivity of glutathione conjugates is probably due to inter-organ co-operation in metabolism and their renal processing to yield the corresponding cysteine conjugate (figure 3.2), which may be a direct-acting nephrotoxin, like S-(2-chloroethyl)cysteine or which may require bioactivation by cysteine conjugated β-lyase, like HCBD-cysteine, to produce toxicity. Renal cysteine conjugate β-lyase catalyses the conversion of cysteine conjugates to pyruvate, ammonia and a reactive thiol moiety. The thiol formed is probably responsible for the toxicity and in some cases mutagenicity. With HCBD, the thiol moiety would be 1,2,3,4,4-pentachloro-1, 3-butadienyl mercaptan, which may rearrange to yield a thionoacyl halide. Further work is needed to identify the structures of the thiols formed and their interactions with renal macromolecules as has been reported for 1,2-dibromoethane (Ozawa and Guengerich, 1983). It is also important to ascertain which are the critical site(s) on macromolecules that are alkylated and to identify the sequence of biochemical events which lead to renal tubular necrosis. There is evidence that the mitochondrion is a prime target for DCVC and the cysteine conjugate of HCBD, where they inter-fere with oxidative phosphorylation (Parker, 1965; Stonard and Parker, 1971a; Stonard, 1973; Schnellman *et al.*, 1986). Little is known about these key enzyme steps in man. *In vitro* studies with human tissue to determine the rate of hepatic conjugation and the activity of renal cysteine conjugate β-lyase are important future steps to help extrapolate these findings from experimental animals to man.

Glutathione conjugation is the body's way of processing these foreign com-pounds for excretion. However, in these cases, it leads to a lethal synthesis. Gluta-thione also scavenges the reactive electrophiles formed, so glutathione plays a role in both the toxication and detoxication of these haloalkene and haloalkane chemicals.

Note added in proof

Cysteine conjugate β-lyase has recently been purified from rat kidney cytosol and appears to be identical to rat kidney cytosolic glutamine transaminase K (Stevens, J. L., Robbins, J. D. and Byrd, R. A. (1986). A purified cysteine conjugate β-lyase from rat kidney cytosol. *J. Biol. Chem.*, **261**, 15529-37).

ACKNOWLEDGEMENTS

The author wishes to thank Dr B. Elliott, Dr T. Green and Dr. M. Stonard, for their constructive criticism of the draft manuscript. I am also indebted to Mrs B. Holroyd for her patience in typing the manuscript.

REFERENCES

Anderson, P. M. and Schultze, M. O. (1965). Cleavage of S-(1,2-dichlorovinyl)-L-cysteine by an enzyme of bovine origin. *Arch. Biochem. Biophys.*, **111**, 593-602

Banerjee, S. and Van Durren, B. L. (1979). Binding of carcinogenic halogenated hydrocarbons to cell macromolecules. *J. Nat. Cancer. Inst.*, **63**, 707-11

Berndt, W. O. and Mehendale, H. M. (1979). Effects of hexachlorobutadiene (HCBD) on renal function and renal organic ion transport in the rat. *Toxicology*, **14**, 55-65

Bhattacharya, R. K. and Schultze, M. O. (1967). Enzymes in bovine and turkey kidneys which cleave S-(1,2-dichlorovinyl)-L-cysteine. *Comp. Biochem. Physiol.*, **22**, 723-35

Bhattacharya, R. K. and Schultze, M. O. (1972). Properties of DNA treated with S-(1,2-dichlorovinyl)-L-cysteine and a lyase. *Arch. Biochem. Biophys.*, **153**, 105-15

Bonhaus, D. W. and Gandolfi, A. J. (1981). Conjugation and bioactivation of chlorotrifluoroethylene. *Life Sci.*, **29**, 2399-405

Boyd, M. R. and Dutcher, J. S. (1981). Renal toxicity due to reactive metabolites formed in situ in the kidney: investigations with 4-ipomeanol in the mouse. *J. Pharmacol. exptl. Ther.*, **216**, 640-6

Branchflower, R. V., Nunn, D. S., Highet, R. J., Smith, J. H., Hook, J. B. and Pohl, L. R. (1984). Nephrotoxicity of chloroform: metabolism to phosgene by the mouse kidney. *Toxicol. appl. Pharmacol.*, 72, 159–68

Buckley, L. A., Clayton, J. W., Nagle, R. B. and Gandolfi, A. J. (1982). Chlorotrifluoroethylene nephrotoxicity in rats: a subacute study. *Fund. appl. Toxicol.*, 2, 181–6

Cater, D. B. and Peters, R. A. (1961). The occurrence of renal changes resembling nephrosis in rats poisoned with fluorocitrate. *Brit. J. exptl. Path.*, 42, 278–89

Chasseaud, L. F. (1979). The role of glutathione and glutathione S-transferases in the metabolism of chemical carcinogens and other electrophilic agents. *Adv. Cancer Res.*, 29, 175–274

Clayton, J. W. (1977). Toxicology of the fluoroalkenes: review and research needed. *Environ. Hlth Perspec.*, 21, 255–67

Davis, M. E. (1984). AT-125 (acividin) does not prevent hexachlorobutadiene (HCBD) nephrotoxicity. *Toxicologist*, 4, 32

Davis, M. E., Berndt, W. O. and Mehendale, H. M. (1980). Disposition and nephrotoxicity of hexachloro-1,3-butadiene. *Toxicology*, 16, 179–91

Dees, J. H., Masters, B. S. S., Muller-Eberhard, U. and Johnson, E. F. (1982). Effect of 2,3,7,8-tetrachlorodibenzo-p-dioxin and phenobarbitone on the occurrence and distribution of four cytochrome P-450 isoenzymes in rabbit kidney. *Cancer Res.*, 42, 1423–32

Dilley, J. V., Carter, V. L. and Harris, E. S. (1974). Fluoride ion excretion by male rats after inhalation of one of several fluoroethylenes or hexafluoropropene. *Toxicol. appl. Pharmacol.*, 27, 582–90

Dohn, A. R. and Anders, M. W. (1982a). The enzymatic reaction of chlorotrifluoroethylene with glutathione. *Biochem. Biophys. Res. Commun.*, 109, 1339–45

Dohn, A. R. and Anders, M. W. (1982b). Assay of cysteine conjugate β-lyase activity with S-(2-benzothiazolyl)cysteine as the substrate. *Anal. Biochem.*, 120, 379–86

Duffel, M. and Jakoby, W. B. (1982). Cysteine S-conjugate N-acetyl-transferase from rat kidney microsomes. *Mol. Pharm.*, 21, 444–8

Duggin, G. G. and Mudge, G. H. (1976). Analgesic nephropathy: renal distribution of acetaminophen and its conjugates. *J. Pharmacol. exptl. Ther.*, 199, 1–9

Earl, L. K., McLean, A. E. M. and Lock, E. A. (1984). Use of isolated kidney cells for studying nephrotoxicity: hexachloro-1,3-butadiene as a model compound. *Human Toxicol.*, 3, 332–3

Elfarra, A. A. and Anders, M. W. (1984). Renal processing of glutathione conjugates: role in nephrotoxicity. *Biochem. Pharmacol.*, 33, 3729–32

Elfarra, A. A., Baggs, R. B. and Anders, M. W. (1985). Structure–nephrotoxicity relationships of S-(2-chloroethyl)-DL-cysteine and analogs: role for an episulphonium ion. *J. Pharmacol. exptl. Ther.*, 233, 512–16

Fowler, B. A., Hook, G. E. R. and Lucier, G. W. (1977). Tetrachlorodibenzo-p-dioxin induction of renal microsomal enzyme systems. Ultrastructural effects on pars recta (S3) proximal tubule cells of the rat kidney. *J. Pharmacol. exptl. Ther.*, 203, 712–21

Fry, J. R., Wiebkin, P., Kao, J., Jones, C. A., Gwynn, J. and Bridges, J. W. (1978). A comparison of drug-metabolising capability in isolated viable rat hepatocytes and renal tubule fragments. *Xenobiotica*, 8, 113–20

Gandolfi, A. J., Nagle, R. B., Soltis, J. J. and Plescia, F. H. (1981). Nephrotoxicity of halogenated vinyl cysteine compounds. *Res. Comm. Path. Pharmacol.*, 33, 249–61

Ganote, C. E., Reimer, K. A. and Jennings, R. B. (1974). Acute mercury chloride nephrotoxicity, an electron microscopic and metabolic study. *Lab. Invest.*, 31, 633–47

Gerdes, R. G., Jones, T. W., Ormstad, K. and Orrenius, S. (1985). The formation of glutathione conjugates of hexachlorobutadiene by isolated liver cells. In *Renal Heterogeneity and Target Cell Toxicity* (eds P. H. Bach and E. A. Lock), John Wiley, Chichester, pp. 145–8

Glaumann, B. and Trump, B. F. (1975). Studies on the pathogenesis of ischemic cell injury. III Morphological changes of the proximal pars recta tubules (P3) of the rat kidney made ischemic in vivo. *Virchows. Arch. B. Cell. Path.*, 19, 303–23

Gradiski, D., Duprat, P., Magadur, J-L. and Fayein, E. (1975). Etude toxicologique experimentale de l'hexachlorobutadiene. *Eur. J. Toxicol.*, 8, 180–7

Grafstrom, R., Ormstad, K., Moldeus, P. and Orrenius, S. (1979). Paracetamol metabolism in the isolated perfused rat liver with further metabolism of biliary conjugate by small intestines. *Biochem. Pharmacol.*, 28, 3573–9

Green, R. M. and Elce, J. S. (1975). Acetylation of S-substituted cysteines by a rat liver and kidney microsomal N-acetyltransferase. *Biochem. J.*, 147, 283–9

Green, T. and Odum, J. (1985). Structure/activity studies of the nephrotoxic and mutagenic action of cysteine conjugates of chloro and fluoroalkenes. *Chem. Biol. Interac.*, 54, 15–31

Guengerich, F. P., Crawford, W. M., Domoradzki, J. Y., Macdonald, T. L. and Watanabe, P. G. (1980). In vitro activation of 1,2-dichloroethane by microsomal and cytosolic enzymes. *Toxicol. appl. Pharmacol.*, 55, 303–17

Harleman, J. H. and Seinen, W. (1979). Short-term toxicity and reproduction studies in rats with hexachloro-1,3-butadiene. *Toxicol. appl. Pharmacol.*, 47, 1–14

Hassall, C. D., Gandolfi, A. J. and Brendel, K. (1983). Effect of halogenated vinyl cysteine conjugates on renal tubular active transport. *Toxicology*, 26, 285–94

Hassall, C. D., Gandolfi, A. J., Duhamel, R. C. and Brendel, K. (1984). The formation and biotransformation of cysteine conjugates of halogenated ethylenes by rabbit renal tubules. *Chem. Biol. Interac.*, 49, 283–97

Hill, D. L., Shih, T. W., Johnston, T. P. and Struck, R. F. (1978). Macromolecular binding and metabolism of the carcinogen 1,2-dibromoethane. *Cancer Res.*, 38, 2438–42

Hirata, E. and Takahashi, H. (1981). Degradation of methyl mercury glutathione by the pancreatic enzymes in bile. *Toxicol. appl. Pharmacol.*, 58, 483–91

Hook, J. B., McCormack, K. M. and Kluwe, W. M. (1979). Biochemical mechanisms of nephrotoxicity. *Rev. Biochem. Toxicol.*, 1, 53–78

Hook, J. B., Ishmael, J. and Lock, E. A. (1983). Nephrotoxicity of hexachloro-1,3-butadiene in the rat: the effect of age, sex and strain. *Toxicol. appl. Pharmacol.*, 67, 121–31

Ilett, K. F., Reid, W. D., Sipes, I. G. and Krishna, G. (1973). Chloroform toxicity in mice: correlation of renal and hepatic necrosis with covalent binding of metabolites to tissue macromolecules. *Exptl. mol. Pathol.*, 19, 215–29

Inoue, M., Okajima, K. and Morino, Y. (1981). Renal transtubular transport of mercapturic acid in vivo. *Biochim. Biophys. Acta*, 641, 122–8

Inoue, M., Okajima, K. and Morino, Y. (1982). Metabolic co-ordination of liver and kidney in mercapturic acid biosynthesis in vivo. *Hepatology*, 2, 311–16

Inoue, M., Okajima, K. and Morino, Y. (1984). Hepato-renal cooperation in biotransformation, membrane transport and elimination of cysteine S-conjugates of xenobiotics. *J. Biochem. (Tokyo)*, 95, 247–54

Inskeep, P. R. and Guengerich, F. P. (1984). Glutathione-mediated binding of dibromoalkanes to DNA: specificity of rat glutathione-S-transferases and dibromoalkane structure. *Carcinogenesis*, 5, 805–8

Jacobsen, N. O. and Jorgensen, F. (1973). Ultrastructural observations on pars descendens of the proximal tubule in the kidney of the male rat. *Z. Zellforsch. Mikrosk. Anat.*, 136, 479–99

Jaffe, D. R., Hassall, C. D., Brendel, K. and Gandolfi, A. J. (1983). In vivo and in vitro nephrotoxicity of the cysteine conjugate of hexachlorobutadiene. *J. Toxicol. Environ. Hlth.*, **11**, 857–67

Jaffe, D. R., Gandolfi, A. J. and Nagle, R. B. (1984). Chronic toxicity of S-(trans-1,2-dichlorovinyl)-L-cysteine in mice. *J. appl. Toxicol.*, **4**, 315–19

Jakoby, W. B. and Habig, W. H. (1980). Glutathione transferases. In: *Enzymatic Basis of Detoxication*, Vol. II (ed. W. B. Jakoby), Academic Press, New York, pp. 63–94

Jakoby, W. B., Stevens, J., Duffel, M. W. and Weisiger, R. A. (1984). The terminal enzymes of mercapturate formation and the thiomethyl shunt. *Rev. Biochem. Toxicol.*, **6**, 95–115

Johnson, M. K. (1965). The influence of some aliphatic compounds on rat liver glutathione levels. *Biochem. Pharmacol.*, **14**, 1383–5

Kluwe, W. M. (1981). The nephrotoxicity of low molecular weight halogenated alkane solvents, pesticides and chemical intermediates. In: *Toxicology of the Kidney* (ed. J. B. Hook), Raven Press, New York, pp. 179–226

Kluwe, W. M., McNish, R., Smithson, K. and Hook, J. B. (1981). Depletion by 1,2-dibromoethane, 1,2- dibromo-3-chloropropane, tris(2,3-dibromopropyl)-phosphate and hexachloro-1,3-butadiene of reduced non-protein sulphydryl groups in target and nontarget organs. *Biochem. Pharmacol.*, **30**, 2265–771

Kluwe, W. M., Abdo, K. M. and Huff, J. (1984). Chronic kidney disease and organic chemical exposures: evaluations of casual relationships in humans and experimental animals. *Fund. appl. Toxicol.*, **4**, 889–901

Kociba, R. J., Schwetz, B. A., Keyes, D. G., Jersey, G. C., Ballard, J. J., Dittenber, D. A., Quast, J. F., Wade, C. E. and Humiston, C. G. (1977a). Chronic toxicity and reproduction studies of hexachlorobutadiene in rats. *Environ. Hlth. Perspect.*, **21**, 49–53

Kociba, R. J., Keyes, D. G., Jersey, G. C., Ballard, J. J., Dittenber, D. A., Quast, J. F., Wade, C. E., Humiston, C. G. and Schwetz, B. A. (1977b). Results of a two year chronic toxicity with hexachlorobutadiene in rats. *Am. Ind. Hyg. Assoc. J.*, **38**, 589–602

Kozak, E. M. and Tate, S. S. (1982). Glutathione-degrading enzymes of microvillus membranes. *J. Biol. Chem.*, **257**, 6322–7

Larsen, G. L., Larson, J. D. and Gustafsson, J-A. (1983). Cysteine conjugate β-lyase in the gastrointestinal bacterium Fusobacterium necrophorum. *Xenobiotica*, **13**, 689–700

Lash, L. H. and Jones, D. P. (1983). Transport of glutathione by renal basal-lateral membrane vesicles. *Biochem. Biophys. Res. Commun.*, **112**, 55–60

Lash, L. H. and Jones, D. P. (1984). Renal glutathione transport. Characteristics of the sodium-dependent system in the basal-lateral membrane. *J. Biol. Chem.*, **259**, 14508–14

Lash, L. H. and Jones, D. P. (1985). Uptake of the glutathione conjugate S-(1,2-dichlorovinyl)glutathione by renal basal-lateral membrane vesicles and isolated kidney cells. *Mol. Pharm.*, **28**, 278–82

Litterst, C. L., Mimnaugh, E. G., Reagan, R. L. and Gram, T. E. (1975). Comparison of *in vitro* drug metabolism by lung, liver and kidney of several common laboratory species. *Drug. Metab. Dispos.*, **3**, 259–65

Litterst, C. L., Mimnaugh, E. G. and Gram, T. E. (1977). Comparative alterations in extrahepatic drug metabolism by factors known to affect hepatic activity. *Biochem. Pharmacol.*, **26**, 749–55

Livesey, J. C. and Anders, M. W. (1979). In vitro metabolism of 1,2-dihaloethanes to ethylene. *Drug Metab. Dispos.*, **7**, 199–203

Lock, E. A. (1982). Renal necrosis produced by halogenated chemicals. In: *Nephrotoxicity: Assessment and Pathogenesis* (eds P. H. Bach, F. W. Bonner, J. W. Bridges and E. A. Lock), John Wiley, Chichester, pp. 396–408

Lock, E. A. and Green, T. (1984). Selective activation of chemicals by the kidney: its relevance to toxicity and mutagenicity. In: *Proceedings 9th International Congress of Pharmacology*, Vol. 1, (eds W. Paton, J. Mitchell and P. Turner) Macmillan, London, pp. 197–202

Lock, E. A. and Ishmael, J. (1979). The acute toxic effects of hexachloro-1,3-butadiene on the rat kidney. *Arch. Toxicol.*, **43**, 47–57

Lock, E. A. and Ishmael, J. (1981). Hepatic and renal non-protein sulphydryl concentration following toxic doses of hexachloro-1,3-butadiene in the rat: the effect of Aroclor 1254, phenobarbitone or SKF 525A treatment. *Toxicol. appl. Pharmacol.*, **57**, 79–87

Lock, E. A. and Ishmael, J. (1985). Effect of the organic acid transport inhibitor probenecid on renal cortical uptake and proximal tubular toxicity of hexachloro-1,3-butadienylcysteine by rat renal cortex. *Arch. Toxicol.*, **59**, 12–15

Lock, E. A., Ishmael, J. and Hook, J. B. (1984). Nephrotoxicity of hexachloro-1,3-butadiene in the mouse: the effect of age, sex, strain, monooxygenase modifiers, and the role of glutathione. *Toxicol. appl. Pharmacol.*, **72**, 484–94

Lock, E. A., Odum, J. and Ormond, P. (1986). Transport of N-acetyl-S-pentachloro-1,3-butadienylcysteine by rat renal cortex. *Arch. Toxicol.*, in press

McIntyre, T. and Curthoys, N. P. (1982). Renal catabolism of glutathione. *J. Biol. Chem.*, **257**, 11915–21

McKinney, L. L., Picken, J. C., Weakley, F. B., Eldridge, A. C., Campbell, R. E., Cowan, J. C. and Biester, H. E. (1959). Possible toxic factor of trichloroethylene-extracted soybean oil meal. *J. Am. chem. Soc.*, **81**, 909–15

Maher, J. F. (1976). Toxic nephropathy. In: *The Kidney* (eds B. M. Brenner and F. C. Rector), Saunders, Philadelphia, pp. 1355–95

Massey, V. and Williams, C. H. (1965). On the reaction mechanism of yeast glutathione reductase. *J. Biol. Chem.*, **240**, 4470–80

Maunsbach, A. B. (1966). Observations on the segmentation of the proximal tubule in the rat kidney. *J. ultrastruct. Res.*, **16**, 239–58

Monks, T. J., Lau, S. S. and Gillette, J. R. (1983). Glutathione conjugates of 2-bromohydroquinone, a metabolite of bromobenzene are nephrotoxic. In: *Abstracts of 1st Int. Symp. on Foreign Compound Metabolism*, West Palm Beach, Florida, USA, 30th October–4th November, p. 48

Monks, T. J., Lau, S. S. and Gillette, J. R. (1984). The metabolism and nephrotoxicity of 2-bromohydroquinone glutathione conjugates. In: *Abstracts of 6th Int. Symp. on Microsomes and Drug Oxidation*, Brighton, Sussex, UK, 5th–10th August, p. 23

Mudge, G. H., Gemborys, M. W. and Duggin, G. G. (1978). Covalent binding of metabolites of acetaminophen to kidney protein and depletion of renal glutathione. *J. Pharmacol. exptl. Ther.*, **206**, 218–26

Nachtomi, E. (1970). The metabolism of ethylene dibromide in the rat: the enzymic reaction with glutathione in vitro and in vivo. *Biochem. Pharmacol.*, **19**, 2853–60

Nachtomi, E., Alumot, E. and Bondi, A. (1966). The metabolism of ethylene dibromide in the rat. I. Identification of detoxication products in urine. *Isr. J. Chem.*, **4**, 239–46

Nachtomi, E., Alumot, E. and Bondi, A. (1968). Biochemical changes in organs of chicks and rats poisoned with ethylene dibromide and carbon tetrachloride. *Isr. J. Chem.*, **6**, 803–11

Nash, J. A., King, L. J., Lock, E. A. and Green, T. (1984). The metabolism and disposition of hexachloro-1,3-butadiene in the rat and its relevance to nephrotoxicity. *Toxicol. appl. Pharmacol.*, **73**, 124–37

Odum, J. and Green, T. (1984). The metabolism and nephrotoxicity of tetrafluoroethylene in the rat. *Toxicol. appl. Pharmacol.*, **76**, 306–18

Oesch, F. and Wolf, C. R. (1986). Properties of the microsomal glutathione transferases involved in hexachlorobutadiene and chloro-2,4-dinitrobenzene conjugation. *Mol. Pharm.*, in press

Olmstead, E. V. (1960). Pathological changes in ethylene dibromide poisoning.
Arch. Ind. Hlth., **21**, 525-9

Ozawa, N. and Guengerich, F. P. (1983). Evidence for formation of an S-[2-(N^7-
guanyl)ethyl] glutathione adduct in glutathione-mediated binding of the carcinogen 1,2-dibromoethane to DNA. *Proc. Nat. Acad. Sci.*, **80**, 5266-70

Parker, V. H. (1965). A biochemical study of the toxicity of S-dichlorovinyl-L-
cysteine. *Fd Cosmet. Toxicol.*, **3**, 75-84

Potter, C. L., Gandolfi, A. J., Nagle, R. and Clayton, J. W. (1981). Effects of
inhaled chlorotrifluoroethylene and hexafluoropropene on the rat kidney.
Toxicol. appl. Pharmacol., **59**, 431-40

Pratt, I. S., Ormond, T. and Lock, E. A. (1986). Metabolism of the mercapturic
acid of hexachloro-1,3-butadiene by rat kidney cytosol *in vitro*. In abstracts.
27th Congress European Soc. Toxicology, Harrogate, UK, 27th-29th May

Rafter, J. J., Bakke, J., Larsen, G., Gustafsson, B. and Gustafsson, J-A. (1983).
Role of the intestinal microflora in the formation of sulphur containing conjugates of xenobiotics. *Rev. Biochem. Toxicol.*, **5**, 387-408

Rankin, B. B. and Curthoys, N. P. (1982). Evidence for the renal paratubular transport of glutathione. *Febs. Lett.*, **147**, 193-6

Rannug, U. and Beije, B. (1979). The mutagenic effect of 1,2-dichloroethane on
Salmonella Typhimurium: II. Activation by the isolated perfused rat liver.
Chem. Biol. Interac., **24**, 265-85

Rannug, U., Sundvall, A. and Ramel, C. (1978). The mutagenic effect of 1,2- di-
chloroethane on Salmonella Typhimurium: I. Activation through conjugation
with glutathione in vitro. *Chem. Biol. Interac.*, **20**, 1-16

Reed, D. J. and Ellis, W. W. (1981). Influence of gamma-glutamyl transpeptidase
inactivation on the status of extracellular glutathione and glutathione conjugates. *Adv. Exp. Med. Biol.*, *136 Pt. A*, 75-86

Reichert, D., Schutz, S. and Metzler, M. (1985). Excretion pattern and metabolism
of hexachlorobutadiene in rats: evidence for metabolic activation by conjugation
reactions. *Biochem. Pharmacol.*, **34**, 399-405

Roch-Ramel, F. and Weiner, I. M. (1980). Renal urate excretion: factors determining
the action of drugs. *Kidney Int.*, **18**, 665-76

Roch-Ramel, F., White, F., Vowels, L., Simmonds, H. A. and Cameron, J. S. (1980).
Micropuncture study of tubular transport of urate and PAH in the pig kidney.
Am. J. Physiol., **239**, F107-F112

Ross, B. D. and Guder, W. G. (1982). Heterogeneity and compartmentation in the
kidney. In: *Metabolic Compartmentation* (ed. H. Sies), Academic Press, London,
pp. 363-429

Rowe, V. K., Spencer, H. C., McCollister, D. D., Hollingsworth, R. L. and Adams,
E. M. (1952). Toxicity of ethylene dibromide determined on experimental
animals. *Arch. Ind. Hyg. Occup. Med.*, **6**, 158-73

Rush, G. F., Smith, J. H., Newton, J. F. and Hook, J. B. (1984). Chemically induced
nephrotoxicity: role of metabolic activation. *CRC. Crit. Rev. Toxicol.*, **13**,
99-160

Saari, J. C. and Schultze, M. O. (1965). Cleavage of S-(1,2-dichlorovinyl)-L-cysteine
by Escherichia Coli B. *Archs. Biochem. Biophys.*, **109**, 595-602

Sakharova, L. N. and Tolgskaya, M. S. (1977). Toxicity and nature of the effect
of some halo derivatives of ethylene-difluoro-dichloroethylene, trifluorochloro-
ethylene and tetrafluoroethylene. *Gig. Tr. Zabol.*, **5**, 36-42

Schasteen, C. S. and Reed, D. J. (1983). The hydrolysis and alkylation activities of

S-(2-haloethyl)-L-cysteine analogs – evidence for extended half-life. *Toxicol. appl. Pharmacol.*, **70**, 423–32

Schnellmann, R. G., Lock, E. A. and Mandel, L. J. (1986). A mechanism of S-(1,1,2,3,4-pentachloro-1,3-butadienyl)-L-cysteine (PCBC) toxicity to rabbit proximal tubules (RPT). *Toxicologist*, **6**, 176

Schultze, M. O., Klubes, P., Perman, V., Mitzuno, N. S., Bates, F. W. and Sautter, J. H. (1959). Blood dyscrasia in calves by S-(dichlorovinyl)-L-cysteine. *Blood*, **14**, 1015–25

Schultze, M. O., Derr, R. F., Mizuno, N. S., Joel, D. D. and Sautter, J. H. (1962). Effect of phenylalanine on toxicity of S-(dichlorovinyl)-L-cysteine in the rat and calf. *Proc. exptl. Biol. Med.*, **111**, 499–502

Shih, T-W and Hill, D. L. (1981). Metabolic activation of 1,2-dibromoethane by glutathione transferase and by microsomal mixed function oxidase: further evidence for formation of two reactive metabolites. *Res. Commun. Chem. Path. Pharm.*, **33**, 449–61

Smith, A. G. and Francis, J. (1983). Evidence for the active renal secretion of S-pentachlorophenyl-N-acetyl-L-cysteine by female rats. *Biochem. Pharmacol.*, **32**, 3797–801

Smith, J. H. and Hook, J. B. (1984). Mechanism of chloroform nephrotoxicity III. Renal and hepatic microsomal metabolism of chloroform in mice. *Toxicol. appl. Pharmacol.*, **73**, 511–24

Spencer, H. C., Rowe, V. K., Adams, E. M., McCollister, D. D. and Irish, D. D. (1951). Vapour toxicity of ethylene dichloride determined by experiments on laboratory animals. *Arch. Ind. Hyg. Occup. Med.*, **4**, 482–93

Stevens, J. L. (1985a). Isolation and characterisation of a rat liver enzyme with both cysteine conjugate β-lyase and kynureninase activity. *J. Biol. Chem.*, **260**, 7945–50

Stevens, J. L. (1985b). Cysteine conjugate β-lyase activities in rat kidney cortex: subcellular localisation and relationship to the hepatic enzyme. *Biochem. Biophys. Res. Commun.*, **129**, 499–504

Stevens, J. L. and Jakoby, W. B. (1983). Cysteine conjugate β-lyase. *Mol. Pharm.*, **23**, 761–5

Stonard, M. D. (1973). Further studies on the site and mechanism of action of S-(1,2-dichlorovinyl)-L-cysteine and S-(1,2- dichlorovinyl)-3-mercaptopropionic acid in rat liver. *Biochem. Pharmacol.*, **22**, 1329–35

Stonard, M. D. and Parker, V. H. (1971a). 2-oxoacid dehydrogenases of rat liver mitochondria as the site of action of S-(1,2-dichlorovinyl)-L-cysteine and S-(1,2-dichlorovinyl)-3-mercaptopropionic acid. *Biochem. Pharmacol.*, **20**, 2417–27

Stonard, M. D. and Parker, V. H. (1971b). Metabolism of S-(1,2-dichlorovinyl)-L-cysteine by rat liver mitochondria. *Biochem. Pharmacol.*, **20**, 2429–37

Sundheimer, D. W., White, R. D., Brendel, K. and Sipes, I. G. (1982). The bioactivation of 1,2-dibromoethane in rat hepatocytes: covalent binding to nucleic acids. *Carcinogenesis*, **3**, 1129–33

Tate, S. S. (1980). Enzymes of mercapturic acid formation. In: *Enzymatic Basis of Detoxication Vol. II* (ed. W. B. Jakoby), Academic Press, New York, pp. 95–120

Tateishi, M., Suzuki, S. and Shimizu, H. (1978). Cysteine conjugate β-lyase in rat liver. *J. Biol. Chem.*, **253**, 8854–9

Terracini, B. and Parker, V. H. (1965). A pathological study on the toxicity of S-dichlorovinyl-L-cysteine. *Fd Cosmet. Toxicol.*, **3**, 67–74

Tisher, C. A. (1976). Anatomy of the kidney. In: *The Kidney* (eds B. M. Brenner and F C. Rector), Saunders, Philadelphia, pp. 3–64

Tomisawa, H., Suzuki, S., Shigeyasa, I., Fukazawa, H. and Tateishi, M. (1984). Purification and characterisation of C–S lyase from Fusobacterium varium. *J. Biol. Chem.*, **259**, 2588–93

Trump, B. F., Berezesky, I. K., Lipsky, M. M. and Jones, T. W. (1985). Heterogeneity of the nephron: significance to nephrotoxicity. In: *Renal Heterogeneity and Target Cell Toxicity* (eds P. H. Bach and E. A. Lock), John Wiley, Chichester, pp. 31–42

Tune, B. M., Burge, M. B. and Patlak, C. S. (1969). Characteristics of p-aminohippurate transport in proximal renal tubule. *Am. J. Physiol.*, **217**, 1057–63

Vadi, H. V., Schasteen, C. S. and Reed, D. J. (1985). Interactions of S-(2-haloethyl)-mercapturic acid analogs with plasmid DNA. *Toxicol. appl. Pharmacol.*, **80**, 386–96

Valtin, H. (1973). *Renal Function: Mechanisms Preserving Fluid and Solute Balance in Health*, Little, Brown, Boston

Van Bladeren, P. J., Breimer, D. D., Rotteveel-Smijs, G. M. T., De Jong, R. A. W., Buijs, W., Van Der Gen, A. and Mohn, G. R. (1980). The role of glutathione conjugation in the mutagenicity of 1,2-dibromoethane. *Biochem. Pharmacol.*, **29**, 2975–82

Venkatchalam, M. A., Bernard, D. B., Donohoe, J. F. and Levinsky, N. G. (1978). Ischemic damage and repair in the rat proximal tubule: differences among the S1, S2 and S3 segments. *Kidney Int.*, **14**, 31–49

Wachsmuth, E. D. (1985). Renal heterogeneity at a light microscopic level. In: *Renal Heterogeneity and Target Cell Toxicity* (eds P. H. Bach and E. A. Lock), John Wiley, Chichester, pp. 13–30

Wallach, D. P. (1961). Studies on the GABA pathway I. The inhibition of γ-aminobutyric acid-α-ketoglutaric acid transaminase in vitro and in vivo by U-7524 (amino-oxyacetic acid). *Biochem. Pharmacol.*, **5**, 323–31

Walther, A., Fischer, H. D., Jaeger, J., Kemmer, C. and Kunze, D. (1969). Biochemical and morphological studies on the toxicity of chlorotrifluoroethylene. *Acta Biol. Med. Ger.*, **23**, 685–706

Weisiger, R. A. and Jakoby, W. B. (1980). S-methylation: thiol S-methyl-transferase. In: *Enzymatic Basis of Detoxication*, Vol. II (ed. W. B. Jakoby), Academic Press, New York, pp. 131–140

Wolf, C. R., Berry, P. N., Nash, J. A., Green, T. and Lock, E. A. (1984). The role of microsomal and cytosolic glutathione-S-transferases in the conjugation of hexachloro-1,3-butadiene and its possible relevance to toxicity. *J. Pharmacol. exptl. Ther.*, **228**, 202–8

Zenser, T. V., Mattammal, M. B. and Davis, B. B. (1978). Differential distribution of the mixed function oxidase activities in rabbit kidney. *J. Pharmacol. exptl. Ther.*, **207**, 719–25

4

Dioxin and Organotin Compounds as Model Immunotoxic Chemicals

J. G. Vos and A. H. Penninks

ABSTRACT

Studies in various animal models indicate that 2,3,7,8-tetrachlorodibenzo-p-dioxin (TCDD, dioxin) and approximate isostereomers produce a similar pattern of toxic responses, including thymic atrophy. Effects on the immune system include suppression of cell-mediated immunity. Also in man, exposure to TCDD-related halogenated aromatic hydrocarbons has been shown to impair thymus-dependent immunity. Several investigations have been performed to clarify the thymus atrophy. TCDD is not directly toxic for thymocytes, nor does it act through an increase of serum corticosteroid levels or a decrease of growth hormone levels. In studies with murine inbred strains differing in sensitivity to TCDD it has been shown that thymic atrophy segregates with the Ah locus and thus appears to be mediated by the Ah receptor. Recent studies indicate that TCDD acts through a receptor in thymic epithelium. Treatment of monolayers of thymic epithelial cells with TCDD resulted in the suppression of epithelium-dependent responsiveness of co-cultured thymocytes to mitogens. These results provide direct evidence that thymic epithelium is a target for TCDD. These findings are consistent with the hypothesis that TCDD stimulates terminal differentiation of reticular thymic epithelial cells to a stage at which they have lost their ability to support thymocyte maturation, thus leading to depletion of cortical thymocytes.

Another group of chemicals which has been thoroughly investigated for immunotoxic properties are the organotins. Thymic atrophy appeared a prominent lesion in the rat after oral administration of butyl and octyl substituted dialkyltins, propyl and butyl substituted trialkyltins, and phenyl substituted triaryltin. Functional studies revealed suppression of thymus-dependent immunity. Like TCDD, the selective thymic effects of the organotins appeared not to be mediated by the adrenals or pituitary. Rather than an indirect mechanism, it seems likely that the dialkyltins interfere with thymocyte proliferation, as indicated by the reduction of DNA synthesis in thymocytes after *in vitro* and *in vivo* exposure. This anti-proliferative activity seems not to be secondary to a limited energy supply. At the molecular level interference of dialkyltins with membrane and/or cytoskeleton-associated sulphydryl groups as cause of the observed anti-proliferative effect is postulated.

INTRODUCTION

The lymphoid tissue is structurally divided into primary and secondary lymphoid organs or tissues. In the primary organs, the antigen-independent proliferation of lymphocytes takes place while generation of T-lymphocytes from stem cells occurs in the thymus. In birds, the bursa of Fabricius has been shown to be the primary organ that supports extensive lymphopoiesis of B-lymphocytes (the mammalian equivalent of the bursa of Fabricius may exist in different sites, e.g. the bone marrow). The secondary lymphoid tissue is where the complex interactions take place which form the basis of the immune response. These secondary tissues include spleen, lymph nodes and mucosa-associated lymphoid tissues in the alimentary and respiratory tract.

In this paper, the action of 2,3,7,8-tetrachlorodibenzo-*p*-dioxin (TCDD, dioxin) as well as certain organotin compounds on thymus and thymus-dependent immunity are discussed. To better understand the thymic atrophy or involution induced by these compounds knowledge of the basic structure of the thymus is necessary.

The thymus derives embryologically from the endoderm of the third and fourth bronchial pouches and reaches its maximum size during neonatal life, after which a gradual process of involution begins. Histologically (figure 4.1), the adult thymus is a lymphoepithelial organ consisting of many lobules, each containing a cortex and medulla. Cortical reticular epithelial cells have long thin processes and constitute a fine network. Medullary reticular epithelial cells are more spindle-shaped and closely packed. Other stromal cells in the thymus are macrophages located in both cortex and medulla and interdigitating cells, exclusively present in the medulla. Stem cells (prothymocytes), which originate from the bone marrow, proliferate predominantly in the outer cortex. Thymocytes appear to migrate from the cortex to the medulla where they further differentiate to immunologically mature cells. Thymocyte maturation, accompanied by a high rate of death of a proportion of the cells, is characterised by several phenotypic changes in the remaining cells including differential expression of cell surface antigens. Subpopulations of mature thymus-derived or T-lymphocytes migrate out of the thymus to seed the T-dependent areas of peripheral lymphoid organs. In the thymic micro-environment direct contact of thymocytes with the epithelium and/or thymic hormones produced by these epithelial cells is thought to be necessary for thymocyte proliferation and differentiation (Stutman, 1978; Haynes, 1984). Thus, chemically induced thymic atrophy may be caused by a direct lymphocytotoxic or antiproliferative activity of the chemical on the thymocyte itself or on thymic epithelium. In addition it may be

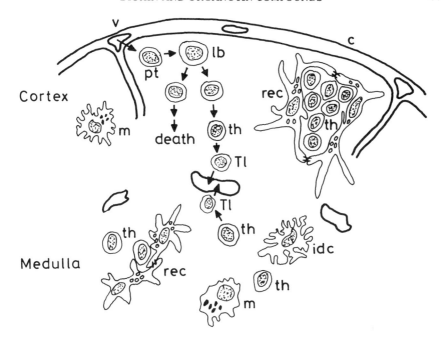

Figure 4.1 Architecture and cellular composition of thymus lobule. v, blood vessel; c, connective tissue capsule; pt, prothymocyte; lb, lymphoblast; th, thymocyte; Tl, T-lymphocyte; rec, reticular epithelial cell; m, macrophage; idc, interdigitating cell

the result of an indirect effect, e.g. increased production of glucocorticosteroids which are known thymolytic agents (White and Goldstein, 1972), or impaired production of growth hormone (Sorkin *et al.*, 1972) which can also lead to thymic atrophy. As a consequence of this, the thymus-dependent immunity may be impaired. Therefore, the effects of dioxin and organotins on the two major arms of acquired immunity will be discussed, namely: (1) cell-mediated immunity, which operates by specifically sensitised T-lymphocytes and is transferable by these cells; and (2) humoral immunity, which involves the production of specific antibodies by plasma cells following sensitisation of B-lymphocytes and is transferable by serum. Regarding the humoral immunity, emphasis will be given to the antibody response to thymus-dependent antigens (i.e. which needs the cooperation of a subset of thymus-derived lymphocytes, so-called T-helper cells).

DIOXIN-INDUCED THYMIC ATROPHY AND SUPPRESSION OF THYMUS-DEPENDENT IMMUNITY

Dioxin-induced thymic atrophy was first described by Buu-Hoi *et al.* (1972). After this initial report, thymic atrophy has been shown to occur following exposure to TCDD or structurally related chlorinated aromatic hydrocarbons in all species investigated, including rat, mouse, guinea pig, hamster, cow, monkey and chicken (Vos *et al.*, 1980; Poland and Knutson, 1982). Reduction in thymus weight appeared to be a very sensitive parameter of TCDD exposure. This finding suggested that TCDD may alter immune responses and initiated immune function studies.

The effects of TCDD on thymus-dependent immunity have been well characterised. These studies comprise functional assessment of immune parameters following exposure of juvenile or young adult animals, as well as investigations after perinatal exposure. Regarding the functional significance of TCDD-induced thymic atrophy, suppression of thymus-dependent immunity is an age-related phenomenon, at least in the rat, in which exposure to TCDD during the development of the immune system seems to be capable of inducing immunosuppression. The effects appear to be focused on cell-mediated immunity, thymus-dependent humoral immunity is also compromised, in most species, but requires higher dosage levels.

Immune function studies in laboratory animals

The cell-mediated and humoral immunity of male weanling guinea pigs after oral exposure (eight weekly doses of 0.008, 0.04, or 0.2 µg TCDD/kg body weight) was investigated by Vos *et al.* (1973). Animals treated with 0.04 or 0.2 µg TCDD/kg showed reduced delayed-type hypersensitivity reactions to tuberculin. In addition, the secondary antibody response to tetanus toxoid was decreased at the 0.2 µg/kg level, while the primary antibody response appeared unaffected. In the same study, the effects of TCDD on thymus-dependent immunity of young adult mice and rats was investigated. In mice, graft versus host reactivity was suppressed following dosages of 5 µg TCDD/kg body weight weekly for 4 weeks. Whereas in rats weekly treatment for a period of 6 weeks with doses up to 5 µg/kg body weight did not impair delayed-type hypersensitivity reactions, despite the occurrence of thymic atrophy. In a subsequent study, in which 1- and 4-month-old mice received four weekly doses of 25 µg TCDD/kg body weight, lymphoproliferative responses of spleen cells following stimulation with phytohaemagglutinin (PHA) were decreased in the younger animals. However, no reduced activity was measured with spleen cells of the older mice, although thymus atrophy was present (Vos and Moore, 1974).

Hinsdill *et al.* (1980) studied various immune parameters in juvenile and adult (4 and 7 weeks old) mice that received dietary concentrations of 10 µg TCDD/kg and higher for at least 5 weeks. Feeding of 10 µg/kg or more reduced the primary and secondary antibody response to both tetanus toxoid and sheep red blood cells (SRBC) in a dose-related fashion. Also, delayed-type hypersensitivity reactions to dinitrofluorobenzene (DNFB) were suppressed, and to a lesser extent the resistance to challenge with either *Salmonella typhimurium* or *Listeria monocytogenes*. Juvenile animals showed greater suppression than adults.

Altered T-lymphocyte function following exposure of adult mice to TCDD was associated with activation of T-suppressor cells and loss of T-lymphocyte cytotoxicity for tumor target cells (Clark *et al.*, 1981, 1983). Mice, 6–8 weeks old, were injected intraperitoneally weekly during 4 weeks with 0.001, 0.01, 0.1, 1 or 10 μg TCDD/kg. The antibody response to SRBC and trinitrophenol-conjugated *Burcella abortus* was impaired following 10 μg TCDD/kg-week. The delayed-hypersensitivity response to oxazalone was impaired significantly by 1 μg TCDD/kg and higher doses, and the *in vitro* generation of alloantigen-specific cytotoxic T cells was sensitive to as little as 0.001 μg TCDD/kg body weight. Thymus cellularity was only decreased in the 1 μg TCDD/kg and 10 μg TCDD/kg groups.

Besides effects on immune responsiveness, TCDD may have other influences that interfere with the ability of the host to overcome deleterious effects of infections. For instance, Thigpen *et al.* (1975) showed that TCDD treatment markedly decreased the resistance of mice to *Salmonella bern* infection. They administered TCDD orally once weekly for 4 weeks to 1-month-old mice at dose levels of 0.5, 1, 5, 10 or 20 μg/kg body weight. Dosages of 1 μg/kg or more, followed by Salmonella infection, resulted in significantly increased mortality, and decreased survival time after infection, the 1 μg/kg dose being one order of magnitude lower than that which caused thymic atrophy. TCDD had no effect on mortality in pseudorabies-infected mice. It was subsequently observed that mice treated with a single or repeated dose of TCDD revealed a markedly increased susceptibility to endotoxin from Gram-negative bacteria (Vos *et al.*, 1978). A similar observation was made by Thomas and Hinsdill (1979). The decreased resistance of TCDD-exposed mice to infection with Salmonella was therefore suspected to be due to an enhanced susceptibility of the animals to the endotoxin of the bacteria rather than a defect in cell-mediated immunity, especially since endotoxin hypersensitivity was recorded below the dose level that produced atrophy of the thymus.

In contrast to the absence of immune suppression in adult rats (Vos *et al.*, 1973), perinatal treatment by maternal exposure impaired the thymus-dependent immunity in the offspring (Vos and Moore, 1974). Oral treatment of dams with 1 μg TCDD/kg body weight on days 11 and 18 of gestation and 0, 7 and 14 post-natally, or with 5 μg TCDD/kg on days 0, 7 and 14 postnatally reduced the ability to reject skin allografts and also the PHA responsiveness and graft versus host activity in the spleen. Perinatal treatment of mice also severely suppressed allograft rejection following maternal oral dosing with 2 or 5 μg TCDD/kg body weight on gestation days 14 and 17 and postnatally on days 1, 8 and 15.

Immune alterations in mice following perinatal exposure were further investigated by Thomas and Hinsdill (1979). Adult female mice were exposed to TCDD for 4 weeks before mating, throughout gestation, and for 3 weeks postparturition, and the immune competence of 5-week-old offspring evaluated. Mice from mothers fed 2.5 or 5.0 μg TCDD/kg demonstrated thymus atrophy and a significantly reduced spleen anti-SRBC plaque forming cell response but had normal serum anti-SRBC antibody levels following primary and secondary immunisation. Delayed-type hypersensitivity reactions to DNFB were reduced in the 1.0, 2.5 and 5.0 μg/kg groups, but only the latter group was significantly reduced from the controls. No effect was observed on the *in vitro* response of the spleen cells to mitogen stimulation, and TCDD treatment did not render the animals more susceptible to a challenge with *Listeria monocytogenes* bacteria. These data are in contrast to the findings of Luster *et al.* (1980), who found in the 5.0 μg TCDD/kg body weight group (maternal oral dosing on day 14 of gestation, and postnatally on days 1, 7 and 14) thymic atrophy, reduced PHA spleen responses, and a significantly decreased resistance to *Listeria monocytogenes*.

Studies to investigate the late consequence of perinatal TCDD exposure of Fischer and Fischer/Wistar rats were reported by Faith and Moore (1977) and Faith and Luster (1979), respectively. Rats were exposed to TCDD though maternal oral dosing (5 μg/kg) on day 18 of gestation and on days 0, 7 and 14 of postnatal life (group I). Another group of rats was exposed through maternal dosing with 5 μg/kg on days 0, 7 and 14 of postnatal life only (group II). In both experiments thymus weights were reduced, in group I up to approximately 5 months of age and group II up to 1 month of age. In the study with Fischer rats, the delayed type hypersensitivity reactions to oxazolone were significantly reduced at days 52, 68 and 145, the effects being more severe in the pre- and postnatally exposed rats. Also the response of spleen cells to the T cell mitogens, PHA and concanavalin A (Con A), was impaired, whereas no significant effect on the serum antibody titres to the thymus-dependent antigen bovine gamma globulin was observed. In the study with Fischer/Wistar rats cell-mediated immunity was similarly impaired as in Fischer rats: delayed hypersensitivity reactions were reduced in group I and II animals at 35 and 133 days of age, as were the lymphoproliferative responses of spleen cells to PHA and Con A. TCDD-exposed animals had recovered normal cell-mediated immune function by 270 days of age.

Immune function studies in man

There are few published reports available in which the effect of TCDD and related compounds on the immune system of humans were studied. Reggiani (1978) reported investigations of the immune status of 44 children (20 had chloracne) residing in the TCDD-contaminated area of Seveso, Italy. These studies revealed no abnormalities in serum immunoglobulin concentrations, levels of circulating complement, and lymphoproliferative responses of T and B cells following mitogen stimulation. However, the immune system of man can be compromised following exposure to TCDD-related halogenated aromatic hydrocarbons. Immunologic evaluation of patients poisoned in 1979 in Taiwan by the consumption of rice oil contaminated with polychlorinated biphenyls (and probably also with polychlorinated dibenzofurans) has been reported by Chang *et al.* (1981, 1982). Serum immunoglobulin concentrations and lymphocyte subpopulations were determined in peripheral blood of 30 patients and 23 healthy controls. In the patients, serum concentrations of IgA and IgM, but not of IgG, were significantly decreased. Also, the percentage of total T-lymphocytes was significantly reduced, apparently due to a decrease in T-helper cells, whereas the percentage of B-lymphocytes was not affected (Chang *et al.*, 1981). The immune system was further investigated by determining the delayed-type hypersensitivity skin response to streptokinase and streptodornase. The response was studied in 30 patients and 50 controls. Results of the study showed that 80% of the normal human subjects had positive hypersensitivity skin tests, compared to only 43% of the patients. When the patients were divided into four groups according to the severity of dermal lesions, the percentage of patients having a positive response decreased with increasing severity; the size of the hypersensitivity skin reactions was negatively correlated with the dermal lesions and also with polychlorinated biphenyl concentrations in whole blood (Chang et al., 1982).

Mechanism of dioxin-induced thymic atrophy

Several attempts have been made to elucidate the mechanism responsible for TCDD-induced thymic atrophy. Although these studies have produced valuable information on the relationship between TCDD and the immune system, these studies have not culminated in definitive findings.

Histologically, the thymic atrophy in TCDD-exposed rats, mice and guinea pigs is reflected almost entirely as a depletion of lymphocytes throughout the cortex without obvious cell necrosis (Buu-Hoi et al., 1972; Gupta et al., 1973; Vos et al., 1973; Poland and Glover 1980); only in moribund animals has lymphocyte necrosis been observed (Vos et al., 1973). Although these histological findings do not completely rule out the possibility for a direct cytotoxic action of TCDD on thymic lymphocytes, such a mechanism seems unlikely as TCDD is not toxic when added directly to cultures of several cell types, including lymphocytes and thymocytes (Kouri et al., 1974; Vos and Moore, 1974; Beatty et al., 1975; Knutson and Poland, 1980). A number of these cell types were inducible for aryl hydrocarbon hydroxylase (AHH) activity, indicating the presence of the cytosolic TCDD receptor. Only Niwa et al. (1975) have reported a cytotoxic action of a very high dose of TCDD (0.48 μg/ml) for mammalian cell types as shown by a decreased viability.

Possible indirect mechanisms that could explain TCDD-induced thymic atrophy have been investigated. In an early study, serum cortisol and corticosterone were measured in guinea pigs exposed to TCDD to evaluate the possible indirect effects of these adrenocorticosteroids. There was, however, no difference in the level of these hormones between the treated and control group. Moreover, adrenal weight was unaltered (Vos et al., 1973). Also, in rats, thymic atrophy is not due to increased levels of corticosteroids, as thymic atrophy occurred in TCDD-exposed animals that had been adrenalectomised (Van Logten et al., 1980). In TCDD-exposed rats, decreased eosinophilia was observed in acidophilic cells of the pituitary, whereas the serum level of growth hormone appeared increased (Vos and Moore, 1974). These changes could indicate a disturbance in the relationship between the pituitary and the thymus that was investigated by Van Logten et al. (1980). Hypophysectomy or treatment with growth hormone, however, failed to prevent thymic atrophy by TCDD. Studies of Van Logten et al. (1981) also indicated that reduced food intake is not the cause of thymic atrophy. Furthermore, neither induction of alpha-fetoprotein nor zinc deficiency appeared to play a role in the thymic atrophy as serum levels were not altered (Vos et al., 1978). Finally, whether a reduced production of thymic hormones could be the cause of TCDD-induced thymic atrophy was investigated. Injections of mice with thymosin fraction 5 obtained from calf thymus, however, failed to restore the TCDD-induced thymus atrophy and reduced lympho-proliferative response of the thymocytes upon stimulation with T-cell mitogens (Vos *et al.*, 1978). It should be noted that the results of this latter study are not conclusive since, besides the action of thymic hormones, an intact thymus micro-environment is important for the maturation and differentiation of T-lymphocytes (Kendall, 1981).

It is currently believed that TCDD-induced thymic atrophy is mediated through a cellular receptor for TCDD. The TCDD receptor was originally described by Poland *et al.* (1976) in hepatic cytosol. Subsequently, Carlstedt-Duke (1979) identified the receptor in a variety of rat tissues; the highest concentration being in the thymus. Studies of Poland and Glover (1980) have indicated that the TCDD-induced thymic atrophy is mediated through the TCDD receptor since thymic atrophy segregates with the *Ah* locus, the gene that determines the cytosol receptor. Thus, C57B1/6 mice who have a high affinity receptor in the thymus are approximately tenfold more sensitive to thymic atrophy than DBA/2 mice that have a receptor with a lower affinity for TCDD. The receptor-mediated mechanism is further supported by the investigations of Clark *et al.* (1983), which showed that a ten to 100-fold greater dose of TCDD was required to suppress cytotoxic T-cells in non-responsive DBA/2 mice as compared with responsive C57B1/6 mice, and by the studies of Nagarkatti *et al.* (1984), which demonstrated that the C57B1/6 × DBA/2 hybrid mouse was susceptible. All these studies are consistent with the dominant inheritance of *Ah.* By using chimeric mice, the latter authors obtained results that could prove to be a major step in the elucidation of the mechanism of TCDD-induced thymic atrophy. They studied the effect of TCDD treatment on murine bone marrow chimeras in which the peripheral lymphoid and thymocyte populations of DBA/2 or C57B1/6 strain mice were replaced with cells of the opposite genotype. They found that susceptibility or resistance to suppression of cytotoxic T-cell generation by TCDD is determined by the *Ah* genotype of the radioresistant non-lymphoid cells of the host and not by that of the grafted lymphomyeloid cells. These results point to the thymic epithelium as a possible target site for TCDD-induced immunotoxicity. Evidence for such a mechanism was recently provided by Greenlee *et al.* (1985). Monolayers of thymic epithelial cells from C57B1/6 mice were treated with varying concentrations of TCDD (1–10 nM) or 2,3,7,8-tetra-chlorodibenzofuran (TCDF, 100 nM) for 48 h, washed and then co-cultured with thymocytes for 48 h. Enhancement of responses of thymocytes to the mitogens PHA and Con A, due to the presence of thymic epithelial monolayers in the culture, was inhibited if the epithelial monolayers were pretreated with TCDD or TCDF (figure 4.2). TCDD treatment did not result in detectable cytotoxicity to these epithelial cells.

From the various studies in which the mechanism of TCDD-induced thymic atrophy has been studied, it can be concluded that TCDD is not directly toxic to thymic lymphocytes. Recent results indicate that TCDD, rather than acting directly on thymocytes, acts through a receptor in epithelial cells. The interaction of TCDD with the receptor on the thymic epithelium perhaps alters the capacity of these cells to support the intrathymic maturation and differentiation of thymic lympho-

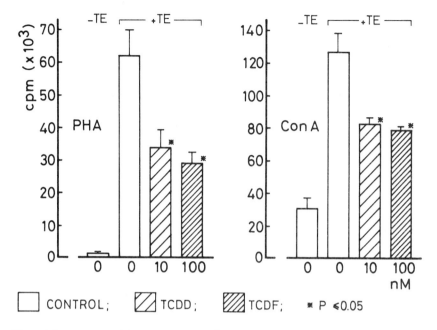

Figure 4.2 Lymphoproliferative responses (^{3}H-thymidine incorporation) of thymocytes from C57B1/6 mice co-cultured on syngeneic thymic epithelial (TE) monolayers treated with TCDD or TCDF (after Greenlee *et al.*, 1985)

cytes, which may be the basis for the well-documented, TCDD-induced thymic atrophy and immunodeficiency.

ORGANOTIN-INDUCED THYMIC ATROPHY AND SUPPRESSION OF THYMUS-DEPENDENT IMMUNITY

Organotin compounds are a group of chemicals having at least one bond between tin and carbon. Major subgroups are referred to as di- and tri-substituted organotins, R_2SnX_2 and R_3SnX respectively. Usually R stands for an alkyl or aryl group and X for chloride, fluoride, oxide, hydroxide, acetate, carboxylate or thiolate.

The first indication for potential immunotoxicity of certain organotin compounds came from toxicity studies in guinea pigs and rats (Verschuuren *et al.*, 1966). Triphenyltin hydroxide (TPTH) and triphenyltin acetate (TPTA) reduced the number of circulating lymphocytes. In the former species also the weights of thymus and spleen were reduced. Gaines and Kimbrough (1968) reported reduced spleen weights in rats after oral exposure to TPTH, whereas Seinen and Penninks (1979) observed thymic atrophy in the same species after feeding diphenyltin dichloride and triphenyltin chloride. The latter compound and TPTA were also active on the lymphoid system of mice as demonstrated by lymphopenia and reduced spleen weights (Ishaaya *et al.*, 1976).

The dialkyltins, in particular di-*n*-butyltin (DBTC) and di-*n*-octyltin (DOTC) dichlorides, are immunotoxic in rats as judged from the prominent decrease of thymus, spleen and lymph node weight; the lower homologues diethyltin and di-*n*-propyltin dichlorides did also reduce thymus weight in rats, although to a lesser extent (Seinen and Willems, 1976; Seinen *et al.*, 1977a). In contrast to rats, no thymolytic activity of DBTC or DOTC was noted in mice, guinea pigs or Japanese quail after oral treatment (Seinen *et al.*, 1977a). However, intravenous injection of DBTC did induce thymic atrophy in mice (Seinen, 1981).

Of the trialkyltin compounds, tri-*n*-butyltin oxide (TBTO) has been shown to cause leukopenia and reduced spleen weights in mice (Ishaaya *et al.*, 1976), and strong thymic atrophy and moderate atrophy of spleen and lymph nodes in rats (Funahashi *et al.*, 1980; Krajnc *et al.*, 1984). Tri-*n*-propyltin chloride also induced atrophy of thymus and spleen in rats (Snoeij *et al.*, 1985).

Immune function studies

The effect of TPTA on the thymus dependent humoral immunity (response to tetanus toxoid) in the guinea pig was studied by Verschuuren *et al.* (1970). Three-week-old female animals were given 15 mg TPTA/kg diet for 49, 77 or 104 days. Serum tetanus-antitoxin titres as well as the number of antitoxin producing plasma cells in the popliteal lymph node were reduced by TPTA treatment. No signs of recovery were seen after an additional period of 2 weeks without TPTA in the diet. A second study with an aryltin compound was done by Vos *et al.* (1984b). In weanling male rats various immune function studies were carried out after 3 or 4 weeks exposure to 25 mg TPTH/kg diet. In two experiments the delayed-type hypersensitivity reactions to ovalbumin and tuberculin, two parameters of cell-mediated immunity, were significantly suppressed. No effect was observed on allograft rejection, splenic clearance of *Listeria monocytogenes* at days 5 and 6 after infection, and lymphoproliferative responses of thymocytes. In contrast, the response of splenic lymphocytes to PHA was significantly suppressed. Regarding the humoral immunity, IgM and IgG responses to tetanus toxoid were unaltered.

Assessment of immune function in trialkyltin-exposed animals has been limited to TBTO. Weanling male rats were fed diets containing 20 or 80 mg TBTO/kg for at least 6 weeks (Vos *et al.*, 1984a). A pronounced suppression of thymus-dependent immunity occurred, as shown by the dose-related depression of delayed-type hypersensitivity reactions to ovalbumin and tuberculin and a reduced response of thymus and spleen cells to T-cell mitogens (the latter phenomenon is explained by reduced number of T-cells as shown by cytofluorometric analysis of cell surface markers). The resistance to the nematode *Trichinella spiralis* was impaired particularly, as noted by a retarded expulsion of adult worms from the small intestine, increased counts of muscle larvae, reduced inflammatory reaction in parasitised musculature, and suppressed serum IgE titres. The secondary mercaptoethanol-resistant (presumably IgG) haemagglutinating antibody titres to SRBC were also significantly reduced, while no significant alterations were found in IgM and IgG titres to *T. spiralis*, ovalbumin and tetanus toxoid. In a subsequent study, the effect of chronic exposure to TBTO was examined (Vos *et al.*, unpublished observations). Weanling male rats were fed diets containing 0.5, 5 or 50 mg TBTO/kg and function tests were performed after 4–6 and 15–17 months exposure. In contrast to results after short-term exposure, delayed-type hypersensitivity was not suppressed after long-term treatment. However, the resistance to *T. spiralis* showed a dose-related depression at 5 and 50 mg/kg as noted by an increased count of muscle larvae and decreased serum IgE titres.

In order to investigate the effects of dialkyltins on immune function Seinen *et al.* (1977b) exposed inbred Wistar (WAG) rats of weaning age to DBTC or DOTC at levels of 50 and 150 mg/kg of diet. The delayed-type hypersensitivity reaction was decreased in a dose-related fashion in rats fed DOTC for 6 weeks. Allograft rejection, another cell-mediated immune response, was significantly delayed in animals receiving DBTC or DOTC at the 150 mg/kg level. Inhibition of the thymus-dependent humoral immunity was noted from a reduction of plaque-forming cells in the spleen as well as from suppressed haemagglutinin and haemolysin titres against SRBC in the serum of DBTC- and DOTC-exposed rats. The developing immune system of rats appeared particularly vulnerable, as the effect of DBTC on allograft rejection was most pronounced when exposure to DBTC started immediately after birth: rejection times were significantly increased in animals given oral doses of either 1 or 3 mg DBTC/kg body weight 3 times a week over a period of 9 weeks. In a subsequent study, Seinen *et al.* (1979) investigated the graft versus host activity and mitogen responsiveness of cell suspensions from lymphoid organs of dialkyltin-exposed rats. Graft versus host activity was significantly decreased in the spleen of rats following dietary DBTC and DOTC exposure at 50 and 150 mg/kg. For the assessment of lymphoproliferative responses rat pups were dosed by gavage from the second day after birth, 3 times a week for 4 weeks, with 5 or 15 mg DOTC/kg body weight. The response of thymocytes to the T-cell mitogens PHA and Con A showed a dose-related decrease and approached the zero level; a similar effect was seen in the response of spleen cells.

In recent investigations by Miller and Scott (1985) no effect of DOTC on the antibody response (haemagglutination titres) to SRBC was observed in rats fed 75 mg DOTC/kg diet for 12 weeks. Also, the graft versus host activity of lymph node cells was not depressed. These results differ from those reported by Seinen and co-workers but young-adult (6- to 8-week-old) rats of a different (PVG) strain were used by Miller and Scott and age at the commencement of treatment could be the most important factor in determining the response. The PVG strain, was however, susceptible to the thymic toxicity of DOTC, as evidenced by thymic atrophy. In addition, the proliferative response of peripheral lymphocytes to PHA was significantly suppressed in the DOTC exposed PVG rats, as was the responsiveness to alloantigenic stimulation, which was measured by mixed leucocyte reactions; findings explained by the DOTC-induced decrease in the number of circulating lymphocytes of the helper/inducer phenotype.

Mechanism of organotin-induced thymic atrophy

Among the organotin compounds in particular the dialkytins DBTC and DOTC have been studied to elucidate the mechanism of their thymolytic activity. These studies point to a mechanism that is different from that involved in dioxin-induced thymic atrophy, although the histological appearance of the thymus is similar: indistinct corticomedullary junctions due to a loss of cortical thymocytes without overt signs of cell destruction at light-microscopic (Seinen and Willems, 1976) or ultrastructural examination (Penninks et al., 1985). As for TCDD also for the dialkyltin possible indirect mechanisms that could explain dialkyltin-induced thymic atrophy have been studied. Although serum corticosteroid levels have not been measured in dialkyltin-treated rats, there is substantial evidence to exclude the involvement of adrenocorticosteroids: (1) in the early studies of Seinen and Willems (1976) it was observed that after dialkyltin treatment neither the adrenal weight nor the histology of the adrenal cortex was affected; (2) thymus weight was equally reduced in adrenalectomised and sham-operated dialkyltin fed rats (Seinen and Willems, 1976). Also a diminished growth hormone production seemed not to be involved. Treatment of rats with growth hormone in amounts that reversed the hypophysectomy-induced thymic atrophy did not restore the DOTC-induced involution of the thymus (Penninks et al., 1985). Furthermore it appeared that the thymic atrophy in the dialkyltin treated rats was much more pronounced than observed in the hypophysectomised rats, and was not associated with severe growth retardation.

Whether a disturbance of the humoral function of the thymus is involved in the dialkyltin-induced thymic atrophy is still doubtful. Based on morphological criteria, conflicting interpretations have been published with regard to a diminished production and/or secretion of thymic hormones. In thymus glands from DOTC-fed rats Miller et al. (1984) observed vacuolisation of reticular epithelial cells together with normal appearing epithelial cells containing an increased amount of secretory droplets. In studies of Penninks et al. (1985) vacuolisation of epithelial cells was also observed, but only when the thymus was already involuted; upon repopulation of the thymic cortex, the vacuolisation rapidly disappeared. An increased amount of secretory granules, as noted by Miller et al. (1984), was not observed. Since the studies of Miller et al. (1984) were performed on rats fed DOTC for at least 2 weeks, the observed vacuolisation may be a consequence, rather than a cause, of thymocyte depletion. This is supported by the fact that extensive vacuolisation of reticular epithelial cells is a common finding in the acutely involuted thymus, when the reticular meshwork of the thymus is collapsed by depletion of cortical thymocytes (Van Haelst, 1967).

An interference of dialkyltins with bone marrow stem cells was also considered. However, after in vivo exposure to dialkyltin compounds neither the number and viability nor the mitotic activity of bone marrow cells were affected (Penninks and Seinen, 1983a; Penninks et al., 1985). Furthermore, no differences were found in colony formation between DBTC-treated and control bone marrow cells (Seinen and Penninks, 1979; Penninks et al., 1985). Although an interaction of dialkyltin compounds with stem cells (prothymocytes) seems unlikely, the results up to now do not definitively exclude interference with prothymocytes since these cells, which represent only a minority of the total bone marrow cell population, were not separated in these studies.

Distribution studies with dialkyltin compounds, either by measurements of tissue Sn content (Hennighausen et al., 1981) or radiolabelled compounds (Penninks and Seinen, 1983a; Penninks, 1985), revealed that the selectivity is not simply due to an accumulation of these compounds in the thymus.

Although the above mentioned studies do not completely rule out the possibility of an indirect effect of dialkyltin compounds on thymocyte maturation, there is substantial evidence to suppose a direct interaction with thymocytes. In contrast to TCDD, dialkyltin compounds are cytotoxic and cytostatic in vitro to several cell types, including thymocytes (Seinen et al., 1977a; Seinen, 1981). Since in vitro the cytolytic activity of dialkyltin compounds is observed at relatively high levels and moreover the disappearance of cortical thymocytes is not associated with histological signs of cell destruction, a direct cytostatic activity seems more likely. This is supported by a decreased DNA synthesis of thymocytes upon low level exposure to dialkyltin compounds (Penninks and Seinen, 1983a,b; Penninks and Seinen, 1986). In short-term in vitro incubations with freshly isolated rat thymocytes, DBTC decreased in a dose-related fashion the basal DNA synthesis, as measured by the incorporation of ^{3}H-thymidine (^{3}H-TdR). Moreover, protein synthesis as well as RNA synthesis were found to be affected. These anti-proliferative effects could not be accounted for by a reduced viability of thymocytes, nor by a limited energy supply as a result of the shift from an aerobic to a more anaerobic metabolism of thymocytes upon exposure to dialkyltin compounds. Although upon in vitro DBTC exposure the glycolytic activity of thymocytes was increased (Penninks and Seinen, 1980), probably because of an inhibition of the α-ketoacid dehydrogenase systems (Aldridge and Cremer, 1955; Aldridge, 1976; Cain et al., 1977; Penninks et al., 1983), the increased glucose metabolism of thymocytes was able to maintain the ATP concentrations at control levels (Penninks and Seinen, 1986).

In vivo exposure of rats to DBTC also resulted in an early and rapid reduction of nucleoside and amino acid incorporation by thymocytes (Penninks and Seinen, 1986). After a single intravenous dose of 2.5 mg DBTC/kg body weight, DNA, RNA and protein synthesis were markedly reduced by 24 h. DNA synthesis was reduced about 50% after 24 h, with a further decrease to 25% of the control value at 48 h; thymus weight and consequently the number of isolated thymocytes started to decrease after 48 h (figure 4.3). Three days post-treatment, ^{3}H-TdR incorporation had started to recover and after an overshoot, returned to normal by seven days. The increased proliferative activity was followed by a recovery of thymus weight and its cellularity. Since the proliferative activity of thymocytes is mainly determined by the population of large dividing thymocytes, these in vitro and in vivo studies point to an interference by DBTC with this cell type. Recent in vivo studies have shown that within 24 h after a single oral dose of DBTC the fraction of large-sized lymphoblasts is strongly reduced (Snoeij, N., Penninks, A. H. and Seinen, W., unpublished results). This early and dramatic reduction in thymo-

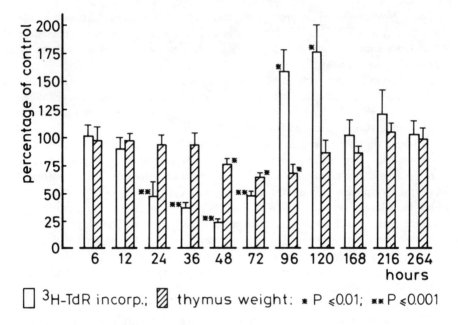

Figure 4.3 Thymus to body weight ratio and basal ^{3}H-thymidine incorporation of rat thymocytes at various time intervals after a single intravenous dose of 2.5 mg DBTC/kg body weight (mean value ± SD of 3 rats). (Results are from Penninks and Seinen, 1986)

cyte blasts was not observed previously, since they only represent about 5% of the total thymocyte population.

In conclusion, these studies indicate that the target cell for the dialkyltin compounds is the proliferating thymocyte; this results in thymic atrophy which leads to suppression of the thymus-dependent immunity. Regarding the molecular mechanism of this anti-proliferative effect, sulphydryl interactions have been postulated (Penninks, 1985), based on the high affinity of dialkyltins for dithiols (Aldridge and Cremer, 1955; Cain *et al.*, 1977; Penninks and Seinen, 1983a). Lymphocytes, which are dependent on cell–cell interactions for their maintenance of normal proliferation and differentiation, are particularly sensitive to SH-reactive agents. Sulphydryl interactions at the level of the plasma membrane (Chaplin and Wedner, 1978; Noelle and Lawrence, 1981) as well as the cytosol, e.g. disruption of the cytoskeleton (Pfeiffer and Irons, 1981, 1983), interfere with lymphocyte blastogenesis. Although similarities in effects of DBTC and known sulphydryl reagents on thymocytes have been observed, further research is needed to validate the postulated interaction of dialkyltins with sulphydryl groups as the mechanism of the observed anti-proliferative effect.

In summary, two groups of chemicals that have severe impact on thymus-dependent immune responses and that have in common a deleterious effect on the thymus, appear to exert their influence by quite different mechanisms. Dioxin and related compounds act on the thymic epithelium, thus impairing thymocyte maturation. DBTC and DOTC, on the other hand, interfere directly with the thymocyte through an anti-proliferative action. Immunotoxicants that do not belong to either of the two groups mentioned above, may exert their immunotoxic action through the mechanisms outlined herein, or through other mechanisms.

REFERENCES

Aldridge, W. N. (1976). The influence of organotin compounds on mitochondrial functions. In: *Organotin Compounds: New Chemistry and Application* (ed. J. J. Zuckermann), American Chemical Society, Washington, D.C., pp. 186–96

Aldridge, W. N. and Cremer, J. E. (1955). The biochemistry of organotin compounds. Diethyltin dichloride and triethyltin sulphate. *Biochem. J.*, **61**, 406–18

Beatty, P. W., Lembach, K. J., Holscher, M. A. and Neal, R. A. (1975). Effects of 2,3,7,8-tetrachlorodibenzo-*p*-dioxin (TCDD) on mammalian cells in tissue culture. *Toxicol. appl. Pharmacol.*, **31**, 309–12

Buu-Hoi, N. P., Chanh, P. H., Sesqué, G., Azum-Gelade, M. C. and Saint-Ruf, G. (1972). Organs as targets of dioxin (2,3,7,8-tetrachlorodibenzo-*p*-dioxin) intoxication. *Naturwissenschaften*, **59**, 174–5

Cain, K., Hyams, R. L. and Griffith, D. E. (1977). Studies on energy linked reactions: inhibition of oxidative phosphorylation and energy linked reactions by dibutyltin dichloride. *FEBS Lett.*, **82**, 23–8

Carlstedt-Duke, J. M. B. (1979). Tissue distribution of the receptor for 2,3,7,8-tetrachlorodibenzo-*p*-dioxin in the rat. *Cancer Res.*, **39**, 3172–6

Chang, K. J., Hsieh, K. H., Lee, T. P., Tang, S. Y. and Tung, T. C. (1981). Immunologic evaluation of patients with polychlorinated biphenyl poisoning: Determination of lymphocyte subpopulations. *Toxicol appl. Pharmacol.*, **61**, 58–63

Chang, K. J., Hsieh, K. H., Tang, S. Y., Tung, T. C. and Lee, T. P. (1982). Immunologic evaluation of patients with polychlorinated biphenyl poisoning: Evaluation of delayed-type skin hypersensitivity response and its relation to clinical studies. *J. Toxicol. Environ. Hlth.*, **9**, 217–23

Chaplin, D. D. and Wedner, H. J. (1978). Inhibition of lectin-induced lymphocyte activation by diamide and other sulfhydryl reagents. *Cell. Immunol.*, **36**, 303–11

Clark, D. A., Gauldie, J., Szewczuk, M. R. and Sweeney, G. (1981). Enhanced suppressor cell activity as a mechanism of immunosuppression by 2,3,7,8-tetrachlorodibenzo-*p*-dioxin. *Proc. Soc. exptl. Biol. Med.*, **168**, 290–9

Clark, D. A., Sweeney, G., Safe, S., Hancock, E., Kilburn, D. G. and Gauldie, J. (1983). Cellular and genetic basis for suppression of cytotoxic T-cell generation by haloaromatic hydrocarbons. *Immunopharmacology*, **6**, 143–53

Faith, R. E. and Luster, M. I. (1979). Investigations on the effects of 2,3,7,8-tetrachlorodibenzo-*p*-dioxin (TCDD) on parameters of various immune functions. *Ann. N.Y. Acad. Sci.*, **320**, 564–71

Faith, R. E. and Moore, J. A. (1977). Impairment of thymus-dependent immune functions by exposure of the developing immune system to 2,3,7,8-tetrachlorodibenzo-*p*-dioxin (TCDD). *J. Toxicol. Environ. Hlth.*, **3**, 451–64

Funahashi, N., Iwasaki, I. and Ide, G. (1980). Effect of bis(tri-*n*-butyltin)oxide on endocrine and lymphoid organs of male rats. *Acta Pathol. Japon.*, **30**, 955–66

Gaines, Th.B. and Kimbrough, R. D. (1968). Toxicity of fentin hydroxide to rats. *Toxicol. appl. Pharmacol.*, **12**, 397–403

Greenlee, W. F., Dold, K. M., Irons, R. D. and Osborne, R. (1985). Evidence for direct action of 2,3,7,8-tetrachlorodibenzo-*p*-dioxin (TCDD) on thymic epithelium. *Toxicol. appl. Pharmacol.*, **79**, 112–20

Gupta, B. N., Vos, J. G., Moore, J. A., Zinkl, J. G. and Bullock, B. C. (1973). Pathologic effects of 2,3,7,8-tetrachlorodibenzo-*p*-dioxin in laboratory animals. *Environ. Hlth. Perspect.*, 5, 125–40

Haynes, B. (1984). The human thymic microenvironment. *Adv. Immunol.*, 36, 87–142

Hennighausen, G., Karnstedt, U. and Lange, P. (1981). Organotin concentrations in liver, spleen and thymus of rats after a single administration of di-*n*-octyltin dichloride. *Pharmazie*, 36, 710–11

Hinsdill, R. D., Couch, D. L. and Speirs, R. S. (1980). Immunosuppression in mice induced by dioxin (TCDD) in feed. *J. Environ. Pathol. Toxicol.*, 4, 401–25

Ishaaya, L., Engel, J. L. and Casida, J. E. (1976). Dietary triorganotins affect lymphatic tissues and blood composition of mice. *Pestic. Biochem. Physiol.*, 6, 270–9

Kendall, M. D. (1981). *The Thymus Gland*, Academic Press, London

Knutson, J. C. and Poland, A. (1980). 2,3,7,8-Tetrachlorodibenzo-*p*-dioxin: Failure to demonstrate toxicity in twenty-three cultured cell types. *Toxicol. appl. Pharmacol.*, 54, 377–83

Kouri, R. E., Ratrie, H., Atlas, S. A., Niwa, A. and Nebert, D. W. (1974). Aryl hydrocarbon hydroxylase induction in human lymphocyte cultures by 2,3,7,8-tetrachlorodibenzo-*p*-dioxin. *Life Sci.*, 15, 1585–95

Krajnc, E. I., Wester, P. W., Loeber, J. G., Van Leeuwen, F. X. R., Vos, J. G., Vaessen, H. A. M. G. and Van der Heijden, C. A. (1984). Toxicity of bis(tri-*n*-butyltin)oxide in the rat. I. Short-term effects on general parameters and on the endocrine and lymphoid systems. *Toxicol. appl. Pharmacol.*, 75, 363–86

Luster, M. I., Boorman, G. A., Dean, J. H., Harris, M. H., Luebke, R. W., Padarathsingh, M. L. and Moore, J. A. (1980). Examination of bone marrow, immunologic parameters and host susceptibility following pre- and postnatal exposure to 2,3,7,8-tetrachlorodibenzo-*p*-dioxin (TCDD). *Int. J. Immunopharmacol.*, 2, 301–10

Miller, K. and Scott, M. P. (1985). Immunological consequences of dioctyltin dichloride (DOTC)-induced thymic injury. *Toxicol. appl. Pharmacol.*, 78, 395–403

Miller, K., Scott, M. P. and Foster, J. R. (1984). Thymic involution in rats given diets containing dioctyltin dichloride. *Clin. Immunol. Immunopathol.*, 30, 62–70

Nagarkatti, P. S., Sweeney, G. D., Gauldie, J. and Clark, D. A. (1984). Sensitivity to suppression of cytotoxic T-cell generation by 2,3,7,8-tetrachlorodibenzo-*p*-dioxin (TCDD) is dependent on the *Ah* genotype of the murine host. *Toxicol. appl. Pharmacol.*, 72, 169–76

Niwa, A., Kumaki, K. and Nebert, D. W. (1975). Induction of aryl hydrocarbon hydroxylase activity in various cell cultures by 2,3,7,8-tetrachlorodibenzo-*p*-dioxin. *Molec. Pharmacol.*, 11, 399–408

Noelle, R. J. and Lawrence, D. A. (1981). Modulation of T-cell function. II. Chemical basis for the involvement of cell surface thiol-reactive sites on T-cell proliferation. *Cell. Immunol.*, 60, 453–69

Penninks, A. H. (1985). *Immunotoxicity of organotin compounds. On the mechanism of dialkyltin induced thymus involution.* Ph.D thesis, University of Utrecht, The Netherlands

Penninks, A. H. and Seinen, W. (1980). Toxicity of organotin compounds. IV. Impairment of energy metabolism of rat thymocytes by various dialkytin compounds. *Toxicol. appl. Pharmacol.*, 56, 221–31

Penninks, A. H. and Seinen, W. (1983a). The lymphocyte as target of toxicity: a biochemical approach to dialkyltin induced immunosuppression. In: *Advances in Immunopharmacology, Vol. 2,* (eds J. W. Hadden, L. Chedid, P. Dukor,

F. Spreafico and D. Willoughby), Pergamon Press, Oxford and New York, pp. 41–60

Penninks, A. H. and Seinen, W. (1983b). Immunotoxicity of organotins. In: *Immunotoxicology*, (eds G. G. Gibson, R. Hubbard and D. V. Parke), Academic Press, London, pp. 427–36

Penninks, A. H. and Seinen, W. (1986). In: *Proceedings of the International Seminar on the Immunological System as Target for Toxic Damage*, Luxembourg, in press

Penninks, A. H., Verschuren, P. M. and Seinen, W. (1983). Di-*n*-butyltin dichloride uncouples oxidative phosphorylation in rat liver mitochondria. *Toxicol. appl. Pharmacol.*, **70**, 115–20

Penninks, A. H., Kuper, F., Spit, B. J. and Seinen, W. (1985). On the mechanism of dialkyltin-induced thymus involution. *Immunopharmacology*, **10**, 1–10

Pfeiffer, R. W. and Irons, R. D. (1981). Inhibition of lectin stimulated lymphocyte agglutination and mitogenesis by hydroquinone: reactivity with intracellular sulfhydryl groups. *Exp. molec. Pathol.*, **35**, 189–98

Pfeiffer, R. W. and Irons, R. D. (1983). Alteration of lymphocyte function by quinones through a sulfhydryl dependent disruption of microtubule assembly. *Int. J. Immunopharmacol.*, **5**, 463–70

Poland, A. and Glover, E. (1980). 2,3,7,8-Tetrachlorodibenzo-*p*-dioxin: Segregation of toxicity with the *Ah* locus. *Molec. Pharmacol.*, **17**, 86–94

Poland, A. and Knutson, J. C. (1982). 2,3,7,8-Tetrachlorodibenzo-*p*-dioxin and related halogenated aromatic hydrocarbons: Examination of the mechanism of toxicity. *Ann. Rev. Pharmacol. Toxicol.*, **22**, 517–54

Poland, A., Glover, E. and Kende, A. S. (1976). Stereospecific, high affinity binding of 2,3,7,8-tetrachlorodibenzo-*p*-dioxin by hepatic cytosol. *J. biol. Chem.*, **251**, 4936–45

Reggiani, G. (1978). Medical problems raised by the TCDD contamination in Seveso, Italy. *Arch. Toxicol.*, **4**, 161–88

Seinen, W. (1981). Immunotoxicity of alkyltin compounds. In: *Immunological Considerations in Toxicology, Vol. 1*, (ed. R. P. Sharma), CRC Press, Boca Raton, pp. 103–119

Seinen, W. and Penninks, A. H. (1979). Immune suppression as a consequence of a selective cytotoxic activity of certain organometallic compounds on thymus and thymus-dependent lymphocytes. *Ann. N.Y. Acad. Sci.*, **320**, 499–517

Seinen, W. and Willems, M. I. (1976). Toxicity of organotin compounds. I. Atrophy of thymus and thymus dependent lymphoid tissue in rats fed di-*n*-octyltin dichloride. *Toxicol. appl. Pharmacol.*, **35**, 63–75

Seinen, W., Vos, J. G., Van Spanje, I., Snoek, M., Brands, R. and Hooykaas, H. (1977a). Toxicity of organotin compounds. II. Comparative *in vivo* and *in vitro* studies with various organotin and organolead compounds in different animal species with special emphasis on lymphocyte cytotoxicity. *Toxicol. appl. Pharmacol.*, **42**, 197–212

Seinen, W., Vos, J. G., Van Krieken, R., Penninks, A., Brands, R. and Hooykaas, H. (1977b). Toxicity of organotin compounds. III. Suppression of thymus-dependent immunity in rats by di-*n*-butyltin dichloride and di-*n*-octyltin dichloride. *Toxicol. appl. Pharmacol.*, **42**, 213–24

Seinen, W., Vos, J. G., Brands, R. and Hooykaas, H. (1979). Lymphocytotoxicity and immunosuppression by organotin compounds. Suppression of graft-versus-host reactivity, blast transformation, and E-rosette formation by di-*n*-butyltin dichloride and di-*n*-octyltin dichloride. *Immunopharmacology*, **1**, 343–55

Snoeij, N. J., Van Iersel, A. A. J., Penninks, A. H. and Seinen, W. (1985). Toxicity of triorganotin compounds: comparative *in vivo* studies with a series of trialkyltin compounds and triphenyltin chloride in male rats. *Toxicol. appl. Pharmacol.*, **81**, 274–86

Sorkin, E., Pierpaoli, W., Fabris, N. and Bianchi, E. (1972). Relation of growth hormone to thymus and the immune response. In: *Growth and Growth Hormone* (eds A. Pecile and E. E. Müller), Excerpta Medica, Amsterdam, p. 132

Stutman, O. (1978). Intrathymic and extrathymic T-cell maturation. *Immunol. Rev.*, **42**, 138–84

Thigpen, J. E., Faith, R. E., McConnell, E. E. and Moore, J. A. (1975). Increased susceptibility to bacterial infection as a sequela of exposure to 2,3,7,8-tetrachlorodibenzo-*p*-dioxin. *Infect. Immun.*, **12**, 1319–24

Thomas, P. T. and Hinsdill, R. D. (1979). The effect of perinatal exposure to tetrachlorodibenzo-*p*-dioxin on the immune response of young mice. *Drug Chem. Toxicol.*, **2**, 77–98

Van Haelst, U. (1967). Light and electromicroscopic study of normal and pathological thymus of the rat. II. The acute thymic involution. *Zeitschr. Zellforsch.*, **80**, 153–82

Van Logten, M. J., Gupta, B. N., McConnell, E. E. and Moore, J. A. (1980). Role of the endocrine system in the action of 2,3,7,8-tetrachlorodibenzo-*p*-dioxin (TCDD) on the thymus. *Toxicology*, **15**, 135–44

Van Logten, M. J., Gupta, B. N., McConnell, E. E. and Moore, J. A. (1981). The influence of malnutrition on the toxicity of tetrachlorodibenzo-*p*-dioxin (TCDD) in rats. *Toxicology*, **21**, 77–88

Verschuuren, H. G., Kroes, R., Vink, H. M. and Van Esch, G. J. (1966). Short-term toxicity studies with triphenyltin compounds in rats and guinea pigs. *Food Cosmet. Toxicol.*, **4**, 35–45

Verschuuren, H. G., Ruitenberg, E. J., Peetoom, F., Helleman, P. W. and Van Esch, G. J. (1970). Influence of triphenyltin acetate on lymphatic tissue and immune response in guinea pigs. *Toxicol. appl. Pharmacol.*, **16**, 400–10

Vos, J. G. and Moore, J. A. (1974). Suppression of cellular immunity in rats and mice by maternal treatment with 2,3,7,8-tetrachlorodibenzo-*p*-dioxin. *Int. Arch. Allergy appl. Immunol.*, **47**, 777–94

Vos, J. G., Moore, J. A. and Zinkl, J. G. (1973). Effects of 2,3,7,8-tetrachlorodibenzo-*p*-dioxin on the immune system of laboratory animals. *Environ. Hlth. Perspect.*, **5**, 149–62

Vos, J. G., Kreeftenberg, J. G., Engel, H. W. B., Minderhoud, A. and Van Noorle Jansen, L. M. (1978). Studies on 2,3,7,8-tetrachlorodibenzo-*p*-dioxin induced immune suppression and decreased resistance to infection: Endotoxin hypersensitivity, serum zinc concentrations and effect of thymosin treatment. *Toxicology*, **9**, 75–86

Vos, J. G., Faith, R. E. and Luster, M. I. (1980). Immune alterations. In: *Halogenated Biphenyls, Terphenyls, Naphthalenes, Dibenzodioxins and Related Products* (ed. R. D. Kimbrough), Elsevier/North Holland, Amsterdam, pp. 241–66

Vos, J. G., De Klerk, A., Krajnc, E. I., Kruizinga, W., Van Ommen, B. and Rozing, J. (1984a). Toxicity of bis(tri-*n*-butyltin)oxide in the rat. II. Suppression of thymus-dependent immune responses and of parameters of nonspecific resistance after short-term exposure. *Toxicol. appl. Pharmacol.*, **75**, 387–408

Vos, J. G., Van Logten, M. J., Kreeftenberg, J. G. and Kruizinga, W. (1984b). Effect of triphenyltin hydroxide on the immune system of the rat. *Toxicology*, **29**, 325–36

Vos, J. G., De Klerk, A., Krajnc, E. I., Kruizinga, W. and Rozing, J. Toxicity of bis(tri-*n*-butyltin)oxide in the rat. III. Suppression of thymus-dependent immune responses and of parameters of nonspecific resistance after chronic exposure. Submitted for publication

White, A. and Goldstein, A. L. (1972). Hormonal control of host immunity. In *Immunogenicity, Frontiers of Biology, Vol. 25* (ed. A. Borek, North-Holland, Amsterdam, pp. 334–64

Part II

Molecular Mechanisms of Toxicity

5

Toxic Lectins and Related Ribosome-inactivating Plant Proteins

Fiorenzo Stirpe

With gratitude I dedicate this review to Norman Aldridge and to all staff of the M.R.C. Toxicology Unit at Carshalton, who greatly contributed to my scientific formation.

'Iron sharpeneth iron; so a man sharpeneth the countenance of his friend' (*Proverbs*, 27, 17)

TOXIC LECTINS

The toxicity of some plants is due to the proteins they contain, which have in common several properties, amongst these the capacity to bind sugars. For this property these toxins are considered as monovalent lectins, as defined by Kocourek and Horejsi (1981).

Five toxins of this type are known (table 5.1): two of them, namely ricin and abrin, were known since the end of the last century; modeccin, identified in 1925 (Green and Andrews, 1925), was purified and characterised more than 50 years later (Refsnes *et al.*, 1977; Stirpe *et al.*, 1978); viscumin was purified as a haemagglutinin (Ziska *et al.*, 1978) and subsequently identified as a toxin similar to ricin (Stirpe *et al.*, 1980); volkensin was identified last (Barbieri *et al.*, 1984).

There are excellent reviews on these toxins (Olsnes and Pihl, 1976, 1982; Jiménez and Vazquez, 1985), and therefore emphasis will be given here to more recent findings, whereas the fundamental, well established knowledge will be recalled only as far as it will be necessary to provide an indispensable background.

Table 5.1 Toxic lectins from plants

Name	Plant source			
	Species	Family	Part	Content (mg/100 g)
Abrin	*Abrus precatorius* (jequirity)	Leguminosae	Seeds	75
Modeccin	*Adenia digitata*	Passifloraceae	Roots*	20–180
Ricin	*Ricinus communis* (castor bean plant)	Euphorbiaceae	Seeds	120
Viscumin	*Viscum album* (mistletoe)	Loranthaceae	Leaves	7
Volkensin	*Adenia volkensii* (kilyambiti)	Passifloraceae	Roots*	37

*Also present in seeds.
Data from Stirpe and Barbieri, 1986.

Purification

The purification of ricin and related toxins is relatively simple nowadays, and is achieved by exploiting their property of binding galactose or galactose-containing sugars. A single-step affinity chromotographic procedure is currently used for the purification of modeccin (Gasperi-Campani *et al.*, 1978), viscumin (Ziska *et al.*, 1978) and volkensin (Stirpe *et al.*, 1985). The seeds of *Ricinus communis* and of *Abrus precatorius* in addition to ricin and abrin contain two other galactose-binding lectins from which the toxins can be separated either by a single-step affinity chromatography, provided it is performed by eluting with a galactose gradient (Thorpe *et al.*, 1981; Simmons and Russell, 1985), or by ion-exchange chromatography (Nicolson *et al.*, 1974; Olsnes *et al.*, 1975a).

All toxins are stable, and can be stored for years, freeze-dried or in frozen solutions, without appreciable loss of activity.

Structure and physico-chemical properties

The toxins considered here have comparable M_r (60 000–65 000) and similar structure, all consisting of two unequal polypeptide chains, a larger one, called B-chain, with sugar-binding properties, and a slightly smaller one, called A-chain (Table 5.2), which is the 'active' part of the molecule, in that it inactivates eukaryotic ribosomes (see below). The two chains are linked to each other by a single disulphide bond that can be cleaved by treatment with a reducing agent. However, under some conditions reduction of the disulphide bond is not sufficient to separate the two chains from each other, thus indicating the presence of other weaker, non-covalent bonds (Lappi *et al.*, 1978; Barbieri *et al.*, 1980; Olsnes *et al.*, 1982; Stirpe *et al.*, 1985).

The complete amino acid sequence of ricin (Funatsu *et al.*, 1978, 1979) and partial sequences of other toxins have been determined. Numerous corresponding sequences were found not only between ricin and the other lectin (agglutinin) of *Ricinus communis* seeds (Cawley *et al.*, 1978; Roberts *et al.*, 1985), but also between the A-chains of ricin and modeccin and the A-chain-like ribosome-inactivating proteins (see below) (Ready *et al.*, 1984; Lappi *et al.*, 1985), which suggests that these proteins may derive phylogenetically from a common ancestor.

Recently, evidence was provided that ricin is synthesised as a 60.5 kD polypeptide, which is proteolytically cleaved to give the A and B chains (Butterworth and Lord, 1983). The existence of this 'preproricin' precursor was confirmed by sequence studies of the genomic ricin clone (Lamb *et al.*, 1985; Halling *et al.*, 1985).

The pI of the toxins is neutral or moderately acidic, and their chains are one acidic, and one near neutral. Forms with different pI have been described for ricin (Ishiguro *et al.*, 1976; Mise *et al.*, 1977), modeccin (Olsnes *et al.*, 1978a; Barbieri *et al.*, 1980) and volkensin (Stirpe *et al.*, 1985).

All toxins are glycoproteins, particularly rich in mannose. As far as it is known, carbohydrates are bound mostly to the B-chains (Olsnes and Pihl, 1982). Abrin, ricin and modeccin bind to concanavalin A, which indicates that their mannose residues are exposed. This is of importance for the uptake of ricin (the only toxin studied in this respect) by macrophages (see below).

The main characteristics of the toxins are summarised in table 5.2.

Table 5.2 Main characteristics of toxic lectins

Toxin	M_r	pI	Total neutral sugar content (%)
Abrin	65 000	6.1	3.7
A-chain	30 000	4.6	Absent
B-chain	35 000	7.2	7.4
Modeccin	63 000	6.2–7.1	2.7
A-chain	28 000	5.8–6.1	
B-chain	31 000	7.3–8.1	
Ricin	62 057	7.1	4.5
A-chain	30 625	7.5	2.6
B-chain	31 432	4.8	6.4
Viscumin	60 000		9.7
A-chain	29 000		
B-chain	32 000		
Volkensin	62 000	7.5–8.2	5.7
A-chain	29 000		
B-chain	36 000		

Data from Stirpe and Barbieri, 1986.

In spite of the many similarities, the toxins have different effects *in vivo*, as it is shown by the diversity of the lesions they cause in poisoned animals, as it will be discussed below. Also, they are immunologically distinct, a partial cross-reactivity having been observed only between modeccin and volkensin (Stirpe *et al.*, 1985), consistent with the taxonomical proximity of the plants producing these two toxins.

Effects on animals

Ricin and similar lectins are exceedingly toxic to animals. Their LD_{50} to mice are reported in table 5.3; it should be added that volkensin shows an even higher toxicity to rats, with an LD_{50} of 50–60 ng/kg, which puts this protein amongst the most potent known toxins. Toxic effects have been observed in human cancer patients receiving abrin intravenously at doses above 0.15 ng/kg (Olsnes and Pihl, 1982). A some 100-fold lower toxicity was observed if the toxin was given by the oral route.

Table 5.3   Toxicity of lectins to mice and to HeLa cells

Toxin	Toxicity to	
	Mice LD_{50} (μg/kg)	HeLa cells ID_{50}^{*} (pM)
Abrin	0.6	3.7
Modeccin	2.1	0.3
Ricin	2.6	1.1
Viscumin	2.4	8.0
Volkensin	1.4	12.3[†]

*Concentration giving 50% inhibition of protein synthesis.
[†]On other cell lines, the ID_{50} of volkensin was some 10-fold lower than that of modeccin (Stirpe *et al.*, 1985).
Data from Stirpe and Barbieri, 1986.

After an admirable description of the lesions produced by ricin and abrin in the rabbit (Flexner, 1897), studies on the pathology of animals poisoned with ricin are surprisingly few, and those concerning other toxins are even scarcer.

A characteristic feature of poisoning by any of the lectins considered here is a latent period without apparent signs of illness, which is present regardless of the dose administered, and lasts 1–3 h. Death never occurs before 6 (volkensin) to 10 h (ricin).

Apart from ascites, which was present in rats poisoned with any of the lectins, significant and sometimes striking differences were observed in the lesions brought about by the toxins in the parenchymal organs of rats (table 5.4). Thus, ricin affects primarily Kupffer cells and the macrophage-rich areas of lymphoid organs such as lymph nodes and the red pulp of the spleen (Flexner, 1897; Derenzini *et al.*, 1976), consistent with the higher sensitivity of macrophages to this toxin

Table 5.4 Lesions* caused by toxic lectins

Toxin		References
Abrin	Necrosis of pancreas acinar cells	1
Modeccin	Massive liver necrosis; ascites	2
Ricin	Necrosis of non-parenchymal liver cells, followed by necrosis of hepatocytes; necrosis of lymph nodes and of splenic red pulp; intestinal necrosis and ascites	3–5
Viscumin	No lesions detectable in parenchymal organs; ascites	6
Volkensin	Massive liver necrosis; ascites	6

1. Barbieri *et al.* (1979a); 2. Sperti *et al.* (1979); 3. Flexner (1897); 4. Waller *et al.* (1966); 5. Derenzini *et al.* (1976); 6. L. Barbieri, M. Derenzini and F. Stirpe (unpublished observations). *The pathological lesions listed were observed in rabbits (reference 3) and in rats (all other references).

(see below). Only if the dose given allowed the animals to survive longer than 24 h, do hepatocytes appear severely damaged. Presumably this sequence of events reflects the occurrence of a two-stage process: necrosis of Kupffer and sinusoidal cells occurs first, and thus sinusoids are deprived of their lining. This leaves the hepatocytes in direct contact with the blood, and causes formation of fibrin clots with subsequent appearance of micro-thrombi and impairment of blood circulation, and damage to hepatocytes (Derenzini *et al.*, 1976).

By contrast, modeccin causes massive liver necrosis, affecting both parenchymal and non-parenchymal cells (Sperti *et al.*, 1979); similar and, possibly, more severe lesions were observed in rats poisoned with volkensin (unpublished observations).

In rats poisoned with lethal doses of abrin, only lesions of acinar pancreatic cells were observed, which could not account for death (Barbieri *et al.*, 1979a). Even more surprising was the lack of any detectable lesions in the parenchymal organs of rats killed with viscumin (unpublished observations). Not only are these results puzzling, but they also cast some doubts on whether the severe pathological lesions observed in the parenchymal organs of rats poisoned with ricin, modeccin and volkensin were in fact the only cause of death.

It has been observed more recently that ricin, abrin and modeccin injected either into peripheral nerves or in certain tissues such as the iris or salivary gland are retrogradely transported along the nerve axons up to the neurons, which are then severely damaged (Dumas *et al.*, 1979; Harper *et al.*, 1980; Wiley *et al.*, 1982; Yamamoto *et al.*, 1983). Besides their intrinsic toxicological interest, these observations may lead to the use of toxic lectins as experimental tools in neurobiological research; moreover, they make one wonder whether a similar 'suicide transport' mechanism may have a role in the poisoning by these toxins, especially in those cases in which no parenchymal lesions severe enough to account for death could be detected. The notion of a neurotoxic action of ricin is supported by the observation that intracerebrally-injected anti-ricin antibodies protect mice from lethal doses of the toxin (Foxwell *et al.*, 1985).

Effects on cells

Ricin and related toxins are lethal to *in vitro* cultured cells, which they kill at concentrations as low as 10^{-12} M (table 5.3). Virtually all animal cells are sensitive to the toxins, although to a variable extent: tumour cells (Lin *et al.*, 1970), virus-transformed fibroblasts (Nicolson *et al.*, 1975a) and macrophages (Refsnes and Munthe-Kaas, 1976) being more sensitive to ricin than HeLa cells or untransformed fibroblasts. Cell mutants resistant to the various toxins have been selected, as will be discussed below.

The effects of the toxins on plant cells are largely unknown; it was observed, however, that the growth of *in vitro* cultured carrot and, to a lesser extent, rice cells was stimulated by ricin (Battelli *et al.*, 1984).

Both the B- and A-chains of the toxins are required for, and contribute to their action on cells, the former providing the binding of the toxin molecule to the cell membrane, a necessary prerequisite for the entry into the cytoplasm of the ribosome-inactivating A-chains.

The first functional change detected in the cells exposed to ricin (and subsequently to the other toxins, see Olsnes and Pihl, 1982) was a severe impairment of protein synthesis that occurred after a lag period which varied with the concentration of the toxin and before the appearance of other signs of functional or structural cell damage. Cell respiration was unaffected, and changes in DNA and RNA synthesis occurred some time after the arrest of protein synthesis, of which presumably they were a consequence (Lin *et al.*, 1971).

This impairment of protein synthesis is due to the action of the A-chains which must enter into the cytoplasm to damage ribosomes. Entry is only possible after the toxin molecules are bound to cells through their B-chains. These bind to galactosyl residues of glycoprotein receptors present on the membrane of virtually all cells, which accounts for the lethal effects of the toxins on all animal cells examined so far. As a consequence the binding, and hence the entry and toxicity, of all lectins to most cells is inhibited in the presence of excess galactose or lactose, which compete with the cell receptors for the galactose-binding sites of toxin B-chains. Conversely, treatment of cells with neuraminidase, which exposes more galactose residues by removing sialic acid, increases the number of binding sites for ricin and the sensitivity of cells to the toxin (Nicolson *et al.*, 1975b; Rosen and Hughes, 1977).

An exception to this is the binding of ricin to, and its uptake by, macrophages, which is scarcely affected by galactose, but is inhibited more effectively by mannose or mannan (Skilleter *et al.*, 1981) and requires the presence of both mannan and galactose to be completely abolished (Simmons *et al.*, 1986). This is because macrophages have receptors on their membranes which bind mannose and mannan, as well as some which bind galactose. Thus ricin binds to cells through two different and in a way opposite mechanisms: with its galactose-binding site to galactose residues on most cells (including macrophages), and with its exposed mannose residues to the receptors for mannose on macrophages. In the former case ricin behaves as a lectin, whilst in the latter instance it is the macrophage receptor that acts as a lectin with respect to ricin. The finding that mannose is more effective than galactose in preventing ricin toxicity to macrophages strongly suggests that binding to mannose receptors provides a more efficient mechanism of internalisation of ricin. An analysis of the binding of ricin to, and of its toxic effects on, macrophages in the presence of ammonium chloride, swainsonine and castanospermine indicates that the toxin taken up via the mannose receptor takes an intracellular route different from that followed by ricin bound to galactosyl residues (Simmons et al., 1986).

The role played by the receptors in the intracellular fate and toxicity of lectins is also suggested by differences amongst the various toxins. For instance, HeLa cells have only 2×10^5 binding sites for modeccin (Olsnes et al., 1978b) as compared with 3×10^7 binding sites for ricin and abrin (Sandvig et al., 1978), and still as few as one hundred molecules of modeccin bound to a cell are sufficient to kill it, whereas some thousand molecules of ricin and abrin must be bound to achieve the same effect. Since it has been calculated that the entry of one toxin molecule into the cytoplasm is sufficient to kill a cell, these results indicate that either the receptors for modeccin are more efficient in delivering the toxin to the cytoplasm or, alternatively, that different toxins are delivered to different intracellular compartments, depending upon the receptors to which they are bound on the cell membrane.

The existence of different mechanisms whereby the various toxins enter into cells is confirmed by the effects of ammonium chloride and chloroquine, which protect cells against modeccin (Sandvig et al., 1979), volkensin (Stirpe et al., 1985) and ricin, the latter when taken up by macrophages via their mannose receptor (Simmons et al., 1986), whilst aggravating the cytotoxic effects of ricin and abrin (Sandvig et al., 1979) and viscumin (Stirpe et al., 1982) taken up via the receptor for their galactose-binding sites.

The exact mechanism whereby toxins are internalised by cells is not clear, although the process is known to exhibit a lag phase, to be temperature- and pH-dependent, and to require Ca^{2+} (this aspect has been reviewed by Olsnes and Sandvig, 1985). Receptor-mediated endocytosis is believed to occur, and by using gold-labelled ricin it has been shown that the toxin is taken up into vesicles near the Golgi apparatus (Van Deurs et al., 1985, 1986).

While there is no doubt that the A-chains must get inside the cells to exert their cytotoxic effects, it is not known whether they enter on their own or, as reported by Ray and Wu (1981), still linked to the B-chains; the latter can also be taken up at least into the environment of the cell membranes (Ishida et al., 1983). In any case, the two chains must be separated from each other (or at least the disulphide bond which joins them must be reduced) for the A-chain to be fully active. The free sulphydryl group does not appear to be necessary for the action of the A-chain, since this is unaffected by sulphydryl reagents such as N-ethylmaleimide (Olsnes et al., 1975a); presumably the A-chains are inactive in the whole toxins because their active site is masked by the B-chains. Reduction of the toxins may occur at the expense of reduced glutathione, possibly through an enzymic process: at least two distinct protein-disulphide oxidoreductases can catalyse this reaction (Barbieri *et al.*, 1982).

Toxin-resistant cell lines have been selected, and can be divided into three categories:

1. Cells that have a decreased capacity to bind the toxins, often due to modifications of the glycoprotein receptors owing to masking of their binding sites by increased sialylation or to defective synthesis of the oligosaccharide chains (Gottlieb *et al.*, 1974; Hyman *et al.*, 1974; Meager *et al.*, 1975, 1976; Fodstad *et al.*, 1977; Olsnes and Refsnes, 1978; Li *et al.*, 1980).
2. Cells that bind a near-normal, normal, or even higher-than-normal number of toxin molecules, but do not internalise them, having 'inefficient' receptors (Meager *et al.*, 1975, 1976; Gottlieb and Kornfeld, 1976; Robbins *et al.*, 1977; Nicolson *et al.*, 1978; Ray and Wu, 1982).
3. A cell line has also been described whose ribosomes are resistant to ricin (Ono *et al.*, 1982).

In the case of insufficient or inefficient binding, ricin can be rendered toxic to resistant cells if it is artificially delivered to the cytoplasm by inclusion into liposomes (Dimitriadis and Butters, 1979; Gardas and Macpherson, 1979) or by osmotically induced microinjection (Ghosh *et al.*, 1984).

Cells resistant to ricin are resistant to abrin and vice versa, but not to modeccin, volkensin or viscumin, and modeccin-resistant cells are cross-resistant to volkensin, but not to ricin, abrin or viscumin (Olsnes and Refsnes, 1978; Sargiacomo and Hughes, 1982; Stirpe *et al.*, 1982, 1985). This indicates the existence of three distinct receptors, one for ricin and abrin, one for modeccin and volkensin, and one for viscumin.

Effects on ribosomes

Ricin and abrin inhibit protein synthesis not only by whole cells, but also by cell-free systems (Olsnes and Pihl, 1972a,b). This effect is due to inactivation of ribosomes (Montanaro *et al.*, 1973), and more precisely of their 60S subunit (Sperti *et al.*, 1973) which becomes unable to bind the elongation factor 2 (Montanaro *et al.*, 1975). This is due to the action of the A-chains of ricin and abrin (Olsnes *et al.*, 1975b) and was observed also with modeccin (Montanaro *et al.*, 1978; Olsnes and Abraham, 1979), although with some differences: thus an excess of elongation factor 2 protects ribosomes from the action of ricin and abrin (Fernandez-Puentes *et al.*, 1976b), whilst aggravating the effects of modeccin (Olsnes and Abraham, 1979). Of all reactions involved in the process of protein synthesis, from the formation of aminoacyl-tRNA to the release of the complete polypeptide chain, the elongation factor 2-catalysed translocation and the elongation factor 2-dependent GTP hydrolysis are the only ones definitely impaired by all toxic lectins examined (as well as by the A-chain-like ribosome-inactivating proteins, see below). Other reported effects, such as an inhibition of the aminoacyl-tRNA binding or an impaired elongation factor 1-dependent GTP hydrolysis (Carrasco *et al.*, 1975; Fernandez-Puentes *et al.*, 1976a) were disproved (Sperti and Montanaro, 1979).

The 60S ribosomal subunit target of the toxic lectins appears damaged both by the toxins *in vitro* and in ribosomes isolated from ricin-treated cells (Onozaki *et al.*, 1975) or from the liver of modeccin-poisoned rats (Sperti *et al.*, 1979).

The nature of the action of the toxins and the change(s) they bring about in ribosomes are still unknown. The toxins act on ribosomes in a less-than-equimolar ratio, suggestive of a catalytic, probably enzymic action. The fact that ribosomes are inactivated in the absence of any cofactor rules out any transfer reaction, and rather suggests a hydrolytic activity. Unspecific protease or RNAase activities have never been detected in the toxins, and only recently a nuclease activity of ricin A-chain on 5S and 5.8S ribosomal RNA was reported, although at toxin concentrations 1000-fold higher than those required to inactivate ribosomes (Obrig *et al.*, 1985).

The inactivating property of the toxins is effective on all mammalian ribosomes examined (with the only exception of those from a ricin-resistant cell line, Ono *et al.*, 1982) and on ribosomes from *Artemia salina*. Ribosomes from protozoa (*Tetrahymena pyriformis*, Wilde *et al.*, 1979; *Acantamoeba castellanii*, Howell and Villemez, 1984) were insensitive to ricin and those from plants either were not affected by the various toxins tested on them, or were damaged by the toxins at concentrations much higher than those effective on mammalian ribosomes (Cawley *et al.*, 1977; Lugnier and Rether, 1981; Harley and Beevers, 1982; Battelli *et al.*, 1984). Ribosomes from *Escherichia coli* and from rat-liver mitochondria were not damaged by ricin (Olsnes *et al.*, 1973; Greco *et al.*, 1974), but those isolated from *Neurospora crassa* and yeast mitochondria were sensitive to this toxin (Lugnier *et al.*, 1976).

Other lectins inhibiting protein synthesis

Some non-toxin or scarcely toxic lectins, including one from a fish roe, inhibit protein synthesis by a cell-free system, although at higher concentrations as compared with the toxic lectins described above (Barbieri *et al.*, 1979b).

Apart from the agglutinin from *Ricinus communis*, which has an A-chain similar to that of ricin (Saltvedt, 1976), the mechanism whereby these lectins inhibit protein synthesis is unknown.

SINGLE-CHAIN RIBOSOME-INACTIVATING PROTEINS

A number of proteins have been isolated from various plant materials (mostly seeds) which inactivate eukaryotic ribosomes, and from the information so far available they appear to act in a manner similar to the A-chains of the toxic lectins. These A-chain-like proteins were provisionally called 'ribosome-inactivating proteins' (RIPs)

Table 5.5 Single-chain ribosome-inactivating proteins

Protein*	Plant source			Inhibitory activity on cell-free protein synthesis[†] ID_{50} (nM)[‡]
	Species	Family	Part	
Agrostin 2 5 6	*Agrostemma githago* (corn cockle)	Caryophyllaceae	Seeds	0.60 0.47 0.57
Peak 2 3 5	*Asparagus officinalis* (asparagus)	Liliaceae	Seeds	0.43 0.37 0.17
Bryodin	*Bryonia dioica*	Cucurbitaceae	Roots	0.12
Dianthin 30 32	*Dianthus caryophyllus* (carnation)	Caryophyllaceae	Leaves	0.30 0.12
Dodecandrin	*Phytolacca dodecandra*	Phytolaccaceae	Leaves	0.043
Gelonin	*Gelonium multiflorum* *Hordeum vulgare* (barley) *Hura crepitans* (sandbox tree)	Euphorbiaceae Gramineae Euphorbiaceae	Seeds Seeds Latex	0.40 0.083–2.13 0.17
Luffin	*Luffa cylindrica*	Cucurbitaceae	Seeds	0.002
Momordin	*Momordica charantia* (bitter gourd)	Cucurbitaceae	Seeds	0.06
PAP[§]	*Phytolacca americana* (pokeweed)	Phytolaccaceae	Leaves	0.24
PAP II			Summer leaves	0.25
PAP-S			Seeds	0.037
Saporin 5 6 9	*Saponaria officinalis* (soapwort)	Caryophyllaceae	Seeds	0.041 0.037 0.037
	Secale cereale (rye)	Gramineae	Seeds	4.00**
Tritin	*Triticum aestivum* (wheat)	Gramineae	Seeds Germ	2.13** 2.30**
	Zea mais (corn)	Gramineae	Seeds	2.13**

*Listed in alphabetical order by name of protein, if available, otherwise by name of plant. Except for dianthins, the number, when present, indicates the peak emerging from the carboxymethyl cellulose column.

[†]Determined on a rabbit reticulocyte lysate, unless stated otherwise.

[‡]Concentration giving 50% inhibition.

[§]Pokeweed antiviral protein.

**Determined on an Ehrlich ascites cell lysate.

Bryodin data were from Stirpe *et al.* (1986); all other data were taken from Stirpe and Barbieri, 1986.

or 'RIPs type 1', as opposed to the toxins, which can be considered as RIPs type 2. A list of the RIPs purified so far is given in table 5.5.

The characteristics of RIPs have been extensively reviewed (Barbieri and Stirpe, 1982; Irvin, 1983; Jiménez and Vazquez, 1985; Roberts and Selitrennikoff, 1986a; Stirpe and Barbieri, 1986) and it will be sufficient here to recall a few noteworthy points.

Ribosome-inactivating proteins have been found in numerous and unrelated plants, although at highly variable concentrations, ranging from less than 1 mg to over 100 mg per 100 g of starting material (Gasperi-Campani et al., 1977, 1980, 1985), and it is even possible that they are present in all plants.

The similarities between the RIPs and the A-chains of the toxins include several structural and functional properties: a similar M_r (30 000 approximately), partial homologies in the respective amino acid sequences (Bjorn et al., 1984; Ready et al., 1984; Lappi et al., 1985), an apparently similar mechanism of action with a comparable specific activity on ribosomes, and a similar relatively low toxicity to intact cells. However, there are also differences between the RIPs and the A-chains, and also between the various RIPs. Thus the pI of all known RIPs is strongly basic, whereas that of the A-chains is in the acidic region. Structural differences reside in the presence and composition of the sugar component, at least two RIPs (PAP and saporin) not containing any sugar. Whether there is a relationship between these differences in structure and the function of the various RIPs is unknown.

Ribosome-inactivating proteins differ from each other in their inhibitory activity on protein synthesis by cell-free systems, and in their toxicity to cells. The latter is much lower than that of toxic lectins, due to lack of the binding B-chain. The ID_{50} of RIPS for most cells is in the region of 10^{-5} M, but is much lower, 10^{-8} M, approximately, for macrophages (Barbieri and Stirpe, 1982). This higher toxicity to macrophages is probably the reason for the immunosuppressive activity of RIPs (Spreafico et al., 1983; Descotes et al., 1985).

This relatively low toxicity to cells is accompanied by a comparably low toxicity to animals, with LD_{50}s of the order of some mg per kg. All RIPs bring about essentially similar lesions, amongst which liver necrosis is particularly evident.

Much more marked are the differences observed in the effects of RIPs on ribosomes from organisms other than animals. Plant ribosomes may or may not be inactivated by RIPs, at concentrations varying by up to 1000-fold, in a manner that is unpredictable for any given RIP and for any ribosomal species. Thus ribosomes from a plant are inactivated by some RIPs but not by others and, conversely, RIPs which are effective on some ribosomes do not affect those from other species. As far as they have been studied in this respect, RIPs do not affect ribosomes from their own plants, and inactivate those from sensitive species at concentrations usually higher than those effective on animal ribosomes (Owens et al., 1973; Coleman and Roberts, 1981; Battelli et al., 1984). Very recently it was observed that a RIP from barley inactivates ribosomes from a mutant of Neurospora crassa and prevents the growth of the same organism and of some, but not of all, other fungal species examined (Roberts and Selitrennikoff, 1986b).

Ribosome-inactivating proteins do not affect ribosomes from *Escherichia coli* nor those from *Sulfolobus sulfataricus*, although gelonin and dianthin 32 at relatively high concentrations inactivate the ribosomes of another Archaebacterium, *Thermoplasma acidophylum* (Cammarano *et al.*, 1985, and personal communication).

On the basis of these observations, the possibility should be considered that some RIPs may exist which do not affect the animal ribosomes commonly used to detect these proteins.

The mechanism whereby RIPs inactivate ribosomes must be catalytic, but the nature of this mechanism is still unknown as is that involved with the toxin A-chains. Proteinase (Montanaro *et al.*, 1985) and RNAase (Obrig *et al.*, 1985) activities associated with gelonin and PAP, respectively, were observed, but the possibility of contaminations cannot be excluded. Whatever their mechanism of action may be, the effects of RIPs (as well as of the toxin A-chains) on ribosomes from different sources indicate that they are enzymes with a strict specificity, which may become valuable research tools, once their mechanism of action has been elucidated.

Ribosome-inactivating proteins can be introduced inside cells, and thus rendered highly toxic, when linked to molecules that bind to, or are taken up by, cells, such as lectins, sugars or neoglycoproteins, or when included into reconstituted viral envelopes or erythrocyte ghosts that can be fused with cells (reviewed by Stirpe and Barbieri, 1986). This possibility is relevant for the use of RIPs in the construction of immunotoxins, as it will be discussed in the next section.

IMMUNOTOXINS

Bacterial and plant toxins are utilised to construct conjugates with various carriers, toxic to the cells which are selective targets for the carriers: the final aim is to use these conjugates to eliminate unwanted, noxious cells. For this purpose toxins have been covalently linked to lectins, to hormones and more frequently to monoclonal antibodies, the latter giving the conjugates ('immunotoxins') with the highest specificity (reviews by Vitetta and Uhr, 1985; Thorpe, 1985; Frankel *et al.*, 1986). As compared with bacterial toxins, plant toxins offer the advantage that there is no widespread immunity against them, which would prevent their use in human therapy. However, conjugates made with whole toxins retain the non-specific toxicity of the parent molecules, due to the property of their B-chains of binding to virtually any cell. For this reason these immunotoxins cannot be administered *in vivo*, and their use is limited to the elimination of cells *in vitro*, where the binding of the B-chains can be prevented by saturating concentrations of lactose.

Better results are obtained by linking the A-chains to antibodies. At least in theory, immunotoxins of this type should be toxic only to the cells bearing the antigen relevant to the antibody used. However, numerous technical problems are caused by the difficulty (and cost) of obtaining absolutely pure A-chains, free of contaminating B-chains or of whole toxin molecules. Moreover, the number of exploitable toxins is probably too limited to overcome the problems arising from the immune response in the case of repeated administration *in vivo*.

Some of these problems can be circumvented by the use of RIPs, which are many, easy and safe to prepare, and also stable. Immunotoxins prepared with RIPs were highly effective in killing the cells target of the antibodies *in vitro* (reviews in Thorpe, 1985; Stirpe and Barbieri, 1986) and some of them significantly prolonged survival of mice carrying transplanted tumours bearing the antigens relevant to the antibodies (Ramakrishnan and Houston, 1984; Thorpe *et al.*, 1985). However, an immunotoxin made with saporin appeared unexpectedly more toxic to mice than free saporin (Thorpe *et al.*, 1985). Presumably, this was due to a longer persistence of the larger immunotoxin molecule in the blood stream, as compared with free saporin which is rapidly excreted through the kidneys. This is an example of some of the problems that still remain to be solved in this field.

FINAL REMARKS

Our knowledge of toxic plant lectins and of the related ribosome-inactivating proteins has increased considerably in the last fifteen years. However, as invariably occurs in science, the new findings have raised a number of new questions.

The first one concerns the role of these proteins in nature. We know that most of the plants so far examined contain in many of their tissues variable and sometimes high amounts of RIPs, most often as single-chain proteins, in some cases as A-chains linked to B-chains with galactose-specific lectin properties. It is likely that many more RIPs exist in the plant kingdom, possibly even in plant materials in which they were not detected, if they contain RIPs with different specificities, not active on the ribosomes used in the assays.

Proteins so widely diffused, and at such high concentrations in some cases (over 5% of total protein in the seeds of *Saponaria officinalis*) must necessarily have an important function, whatever this may be, to be conserved throughout evolution.

The possibility was considered that RIPs may afford protection against predators or parasites. All RIPs have some antiviral activity, but only on plants different from their own, which excludes a role in the prevention of viral infections. Any antibacterial activity is also ruled out by the insensitivity of bacterial ribosomes to RIPs. It is possible, however, that RIPs are toxic to insects or larvae, and recent findings raise the possibility that they may have anti-fungal activity.

The effect of at least some RIPs on ribosomes from heterologous plants led to envisage that they could eliminate their ribosomes if these were faulty, i.e. different from normal ones (Stirpe, 1982) or that they could prevent the taking of grafts that could occur spontaneously amongst plants belonging to different species (Battelli *et al.*, 1984).

Another possibility is that RIPs, being enzymes, have a role in the normal plant metabolism. Obviously, this leads to another unanswered question, namely the nature of their enzymic activity. One may wonder why enzymes of the potency of RIPs should be present in tissues at such high concentrations as found with some

RIPs: it should be considered, however, that the natural conditions under which RIPs are supposed to work may be very different from those found to be optimal for them in experimental situations. Once the nature of their enzymic activity is identified, the role of these proteins will probably become clearer, and, as already pointed out, this may well lead to them becoming useful tools in research and for other purposes.

Another potential application of the toxin A-chains and of single-chain RIPs is in the construction of immunotoxins. It has been shown already that immuno-toxins can effectively remove *in vitro*, in a selective manner, the cells target of the antibodies. This will be useful both experimentally and in therapy for the ex-vivo purging of cancer or T-cells from autologous or allogeneic bone marrow. Hope-fully, immunotoxins will be also useful for *in vivo* therapy of cancer and other diseases, although numerous problems still remain to be solved, as outlined by Thorpe (1985).

Finally, another foreseeable and probably not less important application of RIPs could be their insertion, by genetic engineering, in the genome of plants in which they are scarce, to confer them resistance against fungi or other pathogens.

ACKNOWLEDGEMENTS

The research done in the author's laboratory was supported financially by the Consiglio Nazionale delle Ricerche, Rome, within the Progetti finalizzati 'Con-trollo della crescita neoplastica' and 'Oncologia', by the Ministero della Publica Istruzione, Rome, and by the Pallotti's Legacy for Cancer Research.

REFERENCES

Barbieri, L. and Stirpe, F. (1982). Ribosome-inactivating proteins from plants: properties and possible uses. *Cancer Surveys*, **1**, 489–520

Barbieri, L., Gasperi-Campani, A., Derenzini, M., Betts, C. M. and Stirpe, F. (1979a). Selective lesions of acinar pancreatic cells in rats poisoned with abrin. A morpho-logical and biochemical study. *Virchows Arch. B Cell Path.*, **30**, 15–24

Barbieri, L., Lorenzoni, E. and Stirpe, F. (1979b). Inhibition of protein synthesis *in vitro* by a lectin from *Momordica charantia* and by other haemagglutinins. *Biochem. J.*, **182**, 633–5

Barbieri, L., Zamboni, M., Montanaro, L., Sperti, S. and Stirpe, F. (1980). Purifi-cation and properties of different forms of modeccin, the toxin of *Adenia digitata*. Separation of subunits with inhibitory and lectin activity. *Biochem. J.*, **185**, 203–10

Barbieri, L., Battelli, M. G. and Stirpe, F. (1982). Reduction of ricin and other plant toxins by thiol:protein disulfide oxidoreductases. *Arch. Biochem. Biophys.*, **216**, 380–3

Barbieri, L., Falasca, A. I. and Stirpe, F. (1984). Volkensin, the toxin of *Adenia volkensii* (kilyambiti plant). *FEBS Lett.*, **171**, 277–9

Battelli, M. G., Lorenzoni, E., Stirpe, F., Cella, R. and Parisi, B. (1984). Differential effects of ribosome-inactivating proteins on plant ribosome activity and plant cell growth. *J. exptl. Bot.*, **155**, 882–9

Bjorn, M. J., Larrick, J., Piatak, M. and Wilson, K. J. (1984). Characterization of translational inhibitor from *Phytolacca americana*. Amino-terminal sequence determination and antibody-inhibitor conjugates. *Biochim. Biophys. Acta*, **790**, 154–63

Butterworth, A. G. and Lord, J. M. (1983). Ricin and *Ricinus communis* agglutinin subunits are all derived from a single-size polypeptide precursor. *Eur. J. Biochem.*, **137**, 57–65

Cammarano, P., Teichner, A., Londei, P., Acca, M., Nicolaus, B., Sanz, J. L. and Amils, R. (1985). Insensitivity of archaebacterial ribosomes to protein synthesis inhibitors. Evolutionary implications. *EMBO J.*, **4**, 811–16

Carrasco, L., Fernandez-Puentes, C. and Vazquez, D. (1975). Effects of ricin on the ribosomal sites involved in the interaction of the elongation factors. *Eur. J. Biochem.*, **54**, 499–503

Cawley, D. B., Hedblom, M. L., Hoffman, E. J. and Houston, L. L. (1977). Differential ricin sensitivity of rat liver and wheat germ ribosomes in polyuridylic acid translation. *Arch. Biochem. Biophys.*, **182**, 690–5

Cawley, D. B., Hedblom, M. L. and Houston, L. L. (1978). Homology between ricin and *Ricinus communis* agglutinin: amino terminal sequence analysis and protein synthesis inhibition studies. *Arch. Biochem. Biophys.*, **190**, 744–55

Coleman, W. H. and Roberts, W. K. (1981). Factor requirement for the tritin inactivation of animal ribosomes. *Biochim. Biophys. Acta*, **654**, 57–66

Derenzini, M., Bonetti, E., Marinozzi, V. and Stirpe, F. (1976). Toxic effects of ricin. Studies on the pathogenesis of liver lesions. *Virchows Arch. B Cell Path.*, **20**, 15–28

Descotes, G., Romano, M., Stirpe, F. and Spreafico, F. (1985). The immunological activity of plant toxins used in the preparation of immunotoxins – II. The immunodepressive activity of gelonin. *Int. J. Immunopharmac.*, **7**, 455–63

Dimitriadis, G. J. and Butters, T. D. (1979). Liposome-mediated ricin toxicity in ricin-resistant cells. *FEBS Lett.*, **98**, 33–6

Dumas, M., Schwab, M. E. and Thoenen, H. (1979). Retrograde axonal transport of specific macromolecules as a tool for characterizing nerve terminal membranes. *J. Neurobiol.*, **10**, 179–197

Eiklid, K., Olsnes, S. and Pihl, A. (1980). Entry of lethal doses of abrin, ricin and modeccin into the cytosol of HeLa cells. *Exptl. Cell Res.*, **126**, 321–6

Fernandez-Puentes, C., Carrasco, L. and Vazquez, D. (1976a). Site of action of ricin on the ribosome. *Biochemistry*, **15**, 4364–9

Fernandez-Puentes, C., Benson, C., Olsnes, S. and Pihl, A. (1976b). Protective effect of elongation factor 2 on the inactivation of ribosomes by the toxic lectins abrin and ricin. *Eur. J. Biochem.*, **64**, 437–43

Flexner, S. (1897). The histological changes produced by ricin and abrin intoxication. *J. exptl. Med.*, **2**, 197–216

Fodstad, Ø., Olsnes, S. and Pihl, A. (1977). Inhibitory effect of abrin and ricin on the growth of transplantable murine tumors and of abrin on human cancers in nude mice. *Cancer Res.*, **37**, 4559–67

Foxwell, B. M. J., Detre, S. I., Donovan, T. A. and Thorpe, P. E. (1985). The use of *anti*-ricin antibodies to protect mice intoxicated with ricin. *Toxicology*, **34**, 79–88

Frankel, A. E., Houston, L. L. and Fatham, G. (1986). Prospects for immunotoxin therapy in cancer. *Ann. Rev. Med.*, **37**, 125–42

Funatsu, G., Yoshitake, S. and Funatsu, M. (1978). Primary structure of the Ile chain of ricin D. *Agric. Biol. Chem.*, **41**, 501-3

Funatsu, G., Kimura, M. and Funatsu, M. (1979). Primary structure of Ala chain of ricin D. *Agric. Biol. Chem.*, **43**, 2221-4

Gardas, A. and Macpherson, I. (1979). Microinjection of ricin entrapped into uni-lamellar liposomes into a ricin-resistant mutant of baby hamster kidney cells. *Biochim. Biophys. Acta*, **584**, 538-41

Gasperi-Campani, A., Barbieri, L., Lorenzoni, E. and Stirpe, F. (1977). Inhibition of protein synthesis by seed-extracts. A screening study. *FEBS Lett.*, **76**, 173-6

Gasperi-Campani, A., Barbieri, L., Lorenzoni, E., Montanaro, L., Sperti, S., Bonetti, E. and Stirpe, F. (1978). Modeccin, the toxin of *Adenia digitata*. Purification, toxicity and inhibition of protein synthesis *in vitro*. *Biochem. J.*, **174**, 491-6

Gasperi-Campani, A., Barbieri, L., Morelli, P. and Stirpe, F. (1980). Seed-extracts inhibiting protein synthesis *in vitro*. *Biochem. J.*, **186**, 439-41

Gasperi-Campani, A., Barbieri, L., Battelli, M. G. and Stirpe, F. (1985). On the distribution of ribosome-inactivating proteins amongst plants. *J. Nat. Prod.*, **48**, 446-54

Ghosh, P. C., Wellner, R. B. and Wu, H. C. (1984). Osmotically induced micro-injection of ricin bypasses a ricin internalization defect in a Chinese hamster ovary mutant cell line. *Mol. Cell. Biol.*, **4**, 1320-5

Gottlieb, C. and Kornfeld, S. (1976). Isolation and characterization of two mouse L cell lines resistant to toxic lectin ricin. *J. Biol. Chem.*, **251**, 7761-8

Gottlieb, C., Skinner, A. M. and Kornfeld, S. (1974). Isolation of Chinese hamster ovary cells deficient in plant lectin-binding sites. *Proc. Nat. Acad. Sci. U.S.A.*, **71**, 1078-82

Greco, M., Montanaro, L., Novello, F., Saccone, C., Sperti, S. and Stirpe, F. (1974). Inhibition of protein synthesis by ricin: experiments with rat liver mitochondria and nuclei and with ribosomes from *Escherichia coli*. *Biochem. J.*, **142**, 695-7

Green, H. H. and Andrews, W. H. (1925). The toxicity of *Adenia digitata* Burtt-Davy (*Modecca digitata* Harv.). *Rep. Vet. Res. S. Africa*, **9/10**, 381-92

Halling, K. C., Halling, A. C., Murray, E. E., Ladin, B. F., Houston, L. L and Weaver, R. F. (1985). Genomic cloning and characterization of a ricin gene from *Ricinus communis*. *Nucleic Acid Res.*, **13**, 8019-33

Harley, S. M. and Beevers, H. (1982). Ricin inhibition of in vitro protein synthesis by plant ribosomes. *Proc. Nat. Acad. Sci. U.S.A.*, **79**, 5935-8

Harper, C. G., Gonatas, J. O., Mizutani, T. and Gonatas, N. K. (1980). Retrograde transport and effects of toxic ricin in autonomic nervous system. *Lab. Invest.*, **42**, 396-404

Hyman, R., Lacorbiere, M., Stavarek, S. and Nicolson, G. (1974). Derivation of lymphoma variants with reduced sensitivity to plant lectins. *J. Nat. Cancer Inst.*, **52**, 963-9

Howell, M. D. and Villemez, C. L. (1984). Toxicity of ricin, diphtheria toxin and α-amanitin for *Acantamoeba castellanii* (1983). *J. Parasit.*, **70**, 918-23

Irvin, J. D. (1983). Pokeweed antiviral protein. *Pharmac. Ther.*, **21**, 371-87

Ishida, B., Cawley, D. B., Reue, K. and Wisnieski, B. J. (1983). Lipid-protein inter-actions during ricin toxin insertion into membranes. Evidence for A and B chain penetration. *J. Biol. Chem.*, **258**, 5933-7

Ishiguro, M., Tomi, M., Funatsu, G. and Funatsu, M. (1976). Isolation and chemical properties of a ricin variant from castor bean. *Toxicon.*, **14**, 157-65

Jiménez, A. and Vazquez, D. (1985). Plant and fungal protein and glycoprotein toxins inhibiting eukaryote protein synthesis. *Ann. Rev. Microbiol.*, **39**, 649-72

Kocourek, J. and Horejsi, V. (1981). Defining a lectin. *Nature, Lond.*, **290**, 188

Lamb, F. I., Roberts, L. M. and Lord, J. M. (1985). Nucleotide sequence of cloned cDNA coding for preproricin. *Eur. J. Biochem.*, **148**, 265-70

Lappi, D. A., Kapmeyer, W., Beglau, J. M. and Kaplan, N. O. (1978). Disulfide bond connecting chains of ricin. *Proc. Nat. Acad. Sci. U.S.A.*, **75**, 1096–100

Lappi, D. A., Esch, F. S., Barbieri, L., Stirpe, F. and Soria, M. (1985). Characterization of a *Saponaria officinalis* seed ribosome-inactivating protein: immunoreactivity and sequence homologies. *Biochem. Biophys. Res. Commun.*, **129**, 934–42

Li, I.-C., Blake, D. A., Goldstein, I. J. and Chu, E. H. Y. (1980). Modification of cell membrane in variants of Chinese hamster cells resistant to abrin. *Exptl. Cell Res.*, **129**, 351–60

Lin, J.-Y., Tserng, K.-Y., Chen, C.-C., Lin, L.-T. and Tung, T.-C. (1970). Abrin and ricin: new anti-tumour substances. *Nature, Lond.*, **227**, 292–3

Lin, J.-Y., Liu, K., Chen, C.-C. and Tung, T.-C. (1971). Effect of crystalline ricin on the biosynthesis of protein, RNA, and DNA in experimental tumor cells. *Cancer Res.*, **31**, 921–4

Lugnier, A.-A. J. and Rether, B. (1981). Mechanism of ricin action on a wheat germ cell-free protein synthesizing system. *Plant Sci. Lett.*, **23**, 71–80

Lugnier, A.-A. J., Küntzel, H. and Dirheimer, G. (1976). Inhibition of *Neurospora crassa* and yeast mitochondrial protein synthesis by ricin, a toxic protein inactive on *E. coli* protein synthesis. *FEBS Lett.*, **66**, 202–5

Meager, A., Ungkitchannukit, A., Nairn, R. and Hughes, R. C. (1975). Ricin resistance in bay hamster kidney cells. *Nature, Lond.*, **257**, 137–9

Meager, A., Ungkitchannukit, A. and Hughes, R. C. (1976). Variants of hamster fibroblasts resistant to *Ricinus communis* toxin (ricin). *Biochem. J.*, **154**, 113–24

Mise, T., Funatsu, G., Ishiguro, M. and Funatsu, M. (1977). Biochemical studies on ricin. Part XVIII. Isolation and characterization of ricin E from castor beans. *Agric. Biol. Chem.*, **41**, 2041–6

Montanaro, L., Sperti, S. and Stirpe, F. (1973). Inhibition by ricin of protein synthesis *in vitro*. Ribosomes as the target of the toxin. *Biochem. J.*, **136**, 677–83

Montanaro, L., Sperti, S., Mattioli, A., Testoni, G. and Stirpe, F. (1975). Inhibition by ricin of protein synthesis *in vitro*. Inhibition of the binding of elongation factor 2 and of adenosine diphosphate-ribosylated elongation factor 2 to ribosomes. *Biochem. J.*, **146**, 127–31

Montanaro, L., Sperti, S., Zamboni, M., Denaro, M., Testoni, G., Gasperi-Campani, A. and Stirpe, F. (1978). Effect of modeccin on the steps of peptide chain elongation. *Biochem. J.*, **176**, 371–9

Montanaro, L., Sperti, S. and Zamboni, M. (1985). A metallo-proteinase associated with gelonin, a 'ribosome-inactivating protein'. *Ital. J. Biochem.*, **34**, 1–9

Nicolson, G. L., Blaustein, T. and Etzler, M. E. (1974). Characterization of two plant lectins from *Ricinus communis* and their quantitative interaction with a murine lymphoma. *Biochemistry*, **13**, 196–204

Nicolson, G. L., Lacorbiere, M. and Hunter, T. R. (1975a). Mechanism of cell entry and toxicity of an affinity-purified lectin from *Ricinus communis* and its differential effects on normal and virus-transformed fibroblasts. *Cancer Res.*, **35**, 144–55

Nicolson, G. L., Lacorbiere, M. and Eckhart, W. (1975b). Qualitative and quantitative interactions of lectins with untreated and neuraminidase-treated normal, wild-type, and temperature-sensitive polyoma-transformed fibroblasts. *Biochemistry*, **14**, 172–9

Nicolson, G. L., Smith, J. R. and Hyman, R. (1978). Dynamics of toxin and lectin receptors on a lymphoma cell line and its toxin-resistant variant using ferritin-conjugated, ^{125}I-labeled ligand. *J. Cell Biol.*, **78**, 565–76

Obrig, T. G., Moran, T. P. and Colinas, R. J. (1985). Ribonuclease activity associated with the 60S ribosome-inactivating proteins ricin A, phytolaccin and Shiga toxin. *Biochem. Biophys. Res. Commun.*, **130**, 879–84

Olsnes, S. and Abraham, A. K. (1979). Elongation-factor-2-induced sensitization of ribosomes to modeccin. Evidence for specific binding of elongation factor 2 to ribosomes in the absence of nucleotides. *Eur. J. Biochem.*, **93**, 447–52

Olsnes, S. and Pihl, A. (1972a). Ricin – a potent inhibitor of protein synthesis. *FEBS Lett.*, **20**, 327–9

Olsnes, S. and Pihl, A. (1972b). Inhibition of peptide chain elongation. *Nature, Lond.*, **238**, 459-61

Olsnes, S. and Pihl, A. (1976). Abrin, ricin and their associated agglutinins. In: *The Specificity of Action of Animal, Bacterial and Plant Toxins. Receptor and Recognition* Series B, Vol. 1 (ed. P. Cuatrecasas), Chapman and Hall, London, pp. 129–73

Olsnes, S. and Pihl, A. (1982). Toxic lectins and related proteins. In: *Molecular Action of Toxins and Viruses* (ed. P. Cohen and S. van Heyningen), Elsevier, Amsterdam, New York, pp. 51–105

Olsnes, S. and Refsnes, K. (1978). On the mechanism of toxin resistance in cell variants resistant to abrin and ricin. *Eur. J. Biochem.*, **88**, 7–15

Olsnes, S. and Sandvig, K. (1985). Entry of polypeptide toxins into animal cells. In: *Endocytosis* (ed. I. Pastan and M. C. Willingham), Plenum Publishing Corporation, New York, pp. 195–234

Olsnes, S., Heiberg, R. and Pihl, A. (1973). Inactivation of eukaryotic ribosomes by the toxic plant proteins abrin and ricin. *Mol. Biol. Rep.*, **1**, 15–20

Olsnes, S., Refsnes, K., Christiansen, T. B. and Pihl, A. (1975a). Studies on the structure and properties of the lectins from *Abrus precatorius* and *Ricinus communis. Biochim. Biophys. Acta*, **405**, 1–10

Olsnes, S., Fernandez-Puentes, C., Carrasco, L. and Vazquez, D. (1975b). Ribosome inactivation by the toxic lectins abrin and ricin. Kinetics of the enzymic activity of the toxin A-chains. *Eur. J. Biochem.*, **60**, 281–8

Olsnes, S., Haylett, T. and Refsnes, K. (1978a). Purification and characterization of the highly toxic lectin modeccin. *J. Biol. Chem.*, **253**, 5069–73

Olsnes, S., Sandvig, K., Eiklid, K. and Pihl, A. (1978b). Properties and mechanism of action of the toxic lectin modeccin. Interaction with cell lines resistant to modeccin, abrin and ricin. *J. Supramol. Struct.*, **9**, 15–25

Olsnes, S., Stirpe, F., Sandvig, K. and Pihl, A. (1982). Isolation and characterization of viscumin, a toxic lectin from *Viscum album* L. (mistletoe). *J. Biol. Chem.*, **257**, 13263–70

Ono, M., Kuwano, M., Watanabe, K.-I. and Funatsu, G. (1982). Chinese hamster cell variants resistant to the A chain of ricin carry altered ribosome function. *Mol. Cell. Biol.*, **2**, 599–606

Onozaki, K., Hayatsu, H. and Ukita, T. (1975). Inhibition of protein synthesis in mouse myeloma cells by *Ricinus communis* toxin. *Biochim. Biophys. Acta*, **407**, 99–107

Owens, R. A., Bruening, G. and Shepherd, R. J. (1973). A possible mechanism for the inhibition of plant viruses by a peptide from *Phytolacca americana. Virology*, **56**, 390-3

Ramakrishnan, S. and Houston, L. L. (1984). Prevention of growth of leukemia cells in mice by monoclonal antibodies directed against Thyl. 1 antigen disulfide linked to two ribosomal inhibitors: pokeweed antiviral protein or ricin A chain. *Cancer Res.*, **44**, 1398–1404

Ray, B. and Wu, H. C. (1981). Internalization of ricin in Chinese hamster ovary cells. *Mol. Cell. Biol.*, **1**, 544–51

Ray, B. and Wu, H. C. (1982). Chinese hamster ovary cell mutants defective in the internalization of ricin. *Mol. Cell. Biol.*, **2**, 535–44

Ready, M., Wilson, K., Piatak, M. and Robertus, J. D. (1984). Ricin-like plant toxins are evolutionarily related to single-chain ribosome-inhibiting proteins from *Phytolacca. J. Biol. Chem.*, **259**, 15252–6

Refsnes, K. and Munthe-Kaas, A. C. (1976). Introduction of B-chain-inactivated ricin into mouse macrophages and rat Kupffer cells via their membrane Fc receptors. *J. exptl. Med.*, **143**, 1464–74

Refsnes, K., Haylett, T., Sandvig, K. and Olsnes, S. (1977). Modeccin – a plant toxin inhibiting protein synthesis. *Biochem. Biophys. Res. Commun.*, **79**, 1176–83

Robbins, J. C., Hyman, R., Stallings, V. and Nicolson, G. L. (1977). Cell surface changes in a *Ricinus communis* toxin (ricin)-resistant variant of a murine lymphoma. *J. Nat. Cancer Inst.*, **58**, 1027–33

Roberts, L. M., Lamb, F. I., Pappin, D. J. C. and Lord, J. M. (1985). The primary sequence of *Ricinus communis* agglutinin. Comparison with ricin. *J. Biol. Chem.*, **260**, 15682–6

Roberts, W. K. and Selitrennikoff, C. P. (1986a). Plant proteins that inactivate foreign ribosomes. *Biosci. Rep.*, **6**, 19–29

Roberts, W. K. and Selitrennikoff, C. P. (1986b). Isolation and partial characterization of two antifungal proteins from barley. *Biochim. Biophys. Acta*, **880**, 161–70

Rosen, S. W. and Hughes, R. C. (1977). Effects of neuraminidase on lectin binding by wild-type and ricin-resistant strains of hamster fibroblasts. *Biochemistry*, **16**, 4908–15

Saltvedt, E. (1976). Structure and toxicity of pure ricinus agglutinin. *Biochim. Biophys. Acta*, **415**, 536–48

Sandvig, K., Olsnes, S. and Pihl, A. (1978). Binding, uptake and degradation of the toxic proteins abrin and ricin by toxin-resistant cell variants. *Eur. J. Biochem.*, **82**, 13–23

Sandvig, K., Olsnes, S. and Pihl, A. (1979). Inhibitory effect of ammonium chloride and chloroquine on the entry of the toxic lectin modeccin into HeLa cells. *Biochem. Biophys. Res. Commun.*, **90**, 648–55

Sargiacomo, M. and Hughes, R. C. (1982). Interaction of ricin-sensitive and ricin-resistant cell lines with other carbohydrate-binding toxins. *FEBS Lett.*, **141**, 14–18

Simmons, B. M. and Russell, J. H. (1985). A single affinity step method for the purification of ricin toxin from castor beans (*Ricinus communis*). *Anal. Biochem.*, **146**, 206–10

Simmons, B. M., Stahl, P. D. and Russell, J. H. (1986). Mannose receptor-mediated uptake of ricin toxin and ricin A chain by macrophages. Multiple intracellular pathways for A chain translocation. *J. Biol. Chem.*, **261**, 7912–20

Skilleter, D. N., Paine, A. J. and Stirpe, F. (1981). A comparison of the accumulation of ricin by hepatic parenchymal and non-parenchymal cells and its inhibition of protein synthesis. *Biochim. Biophys. Acta*, **677**, 495–500

Sperti, S. and Montanaro, L. (1979). Ricin and modeccin do not inhibit the elongation factor 1-dependent binding of aminoacyl-tRNA to ribosomes. *Biochem. J.*, **178**, 233–6

Sperti, S., Montanaro, L., Mattioli, A. and Stirpe, F. (1973). Inhibition by ricin of protein synthesis *in vitro*: 60S ribosomal subunit as the target of the toxin. *Biochem. J.*, **136**, 813–15

Sperti, S., Montanaro, L., Derenzini, M., Gasperi-Campani, A. and Stirpe, F. (1979). Effect of modeccin on rat liver ribosomes *in vivo*. *Biochim. Biophys. Acta*, **562**, 485–504

Spreafico, F., Malfiore, C., Moras, M. L., Marmonti, L., Filippeschi, S., Barbieri, L., Perocco, P. and Stirpe, F. (1983). The immunomodulatory activity of the plant proteins *Momordica charantia* inhibitor and pokeweed antiviral protein. *Int. J. Immunopharmac.*, **5**, 335–43

Stirpe, F. (1982). On the action of ribosome-inactivating proteins: are plant ribosomes species-specific? *Biochem. J.*, **202**, 279–80

Stirpe, F. and Barbieri, L. (1986). Ribosome-inactivating proteins up to date. *FEBS Lett.*, **195**, 1–8

Stirpe, F., Gasperi-Campani, A., Barbieri, L., Lorenzoni, E., Montanaro, L., Sperti, S. and Bonetti, E. (1978). Inhibition of protein synthesis by modeccin, the toxin of *Modecca digitata. FEBS Lett.*, **85**, 65–7

Stirpe, F., Legg, R. F., Onyon, L. J., Ziska, P.and Franz, H. (1980). Inhibition of protein synthesis by a toxic lectin from *Viscum album* L. (mistletoe). *Biochem. J.*, **190**, 843–5

Stirpe, F., Sandvig, K., Olsnes, S. and Pihl, A. (1982). Action of viscumin, a toxic lectin from mistletoe, on cells in culture. *J. Biol. Chem.*, **257**, 13271–7

Stirpe, F., Barbieri, L., Abbondanza, A., Falasca, A. I., Brown, A. N. F., Sandvig, K., Olsnes, S. and Pihl, A. (1985). Properties of volkensin, a toxic lectin from *Adenia volkensii. J. Biol. Chem.*, **260**, 14589–95

Stirpe, F., Barbieri, L., Battelli, M. G., Falasca, A. I., Abbondanza, A., Lorenzoni, E. and Stevens, W. A. (1986). Bryodin, a ribosome-inactivating protein from the roots of *Bryonia dioica* L. (white bryony). *Biochem. J.*, in press

Thorpe, P. E. (1985). Antibody carriers of cytotoxic agents in cancer therapy: a review. In: *Monoclonal Antibodies '84: Biological and Clinical Applications* (ed. A. Pinchera, G. Doria, F. Dammacco and A. Bargellesi), Kurtis, Milan, pp. 475–506

Thorpe, P. E., Cumber, A. J., Williams, N., Edwards, D. C. and Ross, W. C. J. (1981). Abrogation of the non-specific toxicity of abrin conjugated to anti-lymphocyte globulin. *Clin. exptl. Immunol.*, **43**, 195–200

Thorpe, P. E., Brown, A. N. F., Bremner, J. A. J., Jr., Foxwell, B. M. J. and Stirpe, F. (1985). An immunotoxin composed of monoclonal anti-Thy1. 1 antibody and a ribosome-inactivating protein from *Saponaria officinalis*: potent antitumor effects *in vitro* and *in vivo. J. Nat. Cancer Inst.*, **75**, 151–9

Van Deurs, B., Ryde Pedersen, L., Sundan, A., Olsnes, S. and Sandvig, K. (1985). Receptor-mediated endocytosis of a ricin-colloidal gold conjugate in Vero cells. *Exptl. Cell Res.*, **159**, 287–384

Van Deurs, B., Tønnessen, T. I., Petersen, O. W., Sandvig, K. and Olsnes, S. (1986). Routing of internalized ricin and ricin conjugates to the Golgi complex. *J. Cell Biol.*, **102**, 37–47

Vitetta, E. S. and Uhr, J. W. (1985). Immunotoxins. *Ann. Rev. Immunol.*, **3**, 197–212

Waller, G. R., Ebner, K. E., Scroggs, R. A., Das Gupta, B. R. and Corcoran, J. B. (1966). Studies on the toxic action of ricin. *Proc. Soc. exptl. Biol.*, **121**, 685–91

Wilde, C. G., Boguslawski, S. and Houston, L. L. (1979). Resistance of *Tetrahymena* to ricin, a toxic enzyme from *Ricinus communis. Biochem. Biophys. Res. Commun.*, **91**, 1082–8

Wiley, R. G., Blessing, W. W. and Reis, D. J. (1982). Suicide transport: destruction of neurons by retrograde transport of ricin, abrin, and modeccin. *Science, N.Y.*, **216**, 889–90

Yamamoto, T., Iwasaki, Y. and Konno, H. (1983). Retrograde transport of toxic lectins is useful for transganglionic tracings of the peripheral nerve. *Brain Res.*, **274**, 325–8

Ziska, P., Franz, H. and Kindt, A. (1978). The lectin from *Viscum album* L. Purification by biospecific chromatography. *Experientia*, **34**, 123–4

6

Mechanisms of Ageing of Organophosphate-inhibited Esterases

F. Berends

INTRODUCTION

The high toxicity of certain organophosphorus (OP) compounds was discovered in the mid-1930s. This finding initiated investigations, which resulted in the development of new insecticides and potential chemical warfare agents, the so-called nerve gases. Table 6.1 gives a few examples of both categories. During World War II, in Germany some of these nerve gases were produced and stockpiled, but fortunately they were not used. After the war research continued, with regard to insecticides and pesticides as well as to chemical warfare agents, and many new effective compounds were developed. These compounds vary considerably in toxicity; the lethal dose for humans of the most toxic nerve gases amounts to a few milligrams, while that of parathion is about 30 mg, whereas for the insecticide malathion values above 3 g have been estimated.

Except for the possible use of Tabun in the current conflict between Iran and Iraq, the military use of nerve gases has remained in abeyance. Nevertheless, the OP compounds have already claimed hundreds of lives, mostly due to accidents with insecticides.

Soon after the discovery of the organophosphates it became clear that their toxicity could be attributed to an interference with the hydrolysis of the neurotransmitter acetylcholine and, thus, interference with the normal function of cholinergic neurones. After the war, the mode of action of these compounds was studied in more detail. It appeared that irreversible inhibition of the enzyme acetylcholinesterase (AChE) in the cholinergic synapses, which leads to a local accumulation of acetylcholine, was responsible for the toxic effects. This inhibition was shown to be due to covalent reaction of the OP compound with a group in the active centre of the enzyme, according to the scheme

$$\text{Enzyme-H} + R,R'P(O)X \longrightarrow \text{Enzyme-P(O)R,R'} + H^+ + X^-$$

Table 6.1 Examples of toxic organophosphorus compounds

Structural formula	Chemical and other names	Properties
$i\text{-}C_3H_7O$, $i\text{-}C_3H_7O$ — P(=O)F	Diisopropyl phosphoro-fluoridate; DFP	Potent cholinesterase-inhibitor, used in treatment of glaucoma
$i\text{-}C_3H_7NH$, $i\text{-}C_3H_7NH$ — P(=O)F	N,N'-diisopropyl phosphoro-diamidofluoridate; Mipafox, Isopestox	Insecticide
C_2H_5O, C_2H_5O — P(=S) O—$C_6H_4NO_2$	Diethyl, p-nitrophenyl phosphorothionate; Parathion	Insecticide; used in many suicide attempts
C_2H_5O, $(CH_3)_2N$ — P*(=O)CN	Ethyl, N-dimethyl phosphor-amidocyanidate; Tabun, GA	Extremely toxic; 'nerve gas'
$i\text{-}C_3H_7O$, CH_3 — P*(=O)F	Isopropyl methylphosphono-fluoridate; Sarin, GB	Extremely toxic; 'nerve gas'
$t\text{-}C_4H_9$, CH_3 — $*CHO$, CH_3 — P*(=O)F	1,2,2-trimethylpropyl (= pinacolyl) methylphos-phonofluoridate; Soman, GD	Extremely toxic; 'nerve gas'; rapid ageing

*Asymmetric atom.

Later it was suggested that this reaction proceeds in analogy with the transient acylation step that occurs during normal catalytic ester hydrolysis, as is illustrated in figure 6.1. We now know that this hypothesis was correct, not only for AChE, but also for a whole group of hydrolytic enzymes, which presently are known as the serine-hydrolyases.

Early studies indicated that the imidazole group of a histidine residue, assumed to be present in the active centre of AChE, was the possible binding site of the phosphorus moeity. However, later chemical analysis showed that the phosphorus

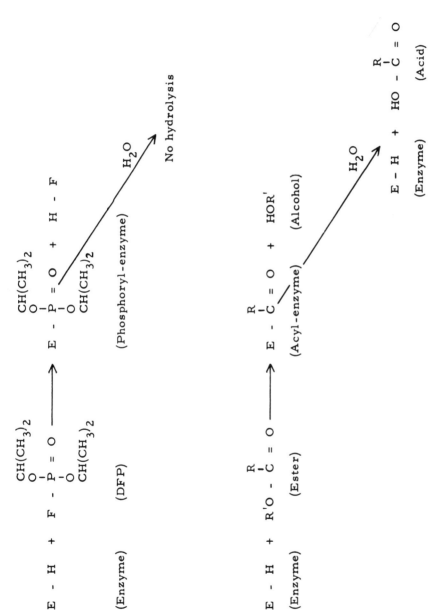

Figure 6.1 Parallelism between the reaction with organophosphates and the formation of an acyl-enzyme during enzyme-catalysed ester hydrolysis

was attached to the oxygen of a serine side chain (Schaffer *et al.*, 1954). At that time this result was ill understood: the hydroxyl group of serine was considered to be of low reactivity towards the type of phosphorus compounds concerned, in contrast to imidazole. Furthermore, histidine-imidazole had the correct pK_a (around 7) to explain the results of the enzyme studies, quite unlike the serine-OH (pK_a approx. 14).

In view of the high toxicity of the OP compounds, during the 1950s several groups started research to find an antidote to intoxication, by looking for chemicals that would be able to reactivate the inhibited AChE. Among the pioneers in this field were scientists such as Hobbiger, Aldridge and Wilson who later became leaders in this and related areas of research. Amazingly good reactivators were rapidly developed, such as hydroxylamine, aliphatic oximes and hydroxamic acids, and by 1955 the first pyridinium oximes were synthesised (PAM, see figure 6.2), and found to be superior to other reactivators (Wilson and Ginsburg, 1955; Childs *et al.*, 1955). Since then many hundreds of other oximes have been synthesised and

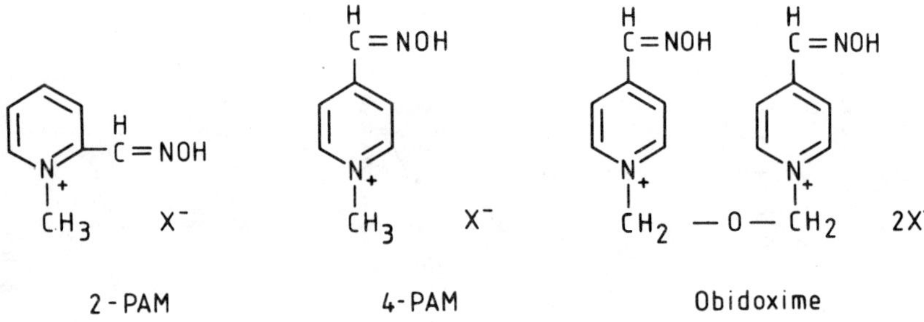

2 - PAM   4-PAM   Obidoxime

Figure 6.2 Some pyridinium oximes used to reactivate OP-inhibited cholinesterase. Other names for 2-PAM: pralidoxime; P2S. In many publications, for obidoxime the trade name Toxogonin[®] is used

tested, and the pyridinium oximes derived from 2- or 4-PAM (such as obidoxime) still give the best results.

With the development of good reactivators came the discovery of the 'ageing' phenomenon for OP-inhibited AChE. In 1955, Hobbiger, Wilson and Jandorf *et al.*, independently came across this phenomenon showing that the susceptibility of the inhibited enzyme to reactivation decreased with time, in a first order manner. An elegant hypothesis to explain this phenomenon was rapidly born. It was suggested that — upon inhibition — the phosphoryl group initially became attached to the imidazole of a histidine residue, where it would be susceptible to reactivation by oximes in analogy to the labile binding of the acyl-enzyme intermediate. Thereafter, in a secondary reaction, a gradual transphosphorylation was supposed to occur from histidine to serine. In this second position, at the serine, the phosphoryl group would be bound stably. This migration should occur only with phosphoryl group, not with the acetyl group of the acyl enzyme. This hypothesis not only explained the ageing process, but also reconciled the kinetic data with the finding of phosphorylated serine residue.

A survey of the literature of this period can be found in Hobbiger (1963).

AGEING: TRANSPHOSPHORYLATION OR DEALKYLATION?

A few years after the discovery of ageing and the attractive mechanistic explanation of this phenomenon, Jansz in our institute investigated the binding site of the phosphorus moiety in DFP-inhibited pseudocholinesterase (or butyrylcholinesterase; BuChE), and found not the expected di-isopropylphosphoryl (DP-)group attached to serine, but a mono-isopropylphosphoryl (MP-)group (Jansz et al., 1959). Evidently, a dealkylation had occurred, which could not be ascribed to the handling of the material. In a study on the ageing of ^{32}P-DFP-inhibited BuChE, we succeeded in demonstrating that the decrease in reactivatability coincided with the conversion of DP-enzyme into MP-enzyme. Figure 6.3 shows the results as they were presented for the first time, at the international biochemical congress in Vienna, 1958 (Berends et al., 1959). Subsequently, using ^{14}C/^{32}P labelled DFP, we showed that in the inhibited enzyme the ^{14}C/^{32}P ratio decreased from a value corresponding to two isopropyl groups per P atom to one, in proportion to the loss of reactivation ability. In addition, ^{14}C-isopropanol was identified in the medium (Berends et al., 1959; Berends, 1964a).

We also showed the parallelism between ageing and dealkylation for ^{32}P-Sarin-inhibited BuChE, while DFP-inhibited chymotrypsin also exhibited a gradual (all be it very slow) conversion to the MP-enzyme (Berends, 1964a; Jansz et al., 1963).

These results offered a good explanation for the oxime resistance of the aged inhibited enzymes, namely repulsion of the oxime anion by the negative charge of the dealkylated phosphoryl group and increased chemical stability to nucleophilic attack of the phospho-diester compared to the original phospho-triester structure (figure 6.4). But at the same time it re-introduced the dilemma of histidine versus serine. It took some time before the elegant and attractive transphosphorylation-hypothesis was discarded, and the dealkylation mechanism accepted. In 1964, 5 years after the first publication, during a visit to the USA, I still met disbelief, and even in 1970 I was asked – in confidence – whether deep inside I really believed that dealkylation was the cause of ageing.

The matter was rapidly settled, however, when other groups started to look into this problem. Between 1965 and 1967 several investigators in the USA and England published on this subject. They studied the ageing of AChE, either in the electric-eel enzyme or in bovine red blood cell preparation, inhibited with a radioactively labelled organophosphate. Fleisher and Harris (1965), using ^{32}P-Soman and ^{32}P-Sarin, found perfect agreement between ageing and dealkylation. They also demonstrated that dealkylation occurs in vivo, in rat brain, at the same rate as in vitro (Harris et al., 1966). Smith and Usdin (1966) measured the release of ^{3}H-isopropanol during ageing of the ^{3}H-sarin-inhibited enzyme. Coult et al. (1966) studied the dealkylation with a whole series of ^{32}P-alkyl methylphosphonates. Finally, Michel et al. (1967), who used both ^{3}H- and ^{32}P-labelled Soman, demonstrated a parallelism between ageing and dealkylation over a wide pH range.

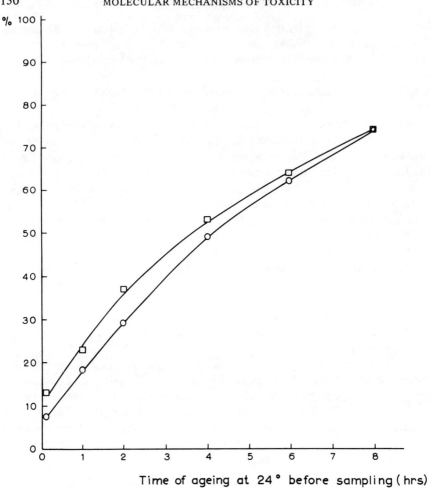

Figure 6.3 Parallelism between ageing (loss of reactivatability; □) and dealkylation (○) during storage of DFP-inhibited BuChE from horse serum (from Berends, 1964a)

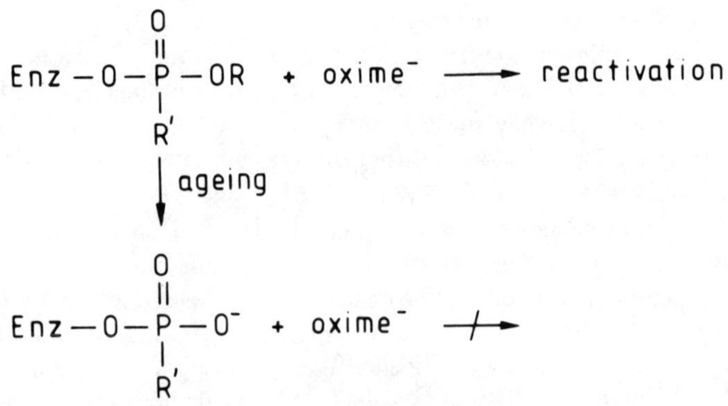

Figure 6.4 Effect of dealkylation on oxime reactivation

In addition, in Russia, Rozengart and Balashova (1965) showed that treatment of DFP-inhibited AChE with the soft nucleophile thiourea, which is known to promote dealkylation, accelerated the formation of the aged inhibited enzyme.

The British group at Porton Down compared the rate of dealkylation or ageing of a series of homologous alkyl methylphosphonates, and found that branching of the leaving alkyl group accelerated the reaction: a group derived from a secondary alcohol resulted in faster ageing than an alkyl group coming from a primary one. The general conclusion was: the easier the alkyl group can form a carbonium ion, the faster dealkylation occurs, which suggested a C-O fission mechanism (Coult *et al.*, 1966; Berry and Davies, 1966).

In Holland, Benschop and coworkers (Benschop and Keyer, 1966; Benschop *et al.*, 1967) studied this phenomenon in more detail. They compared the rate of ageing of inhibited AChE as well as BuChE, with the rate of solvolysis of the corresponding alkyl tosylates. This solvolysis was known to proceed via C-O fission, in a unimolecular reaction during which a carbonium ion is formed and released. In three series of alkyl methylphosphonates they found a satisfactory agreement between the relative rates of ageing and the rates of solvolysis. Table 6.2 shows the results obtained with a series of cycloalkyl compounds.

Table 6.2 Relative rates of solvolysis of cycloalkyl tosylates and of ageing of corresponding cycloalkyl methylphosphonyl enzymes. Temperature $25°C$ (from Benschop *et al.*, 1967)

Cycloalkyl group	Solvolysis of cycloalkyl tosylate	Ageing of cycloalkyl methylphosphonyl enzyme	
		AChE	BuChE
Cyclopropyl	10^{-5}	$\ll 0.1$	$\ll 0.5$
Cyclobutyl	85	130	90
Cyclopentyl	100	100	100
Cyclohexyl	3	1	3
Cycloheptyl	150	11	67
Cyclooctyl	1570	> 1000	> 1000

In each series, the value for the cyclopentyl group has been put at 100.

Direct evidence for C-O scission came from Michel *et al.* (1967), who identified the products released from ^{3}H-Soman-inhibited AChE. Instead of the expected pinacolyl alcohol, $(CH_3)_3C-CH(OH)-CH_3$, two other ^{3}H-products were found, viz. 2,3-dimethylbutene(1-2), $CH_2 = C(CH_3)-CH(CH_3)_2$, and 2,3-dimethylbutane-1-ol, $(CH_3)_2CH-C(OH)(CH_3)_2$. These two products could only have been formed through rearrangement of the originally released carbonium ion:

$$(CH_3)_3C-C^+H-CH_3 \longrightarrow (CH_3)_2C^+ - CH(CH_3)_2$$

So, in 1967 the situation appeared clear: ageing is dealkylation occurring via C-O fission, with a rate depending on the tendency of the alkyl group to form a carbonium ion. Results obtained since then with similar inhibited cholinesterases, by Sun *et al.* (1979), by Clothier *et al.* (1981) and by De Jong *et al.* (1982), are consistent with this conclusion.

SCIENTIFIC AND PRACTICAL ASPECTS OF AGEING

Towards the end of the 1960s, the principle of the ageing reaction appeared to have been firmly established. In all well-performed studies first order kinetics had been observed, all results indicated dealkylation as the cause of the resistance to oxime-reactivation and the data — with a few exceptions (see next section) — argued in favour of dealkylation proceeding via C–O scission. At that time, the problem of the controversy between histidine and serine as the site of attachment of the acyl or phosphoryl group had begun to resolve, mainly owing to results obtained with other serine-hydrolases, such as chymotrypsin. In addition to the original kinetic and chemical data, frequently pointing to different residues, new structural information obtained by X-ray diffraction had become available, which showed the involvement of both amino acids (Blow *et al.*, 1969): in the native enzyme, interactions between a carboxyl group, the imidazole-ring of histidine and the serine-OH resulted in what is now known as the 'charge-relay system', which donates a particular reactivity to the 'active serine'. It appeared rather plausible that a similar structure would be present in AChE.

However, although this notion could account for the reactivity of serine-OH towards OP compounds, and even for the enhanced susceptibility of the P atom in inhibited AChE to nucleophilic attack by oxime-anions, it did not explain the rapid dealkylation frequently observed. With small model peptides, the dialkyl phosphoryl group attached to serine-OH does not show any tendency for dealkylation, unless extreme conditions are applied. The conclusion appeared justified, therefore, that as yet unidentified interactions with the enzyme molecule would play a role in the ageing process.

Notwithstanding the scientific interest of this problem, most investigations into ageing were initiated with a more practical goal in mind. Since ageing results in an inhibited enzyme that is no longer susceptible to reactivation, it may pose a problem in the treatment of victims of OP-poisoning, because of failure of the causal therapy with oximes. Generally, only rapid ageing will interfere with therapy, since the action of most OP compounds (in particular the nerve gases) demands the speedy administration of a rapidly acting reactivator. However, in progressive or prolonged intoxications, which often are seen with the more persistent insecticides that can remain intact in the human body for many days, even a relatively slow ageing process may endanger the patient's recovery.

The rate of ageing showed large variations. It was found to depend on the source of the AChE, but in particular on the structure of the inhibiting phosphorus moiety (see Aldridge and Reiner, 1972, for a survey). In the case of Soman, which ranks high among the potential chemical warfare agents, *in vitro* and *in vivo* half-lifes of ageing in the order of a few minutes had been found. Consequently, Soman-intoxications had to be feared to become therapy-resistant very rapidly, unless ageing could be prevented or retarded. For this reason, many of the more recent studies on ageing have been concentrated on Soman-inhibited enzymes.

THE 'ALTERNATIVE' AGEING PROCESS

Although most data pointed to dealkylation via C–O fission, other results complicated the situation. Lee and Turnbull (1958) reported that diphenyl phosphoryl chymotrypsin spontaneously released phenol and this phenomenon was also observed with trypsin (Lee and Turnbull, 1961). In these cases, P–O scission almost certainly had to take place, with the release of the phenolate anion, as the formation of a carbonium ion of benzene appeared highly improbable.

In 1972, Bender and Wedler studied di(p-nitrophenyl) phosphoryl chymotrypsin, from which p-nitrophenol is released. These authors confirmed the earlier results and demonstrated that after p-nitrophenol had been released, the inhibited enzyme could no longer be reactivated. The pH-dependence showed the influence of a dissociated acidic group with pK_a = 6.8 (figure 6.5). Study of the effect of D_2O and of methanol, and experiments in model systems with imidazole, resulted in the

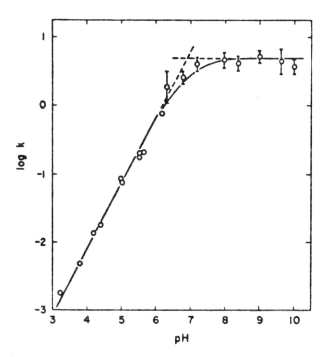

Figure 6.5   The pH-log rate dependence for the first-order ageing reaction of tris(p-nitrophenyl) phosphate inhibited α-chymotrypsin at 25°C; k is in s^{-1}. The solid line is the theoretical curve for a dissociating group with pK_a = 6.80 (from Bender and Wedler, 1972)

conclusion that a histidine residue in the active-centre was probably involved in the reaction, acting as a nucleophile on the tertiary phosphoryl-ester structure by directly attacking the P atom. In this system the imidazole did not act as a general base catalyst, which subtracts a proton from water.

An analogous reaction appeared to occur also with cholinesterases, as was shown by the results of Hovanec and Lieske (1972). With AChE the pH-dependence was bell shaped (figure 6.6). The influence of substituents in the para-position of the leaving phenyl group also agreed with P–O fission, i.e. with the release of the phenolate anion. Similar results were obtained by Wilson and coworkers, who in addition observed a very strong acceleration of the rate of the reaction (up to 70× !) by low concentrations of organic solvents (Wins and Wilson, 1974; Maglothin et al., 1975). Finally, Hamilton et al. (1975) observed the release of a p-nitrophenyl group in p-nitrophenyl methylphosphonyl-inhibited liver carboxylesterase.

Although, technically, this type of ageing results in the same kind of dealkylated, oxime-resistant inhibited enzyme as the more 'classical' ageing reaction, it is a totally different reaction with respect to mechanism. It differs in particular with regard to

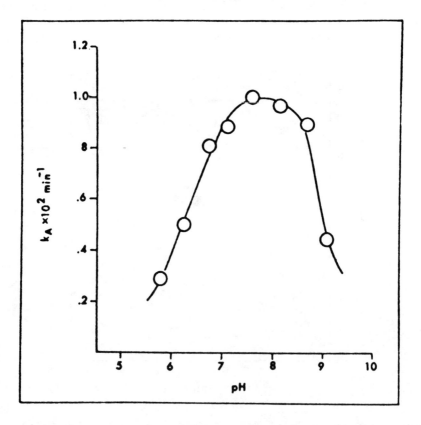

Figure 6.6   pH rate profile for the ageing at 25° of AChE inhibited by p-cyanophenyl methyl-phosphonochloridate (from Hovanec and Lieske, 1972)

the nature of the leaving group. In the 'classical' ageing, phospho-alkyl esters that are rather chemically inert, are involved in the dealkylation reaction, whereas in this case much more reactive structures are present, with partial anhydride character. As the OP compounds used in these studies are rather exceptional, certainly in relation to the practical aspects discussed in the preceding section, the subsequent parts of this review will be devoted to results obtained with the more 'common' OP agents. The final sections, will however, attempt to give a more integrated view.

VARIOUS ASPECTS OF THE AGEING REACTION

After the principle of ageing had been established, many studies have examined various aspects of the mechanism. Two problems arise, however, when we try to discuss the developments in this field: (1) fundamentally, little change has occurred in our insight into the mechanism of ageing since 1970; (2) most publications are the results of more or less isolated studies, sometimes with conflicting results or conflicting conclusions; frequently, results cannot be compared as different systems or different conditions were used. As a consequence, a review would not show much coherence.

A number of determinants of ageing will be discussed below. It will become clear that in all aspects the protein structure is involved, in one way or the other.

pH and temperature

As early as 1956 it was noticed (Hobbiger; Davies and Green) that ageing is pH-dependent. Lowering of the pH increased the rate of ageing. Hobbiger's results suggested a sigmoidal relationship ($pK_a = 7.2$) but other authors concluded that the rate increased in proportion to the H^+-concentration (Berry and Davies, 1966), or observed hardly any effect of pH (Berends, 1964a). It has now become clear that an acidic group in the enzyme is responsible for the pH-dependence of ageing of inhibited cholinesterase (Michel *et al.*, 1967; Keyer, 1971). In an attempt to identify this group and to clarify its role in ageing, Keyer initiated a detailed study on the effect of pH, temperature and ionic strength (Keyer, 1971; Keyer *et al.*, 1974). He used both AChE and BuChE, inhibited with a cycloheptyl methylphosphonyl group which ages fairly rapidly. The pH-dependencies he found are shown in figure 6.7. One thing could be concluded with certainty: in both enzymes ageing is governed by a dissociating group, which must be protonated if ageing is to occur. The pK_as were 5.8 (AChE) and 7.3 (BuChE). That was however, the only finding that was certain, as all efforts to identify the group remained unrewarded. On the basis of the dependency of the pK_a on variations in salt concentration or temperature, a COOH group with a high pK_a appeared an acceptable possibility for AChE, but for BuChE no conclusion at all was possible. A puzzling observation was the strong influence of the nature of the leaving alkyl group, which could shift the pK_a by 1 pH unit, without an apparent correlation with the structure.

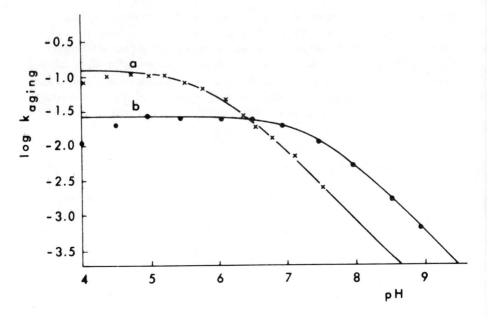

Figure 6.7 Influence of pH on the rate of ageing of cycloheptyl methylphosphonyl cholin-esterase at 25.0°; (a) acetylcholinesterase, (b) butyrylcholinesterase. Dissociation curves of acids with pK_a 5.84 (a) and 7.35 (b) are drawn through the experimental points (from Keyer, 1971).

The final conclusion was that ageing depends on a protonated structure, which is not a free, solvated group but a group which interacts with others. In this context it was suggested that cholinesterases possess a charge-relay system like that found in other serine-hydrolases in which there is an interplay between a carboxyl group, an imidazole ring and the serin-OH. Later studies (Schoene et al., 1980) did not throw new light on these aspects.

Structure of the leaving group

In general, the rate of ageing follows the tendency of the leaving group to form a carbonium ion. Superimposed on this, special effects may be found, as is the case with Soman. In a series of homologous leaving alkyl groups, Benschop et al. (1967) included the pinacolyl group of Soman. According to the solvolysis of the corres-ponding tosylates, Soman-inhibited cholinesterases should age as fast as the enzymes inhibited with the OP compound with one methyl group less. In practice, however, the Soman-inhibited enzymes age $> 20\times$ as fast as can be seen in table 6.3. A simi-lar difference was observed when the ageing of inhibited cholinesterases was com-pared with solvolysis in a model system in which the phosphonyl group was attached to the serine residue of a small peptide. In conclusion: in addition to chemical

Table 6.3 Relative rates of solvolysis of secondary alkyl tosylates and of ageing of corresponding secondary alkyl methylphosphonyl enzymes. Temperature 25°C (from Benschop et al., 1967)

Secondary alkyl group	Solvolysis of secondary alkyl tosylate	Ageing of secondary alkyl methylphosphonyl enzyme	
		AChE	BuChE
C–C–C– with C	1	1	1
C–C–C– with C C	5.8	1.5	3.5
C–C–C* (with C, C)	5.8	$\geqslant 70$	69

*Pinacolyl, the leaving alkyl group in Soman-inhibited cholinesterase (cf. table 6.1)

differences between alkyl groups, specific interactions of the leaving alkyl group with the enzyme may exist which can have a strong effect on the rate of ageing; another indication that groups in or near the active centre of the enzyme can be of great importance.

Effects of ligands

This aspect has attracted considerable attention. In 1966, Berry and Davies reported that N-methylpyridinium retarded ageing and many studies on the effects of pyridinium compounds have followed this earlier observation (Schoene, 1978, 1980; Schoene and Wulf, 1972, Schoene et al., 1980; Raszewski, 1977; Sterri, 1977; Harris et al., 1978; De Jong and Wolring, 1978a,b, 1980; Gray et al., 1985). The practical basis for this interest in the retardation of ageing is clear: since ageing forms an obstacle in the treatment of victims of poisoning by Soman and, possibly, certain other nerve gases, application of retarders of ageing may improve the effect of therapy. In general, however, the results of these studies were disappointing. Schoene and coworkers for instance, performed a series of very thorough studies in which about thirty pyridinium compounds were examined; unfortunately, the data did not throw any new light on the ageing reaction. Studies in which the pyridinium oximes were used as ligands were hampered by the complicated kinetics of simultaneous ageing and reactivation, which had to be solved before the true effects on ageing could be identified (De Jong and Wolring, 1978a,b, 1980). In addition to the pyridinium compounds, curare-like compounds, expected to induce allosteric effects, were used (Crone, 1974; Dawson et al., 1981), as well as imidazole (Sterri, 1977).

The general outcome of the many investigations can be summarised as follows: most quaternary ammonium compounds to some extent retard ageing, but some accelerate; the effects are not very strong and they are rather variable when pH, temperature or ionic strength are changed; sometimes retarders may then become accelerators. The effects were too small and the concentrations needed too high to give any hopes of benefit from practical application. As for the interpretation of the results, De Jong and Wolring (1978b) reached the conclusion that the effects are probably based on influences on the conformation of the active centre of the inhibited enzyme, and that these conformational changes affect the rate of ageing. This is about all that can be concluded, at the present time.

Effects of reactants

Reactivation of diethyl phosphoryl chymotrypsin by hydroxylamine does not proceed beyond 35–40% restored enzyme activity. Erlanger, who mentions this observation, subsequently demonstrated that the fraction of the enzyme that was resistant to the reactivation procedure, carried a monoethyl phosphoryl group (Erlanger et al., 1965). This loss of one ethyl group was shown to be induced by the treatment with hydroxylamine. Similarly, hydroxylamine could induce ageing in diethyl phosphoryl trypsin, but only in the presence of an alkylammonium salt (such salts are well-known activators of the tryptic activity towards aspecific substrates). The mechanism of this induced ageing has not been clarified. The authors postulated an attack by hydroxylamine on the P atom, with the result that either the P–bond with the enzyme is broken, or one of the $P-OC_2H_5$ bonds.

De Jong and Wolring (1978a) found that Tabun-inhibited AChE, which ages very slowly, aged up to 9-fold faster in the presence of certain pyridinium oximes (N-alkyl homologues of 2-PAM). The same pyridinium compounds without the oxime-function *retarded* ageing 2–3 times. So in this case the reactivator also appeared to induce ageing.

As mentioned before, Rozengart and Balashova (1965) could induce dealkylation with the soft nucleophile thiourea, which is known to attack C atoms, and not P atoms.

Beauregard et al. (1981) recently reported that treatment with a specific histidine reagent retarded ageing of DFP-inhibited AChE, whereas compounds reacting with -COOH or $-NH_2$ groups had no effect. It was not established, however, how many histidine residues had reacted, nor whether the retardation was caused by a homogeneous modification of all enzyme molecules or by a total blockade of ageing in a fraction of the molecules.

By themselves, the effect of reactants contribute little to our insight in the mechanism(s) of ageing.

Effects of protein structure

The most important contribution to the process of dealkylation evidently comes from the protein or, to be more precise, from interactions of the inhibiting phosphoryl substituent with groups in the protein. A variety of data support this statement.

1. The effect of protein denaturation, which stops dealkylation (Berends, 1964a; Coult *et al.*, 1966) is in agreement with the lack of reactivity observed in model systems.
2. The effects of structural variations, viz.
   (a) the exceptionally rapid ageing of Soman-inhibited cholinesterases, which was mentioned before;
   (b) the effects of stereoisomerism;
   (c) the differences between enzymes.

With respect to point 2(b), above Berends (1964b) found that in inhibited BuChE only one of the stereoisomers around the P atom ages. As figure 6.8 shows, in the enzyme inhibited with a symmetrical OP compound, DFP, dealkylation runs to completion, whereas in BuChE inactivated with a phosphonyl-inhibitor such as

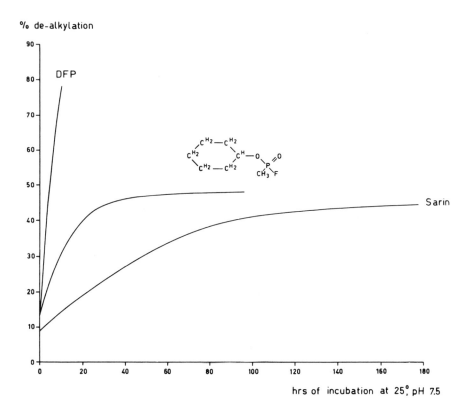

Figure 6.8 Stereospecificity in the ageing of OP-inhibited BuChE. Ageing (dealkylation) was studied after inhibition with a symmetrical OP compound (DFP) or with a racemic inhibitor with an asymmetric P atom ('cyclohexyl sarin'; sarin) (from Berends, 1964)

Sarin, which contains an asymmetric P atom (see table 6.1), ageing does not proceed beyond 50% (since BuChE is not as strongly stereospecific with regard to inhibition as is AChE, an almost racemic inhibited enzyme could be obtained).

In a more complicated manner (inhibition had to be performed with the separate stereoisomers), Keyer and Wolring (1969) demonstrated that with AChE, too, ageing is strictly stereospecific with regard to the configuration around the P atom.

What about the configuration around the C atom of the leaving group, the one that is to become the carbonium ion ? This, too, has an influence, as is shown for the two isomers of sec-octanol bound to a phosphonyl group (Benschop et al., 1967). A difference of a factor of 2 in the rate of ageing is seen (figure 6.9). Surprisingly, in Soman-inhibited cholinesterases, which show such a strong influence of the structure of the alkyl group on the rate of ageing, hardly any effect of the configuration around this C-atom is found, as can be seen in table 6.4.

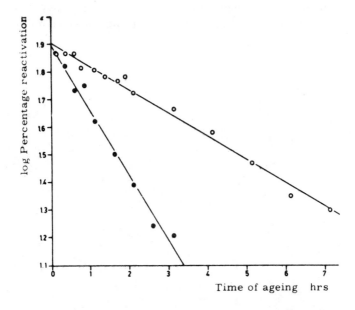

Figure 6.9   Effect of stereoisomerism around the P–O-linked C atom of the leaving alkyl group. Linear relation between log reactivatability (percentage of maximal reactivation) and time, representing ageing, of AChE inhibited by octyl-2-methylphosphonofluoridate derived from: ○ (+)-octanol-2; ● (−)-octanol-2 (from Benschop et al., 1967)

Another aspect of the influence of protein structure can also be seen in table 6.4: the difference in rate of ageing between the AChEs of different species. A 30-fold difference exists between rat and electric-eel AChE, and a difference of 18-fold between AChE from two mammalian species, rat and man. Unfortunately, this difference between rat and man is in the wrong direction, with regard to possible therapy in cases of Soman intoxication. The practical consequence of this is that

Table 6.4 Rate constants of ageing at pH 7.5 and 25° of rat, bovine and human erythrocyte and electric eel acetylcholinesterase after inhibition with racemic soman, C(+)-soman and with C(−)-soman (from De Jong and Wolring, 1984)

| Enzyme inhibited with | Rate constant* (min^{-1}) of inhibited acetylcholinesterase of | | | |
	Rat	Cow	Man	Electric eel
Rac. soman	0.033–0.033	0.13–0.13	0.54–0.66	1.0–1.1
C(+)-soman			0.50–0.59	1.0–1.2
C(−)-soman			0.41–0.51	0.9–1.1

*Values of duplicate experiments.

the treatment regimens that give such promising therapeutic results with Soman-poisoned rats, probably will be of little value in man (Wolthuis *et al.*, 1981).

In this context, the problem may be raised as to what extent do results obtained with isolated AChE preparations reflect the properties of the functional enzyme in the cholinergic synapses. Data presented by Harris *et al.* (1966) showed a good correlation between *in vitro* and *in vivo* ageing of Sarin-inhibited rat-brain AChE. Crone (1974) and Dawson *et al.* (1981), on the other hand, found different effects of salt and curare-like substances when comparing solubilised AChE and the membrane-bound enzyme. More data pertaining to ageing of inhibited AChE *in vivo* will be required before this question can be approached.

A few more examples of the dominating influence of the nature of the enzyme can be given: with AChE of all species studied so far, Soman inhibition leads to an extremely rapid ageing; in chymotrypsin, however, no ageing at all could be observed after inactivation with Soman (Michel *et al.*, 1967; Sun *et al.*, 1979). With cholinesterases only the enzyme inhibited with the P(R) stereoisomers of phosphonyl compounds show ageing, whereas with the neuropathy target esterase it is the P(S) isomer that yields an ageing inhibited enzyme (Johnson *et al.*, 1985).

In summary, a large number of experimental data point to an essential participation of parts of the enzyme molecule in the ageing reaction, and to a mechanism that – in general – is rather sensitive to structural (configurational, conformational) variations.

RECENT DEVELOPMENTS

Although most of the results presented in the preceding sections underline the importance of interactions with elements in the protein structure, they do not help us very much in answering the question which groups in the enzyme are involved in ageing, and how. Actually, in this respect not much progress has been made since 1967. Identification of these groups would not be sufficient, however, because the exact mechanism of their participation in ageing would not have been elucidated unless at the same time insight could be obtained into the spatial positions and interactions of the groups concerned. What is required is a more physical approach, with methods that can give information on bond angles, distances between atoms, electron distributions, bonding and non-bonding interactions, etc., in and around the alkylated phosphorus substituent attached to the active centre of the inhibited enzyme. Attempts in that direction might be made by using OP compounds that carry a 'reporter' group and thus allow studies with fluorescence, ESR or NMR. In a few cases, the interpretation of results of such approaches might be based on potential interactions that can be derived from the three-dimensional structures determined by X-ray diffraction studies on crystallised inhibited enzymes (chymotrypsin; subtilisin).

Around 1970 a few introductory ESR studies were performed on enzymes inhibited with OP compounds that contained a substituent with a nitroxide radical, but unfortunately this approach was not pursued. More recently, fluorescent reporter groups were introduced into the OP inhibitor (Amitai et al., 1980a,b). Specific reaction with the active site of AChE could be demonstrated for two compounds, one giving a reactivatable inhibited AChE, the other the corresponding aged (i.e. dealkylated) form. A substantial difference was seen in the fluorescence quantum yield between the two forms, which was interpreted as an ageing-induced conformational change resulting in less accessibility of the OP moiety to the external medium (Amitai et al., 1980a,b, 1982). It is hoped that this method, when applied together with other techniques, will lead to more concrete information.

An approach that in principle should be perfect for studying OP-inhibited enzymes is ^{31}P-NMR. This technique tells something about the electron configuration around the P atoms present in the material studied. And since the inhibited enzyme contains only one P atom, this information is very relevant. In general, with ^{31}P-NMR, information can be obtained on bond-angle changes, and other interactions that lead to a shift of electrons, such as hydrogen-bond formation. Recently, this technique has been applied to three serine-enzymes, viz. a bacterial atropinesterase, which in some respects resembles the cholinesterases and two proteases with a resolved three-dimensional structure, chymotrypsin and subtilisin; the inhibitor was DFP (Van der Drift, 1983, 1985; Van der Drift et al., 1985).

The NMR spectra of the three inhibited enzymes are shown in figure 6.10. These spectra show the location of the ^{31}P peak in relation to a reference compound, phosphoric acid, the so-called chemical shift (δ). The fact that all three enzymes show the peak in a different position, although they all have the same covalent structure (a diisopropyl phosphoryl (DP-) group attached to serine-OH) demonstrates the influence of interaction with the protein on the bonds around the P atom. After denaturation, all three preparations gave the same peak, which was identical with that of model phospho-triester compounds. Variation of pH strongly influenced the chemical shift, in the manner shown in figure 6.11.

Figure 6.10 ^{31}P-NMR spectra of DFP-inhibited serine-hydrolases (pH 7.5–7.6; 4°C). AtrE: atropinesterase (from Pseudomonas bacteria); Chymogen: chymotrypsinogen; Chymo: α-chymotrypsin; Sub: subtilisin. The chemical shift is indicated relative to the peak of the reference compound, H_3PO_4 (from Van der Drift, 1983)

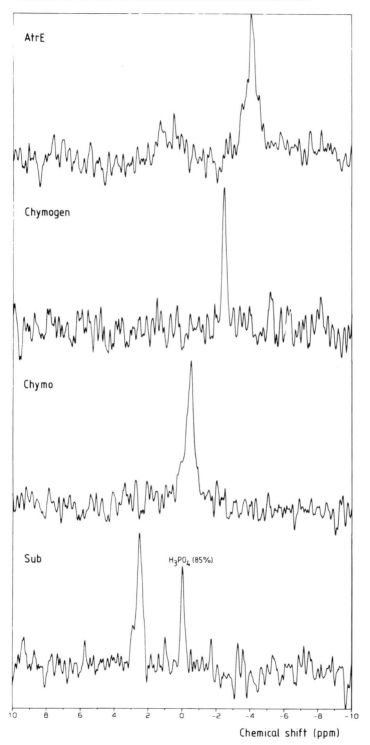

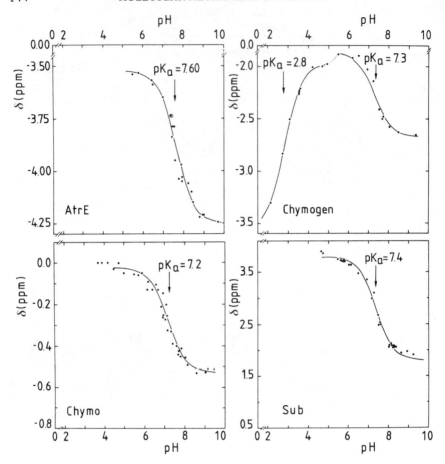

Figure 6.11   pH-dependence of the chemical shift (δ) in the ^{31}P-NMR spectra of DFP-inhibited serine-hydrolases; abbreviations as in figure 6.10. Theoretical dissociation curves (pK_as as indicated) have been fitted to the experimental points (from Van der Drift, 1983)

During storage of the DP enzymes, a second peak appeared in the NMR spectra, which increased at the expense of the original one. Finally, only the second peak remained, as can be seen in figure 6.12. Upon denaturation of the inhibited enzymes this second peak shifted to the position of a phospho-diester, which identified this peak as to represent the dealkylated monoisopropyl phosphoryl (MP-) enzyme. The MP peaks were pH-independent.

By studying the DP and the MP peaks, Van der Drift could follow ageing by NMR measurements, also at different pHs. Remarkably, the pH-dependence of ageing coincided with the pH dependence of the chemical shifts of the three DP-enzymes (figure 6.11). This result suggests that the same dissociating group that is

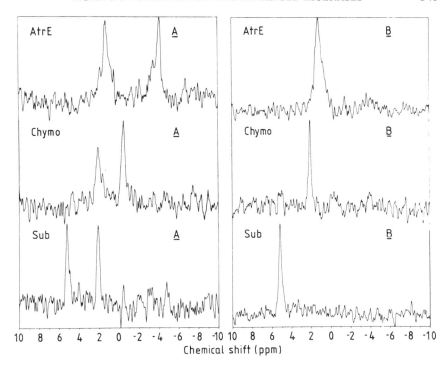

Figure 6.12 ^{31}P-NMR spectra of partially (A) and completely aged (B) DFP-inhibited serine-hydrolases (pH 7.8–8.2; 4°C); abbreviations as in figure 6.10 (from Van der Drift, 1983)

responsible for the pH-dependence of the chemical shift in each of these enzymes, also plays an essential role in the dealkylation reaction.

To see whether ageing of these DP enzymes proceeds via C–O or via P–O fission, ageing was allowed to take place in ^{18}O-water. Subsequently, mass spectrometry revealed that all the isopropanol formed had the same ^{18}O/^{16}O ratio as the water used, so only C–O fission occurred (table 6.5). In addition to isopropanol, a certain amount of propene was found, in substantial proportions with atropinesterase, insignificantly with chymotrypsin, which suggests almost complete S_N2 character for the reaction in the latter enzyme and partial S_N1 character in case of atropin-esterase. Unfortunately, the author did not offer an explanation for the low recovery of the released isopropyl group for subtilisin and atropinesterase.

On the basis of these NMR results, of NMR data obtained with model compounds and – very important – of the knowledge of the three-dimensional structure of two of the enzymes, Van der Drift came to the following conclusions: (1) In the inhibited enzymes, the oxygen of the P=O is locked into position in the so-called oxy-anion hole and kept in place by hydrogen bonding, which stretches the P=O bond. (2) Dealkylation is governed by intramolecular general acid catalysis. Very likely, the proton is provided by the imidazole-Nϵ2 atom of the histidine in the charge-

Table 6.5 Results of mass-spectrometric analysis of products formed upon ageing of DP-enzymes in aqueous solution at $36.0°C$ (from Van der Drift, 1983)

		Chymotrypsin	Subtilisin	Atropinesterase
Isopropanol (%)	(1)	97 ± 13	42 ± 6	18 ± 14
Propene (%)	(1)	1.2 ± 0.2	3.8 ± 0.6	11.3 ± 5.5
$^{18}O/^{16}O$ ratio	(2)	0.99 ± 0.03	1.01 ± 0.01	0.98 ± 0.05

(1) The amount measured after complete ageing at $36.0°C$ (± sem) expressed as percentage of the amount expected on the basis of the concentration of phosphorylated enzyme. Ageing was completed at pH = 5.7 for chymotrypsin and subtilisin, and at pH = 6.7 for atropinesterase in either 0.1 M citric acid–sodium citrate buffer or 0.05 M sodium sulphate. Since the results in these media did not differ significantly, the averaged values of both media are given. In some experiments also a small mount of acetone was found, presumably due to contamination.

(2) The ratio (± sem) between $(H_2^{18}O/H_2^{16}O)$ and $(^{18}O\text{-isopropanol}/^{16}O\text{-isopropanol})$ is given.

relay system (known to be present in chymotrypsin and subtilisin, and probably also in atropinesterase). (3) Via this proton, the histidine hydrogen-bonds to the oxygen atom of the ester bond between the phosphorus atom and the (potentially) leaving alkyl group; whether it is released depends on its ability to form a carbonium ion. (4) After dealkylation, the direct interaction of the phosphoryl group with this histidine is lost. (5) Non-bonding interactions between the protein and the non-scissile isopropyl group may play a role in stabilising the transition state.

Although part of the conclusions need confirmation, these results already show the great possibilities of the application of ^{31}P-NMR to the study of ageing. It is hoped that in the near future more investigators will adopt this approach, to contribute to our understanding of the mechanism of ageing. Unfortunately, because of its high molecular weight, AChE itself is not readily accessible to this technique, but the studies on smaller model enzymes have shown the high value of the information that can be obtained; moreover, now that equipment with a high magnetic field strength is becoming more general, even AChE may be tackled.

PRESENT VIEWS

Attempts to draw conclusion with regard to the mechanism(s) of ageing should start with taking into account the particular properties of the inhibited enzymes. The assumption appears warranted that all serine-hydrolases possess a kind of charge-relay system similar to that present in enzymes belonging to the chymotrypsin and subtilisin families, with a strategically positioned histidine residue. The imidazole ring of this residue is involved in the reactivity of the serine-OH towards OP compounds; probably it plays a role also in the dephosphorylation, either spontaneous or oxime-mediated. And, according to the ^{31}P-NMR studies, it is intimately involved in ageing.

The experimental data indicate that in the inhibited enzymes the phosphorus moiety is susceptible to nucleophilic attack. In part, this may be attributed to the fixation of the double-bonded O atom in the oxy-anion hole and the resulting shift of elections towards this atom. The nucleophilic attack on the P atom may come

$$
\begin{array}{c}
\text{ser—O} \qquad \text{O}^{\,\delta-} \\
\diagdown \qquad \diagup\diagup \\
\text{P} \\
\diagup \qquad \diagdown \\
\text{R—O} \qquad \text{X} \qquad \text{(R = alkyl; aryl)}
\end{array}
$$

from the imidazole when in the dissociated (non-protonated) form, via the free electrons of an N atom, or from an external agent, e.g. an oxime anion. In the latter case, the possibility exists that the protonated imidazole contributes to the reaction by interacting with serine-O via an intermediary water molecule. The role attributed here to the imidazole ring is consistent with most data on spontaneous and oxime-assisted reactivation.

Usually, a nucleophilic attack on the P atom will result in disruption of the P-O bond with the serine residue (= reactivation), because the enzyme is a good leaving group. However, when RO^- can compete with the enzyme in this respect, it is to be expected that in a certain proportion of the molecules the RO-P bond will be split, yielding an aged inhibited enzyme. Evidently, in AChE this situation exists when R is an aryl group: then, spontaneous reactivation and ageing take place simultaneously (unless release of RO^- is too fast for reactivation to compete, as is the case with R = p-nitrophenyl; Hovanec and Lieske, 1972). Chymotrypsin and trypsin appear to be poorer leaving groups than is AChE (in agreement with the very high rate constant of deacylation of the latter enzyme), since after inhibition with an aryl-O-P compound ageing prevails.

In these cases the mere reactivity of the RO-P bond may explain the outcome of the reaction, although a closer view indicates an additional effect of the micro-environment of group R in inhibited AChE (Hovanec and Lieske, 1972).

Less clear is the mechanism of the reactivator-induced ageing mentioned before: above, as is the case with NH_2OH for diethyl phosphoryl(chymo)trypsin and with pyridinium oximes for Tabun-inhibited AChE. A similar explanation, i.e. attack on the P atom followed by partial fission of the 'wrong' P-O bond, demands release of an ethoxy group in both cases. It is not likely, however, that this group by itself can compete with the enzyme as a leaving group. Presumably, interactions with the protein play a role, with a possible extra contribution from a conformational change: in trypsin induced ageing occurred only in the presence of alkylammonium ions (Erlanger et al., 1965), and the induction of conformational changes in the active centre of AChE by pyridinium compounds appears very probable (De Jong and Wolring, 1978b). In Tabun-inhibited AChE, nucleophilic attack of the oxime anion on phosphorus resulting in protein-facilitated P-OEt fission seems fairly plausible, since ageing via C-O scission is known to be retarded by the identical pyridinium compounds without the oxime function (De Jong and Wolring, 1978b). The NH_2OH-induced reaction poses more problems, since the mechanism of reactivation by hydroxylamine, which is unlikely to proceed via the anion, has not been clarified.

With respect to 'classical' ageing, i.e. dealkylation via C–O fission, hydrogen-bonding of the protonated imidazole to the oxygen of the R–O–P connection appears the driving force — probably assisted by the partial positive charge on the P atom. Such a mechanism was already proposed by Keyer et al. (1974) for cholinesterases; it is now strongly supported by the ^{31}P-NMR data on three other enzymes. The strength of this hydrogen bond together with the tendency of group R to form a carbonium ion seems to determine the rate of dealkylation, but this rate may be modulated by other structural elements, such as the non-bonding interactions mentioned by Van der Drift (1983). More experimental data are needed before it can be decided how these modulations are brought about, e.g. by interactions that facilitate or hamper the formation of the transition state. It is also uncertain whether such secondary interactions might change the strength of the hydrogen bond. The observation by Keyer et al. (1974) that the size or nature of group R may shift the pK_a by as much as 1 pH unit, would indicate a potentially strong effect on the local structure, but this seems in conflict with the relatively small influence on the rate of ageing. So, for the time being this observation remains unexplained.

Other factors, too, may affect ageing: whether dealkylation proceeds as a unimolecular or as a bimolecular reaction may depend on the degree of exposure to the solvent of the groups involved, or on the possible presence of water molecules in the active centre. An *active* contribution of other groups in the enzyme acting as acceptor for R^+ is not very likely; during ageing of the inhibited neuropathy target esterase (see chapter by Johnson in this volume), the leaving group becomes attached to functional groups of the protein, but there are no data as yet to indicate an *active* role of the latter groups in the ageing process.

The strong influence of stereoisomerism around the P atom cannot be based on weak, modulating interactions. Unfortunately, no data are available on structural differences between the R- and S-forms of the inhibited enzymes. A plausible explanation would be that fixation of the P=O in the oxy-anion hole forces the rest of the phosphonyl group into such a position that in only one of the two configurations a hydrogen bond between imidazole and the R–O–P oxygen can be formed. In this interpretation it is not clear, however, why in the same stereoisomer of inhibited cholinesterase ageing and oxime reactivation are blocked together. Also the absence of ageing in Soman-inhibited chymotrypsin remains puzzling, in view of the dealkylation-favouring properties of the pinacolyl group. It might be wondered whether with this enzyme stereospecificity of the inhibition — which is known to be present — could result in an inhibited enzyme that contains the phosphorus moiety in the 'wrong' configuration. A number of these questions might be approached experimentally; again, application of ^{31}P-NMR could be very helpful.

CONCLUSIONS

When a P–O–R structure is present in organophosphate-inhibited enzymes, release of group R may occur (ageing), either spontaneously or induced by chemicals. This dealkylation can proceed via P–O or via C–O fission, mainly determined by the nature of R. In both mechanisms, the imidazole of the active-centre histidine of the enzyme is thought to play an essential role. In the case of P-O fission, nucleophilic attack on the P atom appears to be the driving force, while in the other case it is hydrogen-bonding of the protonated imidazole to the O atom. In addition, the reactions are governed by the other interactions with the protein, such as strong fixation of (P=)O in the 'oxy-anion hole' and non-bonding interactions. Configuration, conformation and the precise spatial position of the groups relative to each other are the important determinants. For insight into the exact mechanisms, more detailed structural information is required.

REFERENCES

Aldridge, W. N. and Reiner, E. (1972). Enzyme inhibitors as substrates. In: *Frontiers of Biology*, Vol. 26, North-Holland, Amsterdam, pp. 79–90

Amitai, G., Ashani, Y., Gafni, A. and Silman, I. (1980a). New fluorescent organo-phosphates as probes for studying aging-induced conformational changes in inhibited acetylcholinesterase. *Neurochemistry International*, 2, 199–204

Amitai, G., Ashani, Y., Sharar, A., Gafni, A. and Silman, I. (1980b). Fluorescent organophosphates: Novel probes for studying aging-induced conformational changes in inhibited acetylcholinesterase and for localization of cholinesterase in nervous tissue. *Monogr. Neural Sci.*, Vol. 7, Karger, Basel, pp. 70–84

Amitai, G., Ashani, Y., Gafni, A. and Silman, I. (1982). Novel pyrene-containing organophosphates as fluorescent probes for studying aging-induced conformational changes in organophosphate-inhibited acetylcholinesterase. *Biochemistry*, 21, 2060–9

Beauregard, G., Lum, J. and Roufogalis, B. D. (1981). Effect of histidine modification on the aging of organophosphate-inhibited acetylcholinesterase. *Biochem. Pharmacol.*, 30, 2915–20

Bender, M. L. and Wedler, F. C. (1972). Phosphate and carbonate ester aging reactions with α-chymotrypsin. Kinetics and mechanism. *J. Am. Chem. Soc.*, 94, 2101–9

Benschop, H. P. and Keyer, J. H. (1966). On the mechanism of ageing of phosphonylated cholinesterases. *Biochim. Biophys. Acta*, 128, 586–8

Benschop, H. P., Keyer, J. H. and Kienhuis, H. (1967). On the mechanism of ageing of phosphorylated cholinesterases. In: *Proceedings of the Conference on Structure and Reactions of DFP-sensitive Enzymes* (ed. E. Heilbronn), Försvaret Forskningsanstalt, Stockholm, pp. 193–9

Berends, F. (1964a). Reactivation and 'ageing' of organophosphate-inhibited esterases. Ph.D. thesis, University of Leiden, The Netherlands

Berends, F. (1964b). Stereospecificity in the reactivation and ageing of butyryl-cholinesterase inhibited by organophosphates with an asymmetrical P-atom. *Biochim. Biophys. Acta*, 81, 190–3

Berends, F., Posthumus, C. H., v.d. Sluys, I. and Deierkauf, F. A. (1959). The chemical basis of the 'ageing process' of DFP-inhibited pseudocholinesterase. *Biochim. Biophys. Acta*, 34, 576–8

Berry, W. K. and Davies, D. R. (1966). Factors influencing the rate of 'aging' in a series of alkyl methylphosphonyl-acetylcholinesterases. *Biochem. J.*, 100, 572–6

Blow, D. M., Birkstoft, J. J. and Hartley, B. S. (1969). Role of a buried acid group in the mechanism of action of chymotrypsin. *Nature, Lond.*, 221, 337–40

Childs, A. F., Davies, D. R., Green, A. L. and Rutland, J. P. (1955). The reactivation by oximes and hydroxamic acids of cholinesterase inhibited by organophosphorus compounds. *Brit. J. Pharmacol.*, **10**, 462–5

Clothier, B., Johnson, M. K. and Reiner, E. (1981). Interaction of some trialkyl phosphorothiolates with acetylcholinesterase. Characterization of inhibition, aging and reactivation. *Biochim. Biophys. Acta*, **660**, 306–16

Coult, D. B., Marsh, D. J. and Read, G. (1966). Dealkylation studies on inhibited acetylcholinesterase. *Biochem. J.*, **98**, 869–873

Crone, H. D. (1974). Can allosteric effectors of acetylcholinesterase control the rate of ageing of the phosphonylated enzyme? *Biochem. Pharmacol.*, **23**, 460–3

Davies, D. R. and Green, A. L. (1956). The kinetics of reactivation, by oximes, of cholinesterase inhibited by organophosphorus compounds. *Biochem. J.*, **63**, 529–35

Dawson, R. M., Crone, H. D., Bladen, M. P. and Poretski, M. (1981). A comparison of the effects of ionic strength on three preparations of acetylcholinesterase in the presence and absence of gallamine. *Neurochemistry International*, **3**, 335–41

De Jong, L. P. A. and Wolring, G. Z. (1978a). Effect of 1-(ar)alkyl-2-hydroxyiminomethyl-pyridinium salts on reactivation and aging of acetylcholinesterase inhibited by ethyl dimethylphosphoramidocyanidate (tabun). *Biochem. Pharmacol.*, **27**, 2229–35

De Jong, L. P. A. and Wolring, G. Z. (1978b). Reactivation and aging of cyclopentyl methylphosphonylated acetylcholinesterase in the presence of some 1-alkyl-2-hydroxyiminomethyl-pyridinium salts. *Biochem. Pharmacol.*, **27**, 2911–17

De Jong, L. P. A. and Wolring, G. Z. (1980). Reactivation of acetylcholinesterase inhibited by 1,2,2′-trimethylpropyl methylphosphonofluoridate (soman) with HI-6 and related oximes. *Biochem. Pharmacol.*, **29**, 2379–87

De Jong, L. P. A., Wolring, G. Z. and Benschop, H. P. (1982). Reactivation of acetylcholinesterase inhibited by methamidophos and analogous (di)methylphosphoramidates. *Arch. Toxicol.*, **49**, 175–83

De Jong, L. P. A. and Wolring, G. Z. (1984). Stereospecific reactivation by some Hagendorn-oximes of acetylcholinesterases from various species including man, inhibited by soman. *Biochem. Pharmacol.*, **33**, 1119–25

Erlanger, B. F., Cohen, W., Vratsanos, S. M., Castleman, H. and Cooper, A. G. (1965). Postulated chemical basis for observed differences in the enzymatic behaviour of chymotrypsin and trypsin. *Nature, Lond.*, **205**, 868–71

Fleisher, J. H. and Harris, L. W. (1965). Dealkylation as a mechanism for aging of cholinesterase after poisoning with pinacolyl methylphosphonofluoridate. *Biochem. Pharmacol.*, **14**, 641–50

Gray, A. P., Platz, R. D., Chang, T. C. P., Leverone, T. R., Farrick, D. A. and Kramer, D. N. (1985). Synthesis of some quaternary ammonium alkylating agents and their effects on soman-inhibited acetylcholinesterase. *J. Med. Chem.*, **28**, 111–16

Hamilton, S. E., Dudman, N. P. B., de Jersey, J., Stoops, J. K. and Zerner, B. (1975). Organophosphate inhibitors: the reactions of bis(p-nitrophenyl) methyl phosphate with liver carboxylesterase and α-chymotrypsin. *Biochim. Biophys. Acta*, **377**, 282–96

Harris, L. W., Fleisher, J. H., Clark, J. and Cliff, W. J. (1966). Dealkylation and loss of capacity for reactivation of cholinesterase inhibited by sarin. *Science, N.Y.*, **154**, 404–7

Harris, L. W., Heyl, W. C., Stitcher, D. L. and Broomfield, C. A. (1978). Effects of 1,1′-oxydimethylene bis-(4-tert-butylpyridinium chloride)-(SAD-128) and decamethonium on reactivation of soman- and sarin-inhibited cholinesterase by oximes. *Biochem. Pharmacol.*, **27**, 757–61

Hobbiger, F. (1955). Effect of nicotinhydroxamic acid methiodide on human plasma cholinesterase inhibited by organophosphates containing a dialkyl phosphato group. *Brit. J. Pharmacol.*, **10**, 356–62

Hobbiger, F. (1956). Chemical reactivation of phosphorylated human and bovine true cholinesterases. *Brit. J. Pharmacol.*, **11**, 295–303

Hobbiger, F. (1963). In: *Cholinesterases and Anticholinesterase Agents* (ed. G. B. Koelle), Springer Verlag, Berlin, pp. 921–88

Hovanec, J. W. and Lieske, C. N. (1972). Spontaneous reactivation of acetylcholinesterase inhibited with para-substituted phenyl methylphosphonochloridates. *Biochemistry*, **11**, 1051–6

Jandorf, B. J., Michel, H. O., Schaffer, N. K., Egan, R. and Summerson, W. H. (1955). The mechanism of reaction between esterases and phosphorus-containing anti-esterases. *Disc. Farad. Soc.*, **20**, 134–42

Jansz, H. S., Brons, D. and Warringa, M. G. P. J. (1959). Nature of the diisopropyl phosphorofluoridate-binding site of pseudocholinesterase. *Biochim. Biophys. Acta*, **34**, 573–5

Jansz, H. S., Oosterbaan, R. A., Berends, F. and Cohen, J. A. (1963). *Proc. 5th Int. Congr. Biochem.*, Moscow, 1961, Vol. 4, Pergamon Press, Oxford, pp. 45–56

Johnson, M. K., Read, D. J. and Benschop, H. P. (1985). Interaction of the four stereoisomers of soman (pinacolyl methylphosphonofluoridate) with acetylcholinesterase and neuropathy target esterase of hen brain. *Biochem. Pharmacol.* **34**, 1945–51

Keyer, J. H. (1971). Aging of phosphonylated cholinesterases. Ph.D. thesis, University of Leiden, The Netherlands

Keyer, J. H. and Wolring, G. Z. (1969). Stereospecific aging of phosphonylated cholinesterases. *Biochim. Biophys. Acta*, **185**, 465–8

Keyer, J. H., Wolring, G. Z. and De Jong, L. P. A. (1974). Effect of pH, temperature and ionic strength on the aging of phosphonylated cholinesterases. *Biochim. Biophys. Acta*, **334**, 146–55

Lee, W. and Turnbull, J. H. (1958). Liberation of phenol from diphenylphosphoryl chymotrypsin. *Biochim. Biophys. Acta*, **30**, 655

Lee, W. and Turnbull, J. H. (1961). An ageing effect in inhibited esterases: elimination of phenol from DPC1P-inhibited chymotrypsin and trypsin. *Experientia*, **18**, 360–1

Maglothin, J. A., Wins, P. and Wilson, I. B. (1975). Reactivation and aging of diphenyl phosphoryl acetylcholinesterase. *Biochim. Biophys. Acta*, **403**, 370–5

Michel, H. O., Hackley, B. E. Jr., Berkowitz, L., List, G., Hackley, E. B., Gillilan, W. and Pankau, M. (1967). Ageing and dealkylation of soman-inactivated eel cholinesterase. *Arch. Biochem. Biophys.*, **121**, 29–34

Raszewski, W. (1977). Protective action of a series of new monopyridinium salts and their effect on 'aging' of acetylcholinesterase inhibited by fluostigmine. *Pol. J. Pharmacol. Pharm.*, **29**, 603–7

Rozengart, V. I. and Balashova, E. K. (1965). The aging mechanism of cholinesterase inhibited by organophosphorus inhibitors. *Dokl. Akad. Nauk. SSSR*, **164**, 937–40

Schaffer, N. K., May, C. S. and Summerson, W. H. (1954). Serine phosphoric acid from diisopropylphosphoryl derivative of eel cholinesterase. *J. Biol. Chem.*, **206**, 201–7

Schoene, K. (1978). Aging of soman-inhibited acetylcholinesterase: Inhibitors and accelerators. *Biochim. Biophys. Acta*, **525**, 468–71

Schoene, K. (1980). Pyridinium salts as organophosphate antagonists. *Monogr. Neural Sci.*, Vol. 7, Karger, Basel, pp. 85–98

Schoene, K. and Wulf, R. (1972). Retarding effect of pyridinium salts on aging of soman-inhibited acetylcholinesterase. *Arzneim.-Forsch. (Drug Res.)*, **22**, 1802

Schoene, K., Steinhanses, J. and Wertmann, A. (1980). Aging of soman-inhibited acetylcholinesterase; pH-rate profiles and temperature dependence in absence and in presence of effectors. *Biochim. Biophys. Acta*, **616**, 384–8

Smith, T. E. and Usdin, E. (1966). Formation of nonreactivatible isopropylmethyl-phosphonofluoridate-inhibited acetylcholinesterase. *Biochemistry*, **5**, 2914–8

Sterri, S. H. (1977). Effect of imidazoles and pH on aging of phosphylated acetyl-cholinesterase. *Biochem. Pharmacol.*, **26**, 656–8

Sun, M. C., Chang, Z. G., Shan, M. Z., Huang, R. H. and Chou, T. C. (1979). The mechanism of ageing of phosphonylated acetylcholinesterase. *Eur. J. Biochem.*, **100**, 527–30

Van der Drift, A. C. M. (1983). Physico-chemical characterization of atropinesterase from *Pseudomonas putida*. Ph.D. thesis, University of Utrecht, The Netherlands

Van der Drift, A. C. M. (1985). A comparative study of the aging of DFP-inhibited serine-hydrolases by means of ^{31}P-NMR and mass spectrometry. In: *Molecular Basis of Nerve Activity*, (eds Changeux *et al.*), W. de Gruyter & Co., Berlin, New York, pp. 753–64

Van der Drift, A. C. M., Beck, H. C., Dekker, W. H., Hulst, A. G. and Wils, E. R. J. (1985). ^{31}P-NMR and mass spectrometry of atropinesterase and some serine proteases phosphorylated with a transition-state analogue. *Biochemistry*, **24**, 6894–903

Wilson, I. B. (1955). Promotion of acetylcholinesterase activity by the anionic site. *Disc. Farad. Soc.*, **20**, 119–25

Wilson, I. B. and Ginsburg, S. (1955). A powerful reactivator of alkylphosphate-inhibited acetylcholinesterase. *Biochim. Biophys. Acta*, **18**, 168–70

Wins, P. and Wilson, I. B. (1974). The inhibition of acetylcholinesterase by organo-phosphorus compounds containing a P–Cl bond. *Biochim. Biophys. Acta*, **334**, 137–45

Wolthuis, O. L., Vanwersch, R. A. P. and Van der Wiel, H. J. (1981). The efficacy of some bispyridinium oximes as antidotes to soman in isolated muscles of several species including man. *Eur. J. Pharmacol.*, **70**, 355–69

7

Mechanisms of Genotoxicity of Chlorinated Aliphatic Hydrocarbons

D.Henschler

I. INTRODUCTION

Chlorinated aliphatic hydrocarbons constitute a variety of chemically closely related compounds which share one common physical feature: high solubility in fat, paraffins and other apolar chemical systems. All other properties differ widely, sometimes to the extremes, such as vapor pressure: their physical states vary from gases with very low boiling points (e.g. vinyl chloride) through liquids (most members) to solids (e.g. hexachloroethane). The chemical stability ranges from very high (e.g. hexachlorobutadiene) to low (carbon tetrachloride, methyl chloroform). Usage is many fold: as organic solvents in lacquer preparations, degreasing agents in metal processing, tissue cleaning, propellants in dry aerosol devices, intermediates in organic synthesis, plastic monomers and many others. The inexpensiveness of electrolytic chlorine production and the easy availability of petrochemical aliphatic structures as starting materials makes chlorinated aliphatic hydrocarbons one of the bulk chemical classes.

The toxicology of chlorinated aliphatics started some 140 years ago with the introduction of chloroform as a general anaesthetic. The central nervous system depressing activity is another feature which is, to a greater or lesser extent, shared by all members of this comprehensive class of chemicals. All other toxic properties, such as cardiotoxicity, peripheral neuropathy and particularly cell damage to the parenchymal organs, liver and kidney, are rather unequally distributed in the series. The reason for the major differences encountered between these activities lies in the multitude of biotransformation pathways and, with certain representatives of this class of chemicals, in the unexpected preferences given to some bioactivation and degradation mechanisms by some species, strains or tissues.

This holds particularly true for the covalent interaction of chlorinated aliphatics and/or of their metabolites with the genetic material resulting in mutagenic and carcinogenic effects. The first description of the production of malignant tumours, namely liver haemangiosarcomas in animals after inhalation exposure to vinyl chloride (Viola *et al.*, 1971; Maltoni and Lefemine, 1974), as well as after occupational exposure in humans (Creech and Johnson, 1974), came as late as three and a half decades after its introduction into large scale production. The bioactivation pathway of vinyl chloride was soon elucidated by two groups (Hefner *et al.*, 1975; Green and Hathway, 1975) as the P450 mixed function oxidase catalysed formation of a highly reactive epoxide. Almost simultaneously, it was speculated that the same pathway would prevail with the analogues, the higher chlorinated ethylene derivatives (van Duuren, 1975), some of which, e.g. trichloroethylene and tetrachloroethylene, were widely used as industrial and household chemicals. In fact, the suspicion that these compounds were also mutagenic and/or carcinogenic soon seemed to be confirmed by positive findings in whole animal carcinogenicity studies with vinylidene chloride (Lee *et al.*, 1978), trichloroethylene (NCI, 1976) and tetrachloroethylene (NTP, 1983).

However, these early results were received with uncertainty and doubts, in part because of controversial explanations and validations of the type and numbers of tumours observed in just one animal species, in part because of the lack of any epidemiological evidence of tumourigenicity in spite of the extensive use of and exposure to the chemicals as anaesthetics and technical solvents for many decades in large populations. A more detailed analysis of the mechanisms of toxicity and bioactivation was deemed necessary for an appropriate safety evaluation of the whole group of chlorinated ethylenes and of chemically related molecules which might exert similar toxic activities. The following report deals with the work of one group which initiated a rather unconventional approach to the solution of a problem which seemed rather simple from the outset, but which turned out to be rather complicated as the results came in and still needs additional work to fill some gaps in our knowledge.

The approach may be characterisied by the following series of steps: initial consideration of the chemical stability — prediction of pathways of metabolic activation and detoxication — identification of metabolites in a system mimicking *in vivo* conditions — comparison of predicted with identified metabolites and from this extrapolation of reactive metabolic intermediates — prediction of covalent interactions of electrophiles with DNA and of resulting mutagenic events — testing of the compounds in a simple mutagenicity assay — elaboration of structure/activity relationships and from these identification of the toxic molecular moiety — prediction of safe alternatives of similar chemical and technological properties — and, finally, particularly in case of remaining uncertainty, conduct of whole animal carcinogenicity tests to confirm or reject the proposed structure/activity relationships.

II. CONSIDERATION OF CHEMICAL REACTIVITY AS A PREDICTION OF METABOLIC TRANSFORMATION

The chemical stability of chlorinated aliphatic hydrocarbons is governed by the differences in the electron densities of the chlorine atom and the neighbouring carbon atom. The electron withdrawing capacity of the chlorine substituent induces, however, completely different effects in saturated as compared to unsaturated C2 systems (Bonse and Henschler, 1976): in the case of ethanes (and homologues), it produces a labilisation of the C−Cl and C−C bonds which leads either to chlorine and/or hydrochloride elimination with the formation of olefinic structures, or to the formation of free radicals:

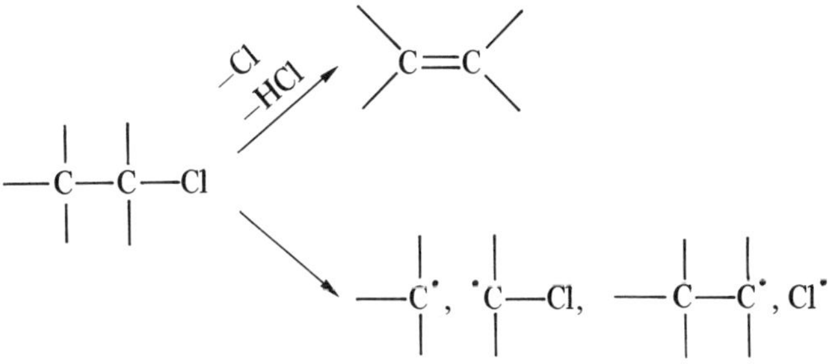

In the case of chlorinated ethenes, the electronegativity of the chlorine atom leads to an electron deprivation of the double bond system and thus to its stabilisation. Consequently, mixed function oxidation as the major metabolic activity in mammalian liver leads to the insertion of activated oxygen with the formation of oxiranes as electrophilic intermediates:

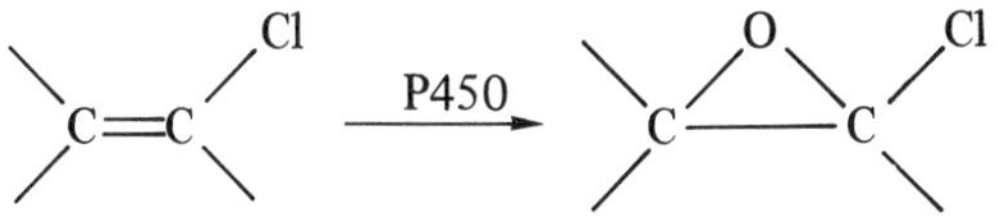

An increase in the number of chlorine substitutions should be expected to increase stability and hence decrease the rate of metabolic transformation. Also, a steric protection of the bulky chlorine residues might add to a decrease in the oxidative metabolic rate, which then should be expected to follow the sequence: $Cl_4 < Cl_3 < Cl_2 < Cl_1$.

With the ethynes, in turn, the electron withdrawing effect induces destabilisation of the triple bond system which renders chlorinated acetylenes extremely unstable in the presence of oxygen:

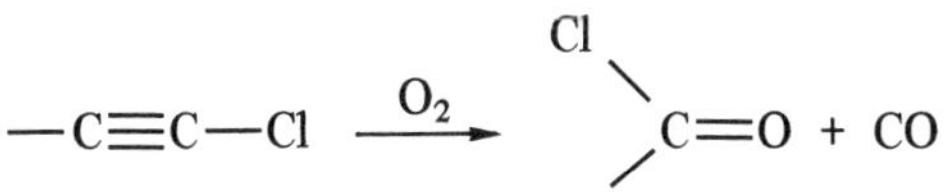

Completely different conditions are encountered with chlorinated allylic compounds in which the chlorine atom constitutes a good leaving group and the propene cation formed is stabilised by resonance, thus producing alkylating properties:

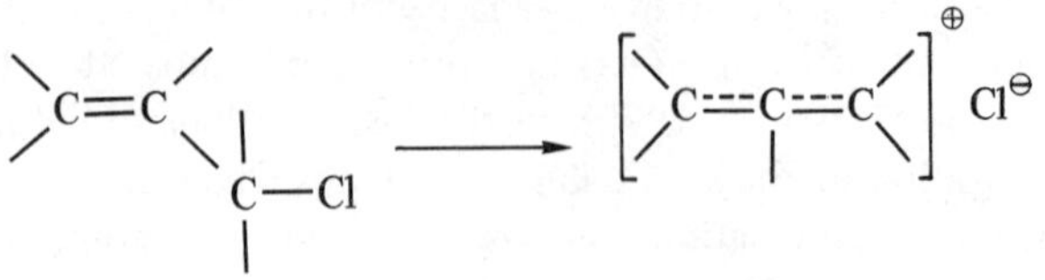

There are, however, at least three conceivable competing mechanisms with chlorinated propenes with an allylic structure: first, simple hydrolysis leading to the formation of allylic alcohols which may subsequently be oxidised by dehydrogenases to highly reactive α/β-unsaturated carbonyls (derivatives of acrolein):

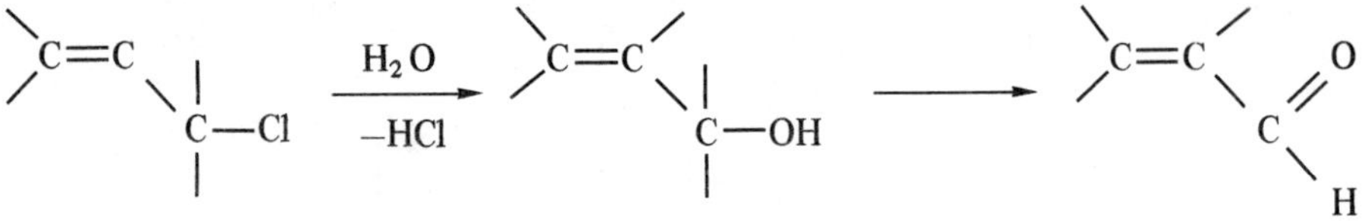

Secondly, the olefinic structure may undergo epoxidation leading to extremely reactive bifunctional molecules such as epichlorohydrins:

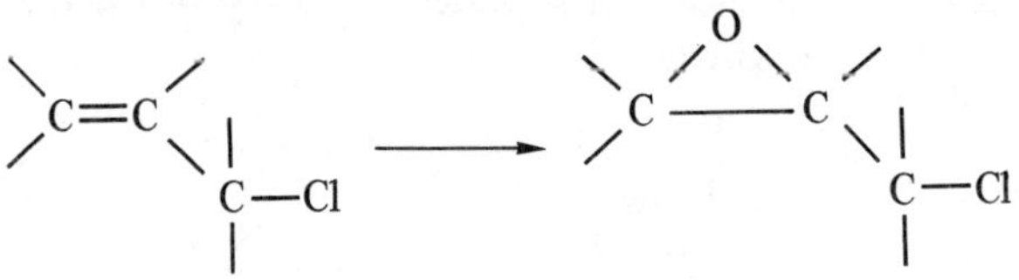

Thirdly, the chlorinated allylic structure may react enzymatically as an electrophile with glutathione which results, after further metabolic processing in the formation (and excretion) of mercapturic acid derivatives:

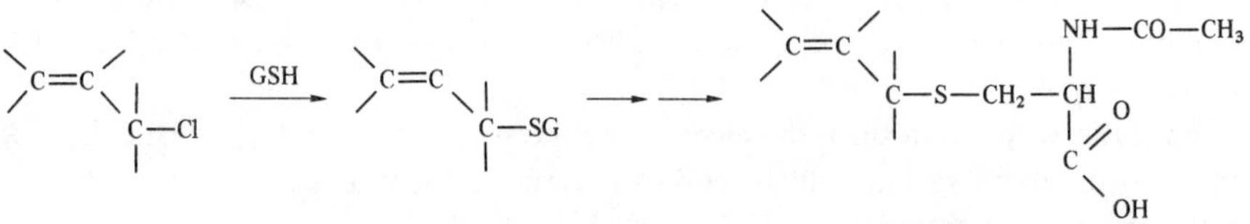

or, alternatively, to the formation of alkylating species:

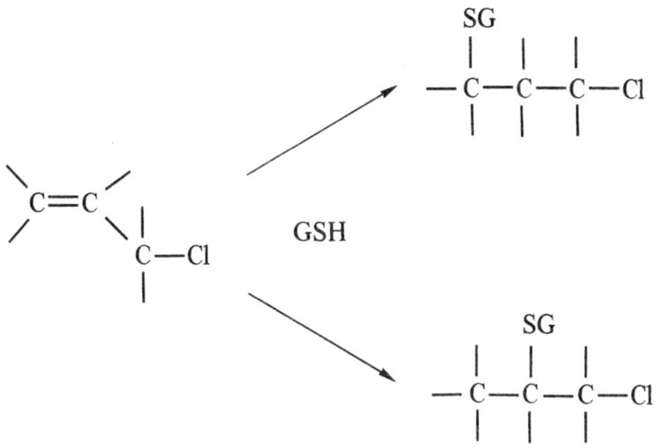

The (enzymic) conjugation with glutathione seems to be possible with chlorinated ethenes as well. If these bear two or more chlorine atoms, the resulting cysteine adducts may lead to another type of alkylating species or undergo further metabolic processing to reactive intermediates:

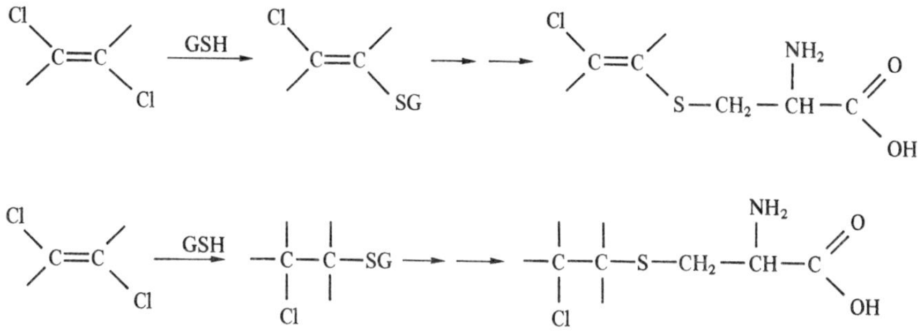

The complexity of the widely varying metabolic activation pathways, in conjunction with further transformation of the primary metabolites to less reactive molecules, and the large variety of potential covalent interactions of primary and secondary transformation products with macromolecules makes it difficult to predict precisely, from simple theoretical considerations, the actual pathways of biotransformation and thus the types of toxicity. Therefore, this exercise can only be regarded as a first step in the effort to evaluate metabolism and toxicity in intact organisms. The second step in this strategic concept must therefore be to study what happens with representative members of different groups of compounds under the influence of integrated mammalian xenobiotic metabolism.

III. COMPARATIVE METABOLISM OF CHLORINATED ETHENES

Epoxidation of a chlorinated ethene was first proposed for trichloroethylene as a preliminary step in a metabolic pathway explaining the formation of its major metabolites, trichloroethanol and trichloroacetic acid (Powell, 1945). A verification of the validity of this concept was provided for vinyl chloride by Hefner *et al.* (1975) and Green and Hathway (1975). These chlorinated epoxides may undergo a variety of secondary reactions, as outlined in figure 7.1: alkylation of nucleophilic sites of cellular macromolecules; conjugation with glutathione which may be a deactivation as well as an activation reaction if one (or two) chlorine residues persist in the β-carbon position to produce an alkylating moiety; hydrolysis to vicinal diols as very unstable intermediates; and — particularly important for this class of compounds — intramolecular rearrangement, with or without chlorine migration, to form chlorinated aldehydes or acetic acid chlorides, both with the capacity of reacting with nucleophilic sites of macromolecules although less potent than the original oxirane structures.

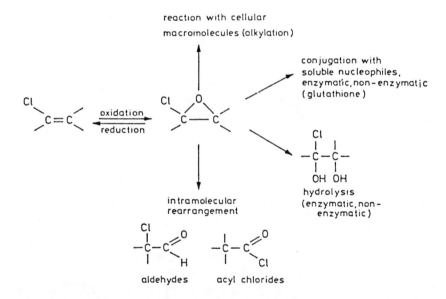

Figure 7.1 Possible reactions of epoxides of chlorinated ethenes (for explanations, see text)

Since these rearrangements may presumably play a significant role in the biotransformation, and may allow us to predict the major metabolites, we have synthesised all of them and investigated the rearrangement products in vitro under normal temperature conditions (Bonse *et al.*, 1975). As can be seen from figure 7.2, some of the products constitute acyl chlorides (tetra-, tri-, 1,1-dichloroethylene); others are chlorinated aldehydes (1,2-dichloroethylene cis and trans, vinyl chloride). Chlorine migration is observed with tetra- and 1,2-dichloroethylenes cis and trans.

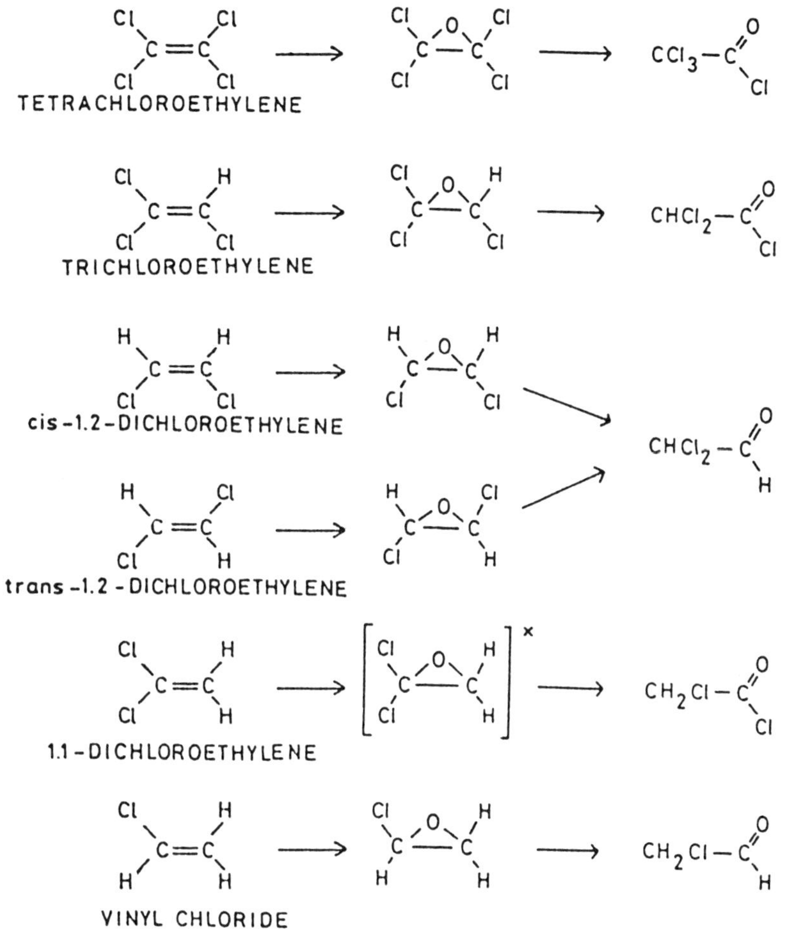

Figure 7.2 Rearrangement mechanisms of epoxides of chlorinated ethenes

The expected metabolites, as secondary products of these rearranged molecules, would in all cases be chlorinated acetic acids, resulting either from the hydrolysis of acyl chlorides or from oxidation of the chlorinated aldehydes by dehydrogenases. Other metabolites may stem from glutathione conjugates which form, in a well known sequence of metabolic processing, mercapturic acids or from epoxide hydrolysis and subsequent chlorine elimination.

We have investigated the metabolism of the higher chlorinated ethenes in the isolated perfused rat liver preparation (Bonse et al., 1975) and found — with a few exceptions to be discussed in more detail later — a confirmation of the hypothesised pathways. With tetrachloroethylene, the following metabolic sequence could be verified (identified metabolites underlined):

$$Cl_2C{=}CCl_2 \longrightarrow \left[\begin{array}{c} Cl_2C\underset{O}{\overset{O}{-}}CCl_2 \end{array}\right] \longrightarrow Cl_3C{-}C\underset{Cl}{\overset{O}{=}} \xrightarrow[-HCl]{H_2O} Cl_3C{-}C\underset{OH}{\overset{O}{=}}$$

$$\downarrow \qquad\qquad \left[Cl_3C{-}C\underset{Prot.}{\overset{O}{=}} \right] \xrightarrow{H_2O}$$

A part of the total amount of trichloroacetic acid could only be detected after strong acid hydrolysis of the rat liver tissue, indicating a covalent binding of the acyl chloride (and maybe the epoxide) to protein or other macromolecules.

With trichloroethylene, the expected dichloroacetic acid could not be identified under the conditions of exposure to concentrations which are in the range of normal occupational conditions (250 ppm in the gas phase of the perfusion medium). Instead, exclusively 1,1,1-trichloro compounds were found:

$$Cl_2C{=}CHCl \longrightarrow \left[Cl_2C\underset{O}{\overset{O}{-}}CHCl \right] \longrightarrow Cl_3C{-}C\underset{H}{\overset{O}{=}} \xrightarrow{ADH}$$

$$\nearrow \quad Cl_3C{-}C\underset{OH}{\overset{O}{=}}$$

$$\searrow \quad Cl_3C{-}CH_2{-}OH$$

$$\downarrow$$

$$Cl_3C{-}CH_2{-}O{-}gluc.$$

This implicates a pathway different from the thermal rearrangement of the epoxide to dichloroacetyl choride, namely, the formation of chloral (which in fact has been identified as such at low levels) which then is converted by dehydrogenases (ADH) either to trichloroacetic acid, or to trichloroethanol which is largely conjugated with glucuronic acid. The reasons for this discrepancy have been elucidated by further studies but will be dealt with on p. 171.

1,2-Dichloroethenes cis and trans form dichloroacetic acid and dichloroethanol which indicates the simple, expected pathways:

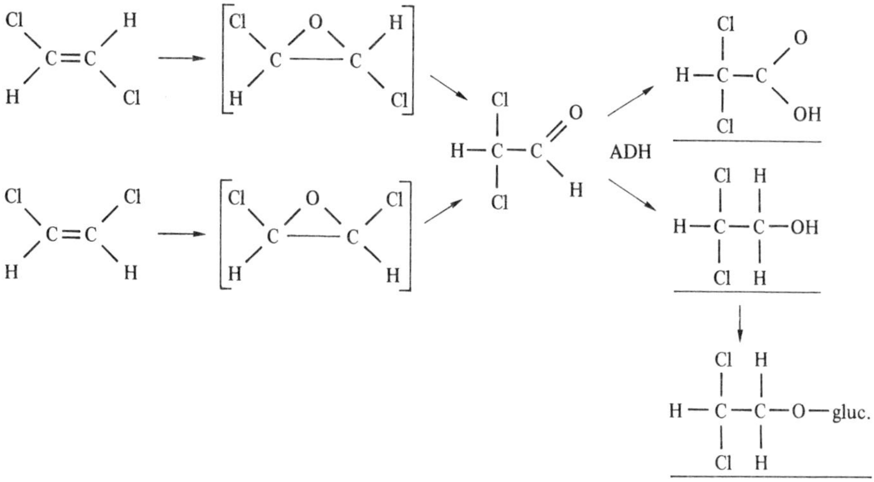

Vinylidene chloride was found to form monochloroacetic acid but no chloro-ethanol, which is in line with the prediction from the known rearrangement of the intermediate epoxide to monochloroacetic acid chloride:

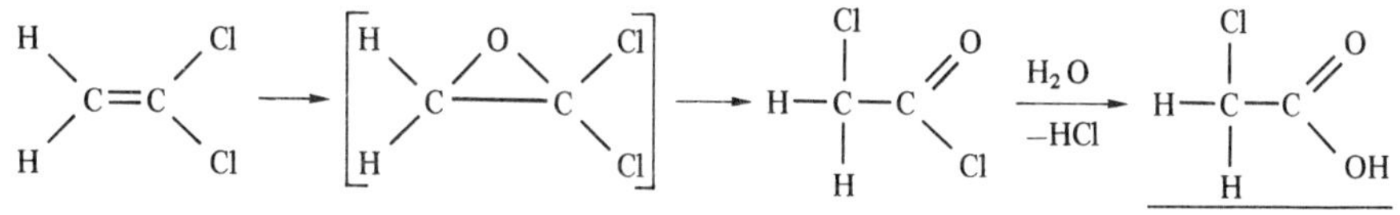

Other authors have identified thioethers formed in intact rats (Jones and Hathway, 1978; McKenna *et al.*, 1978), which has been confirmed by our own group (Reichert *et al.*, 1979), and indicates conjugation with glutathione:

In addition, we have identified an alternative pathway which indicates an attack of an electrophilic intermediate on phosphatidyl ethanolamine (Reichert *et al.*, 1979):

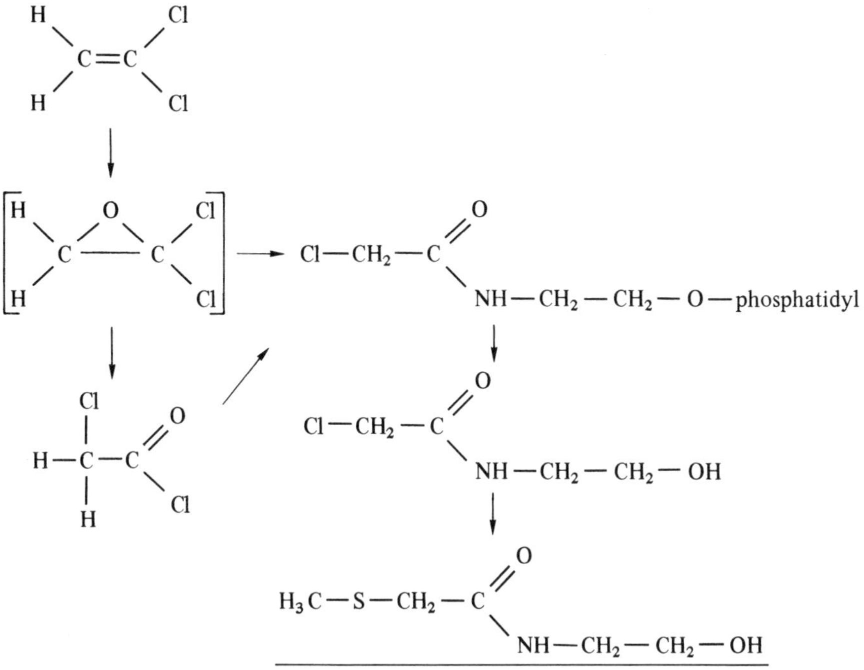

The new metabolite, methylthioacetylaminoethanol, is a subsequent fission product of an adduct with a phosphatidyl moiety which is the major component of lipid membranes. This may explain the mechanism underlying the strong hepatotoxic activity of vinylidene chloride-damage to membrane structures.

Vinyl chloride metabolism has been extensively studied by other groups and can easily be explained by primary formation of the epoxide, which itself, or after rearrangement to chloroacetaldehyde, will either alkylate nucleophilic sites of macromolecules or be conjugated with glutathione to form mercapturic acids, as shown in figure 7.3 (for review, see Henschler 1985).

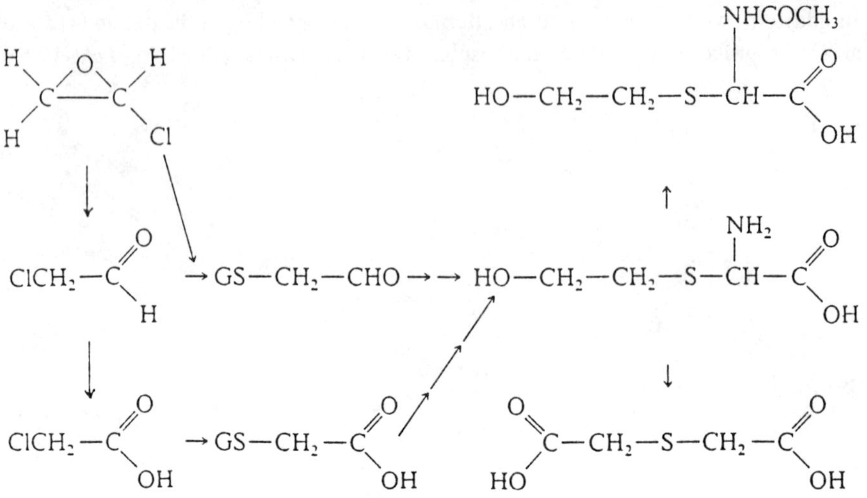

Figure 7.3 Scheme of vinyl chloride metabolism

Some DNA and RNA adducts were formed after exposure of rats to vinyl chloride (Laib and Bolt, 1977, 1978; Green and Hathway, 1978; Osterman-Golkar et al., 1977; Doerjer and Oesch, 1981):

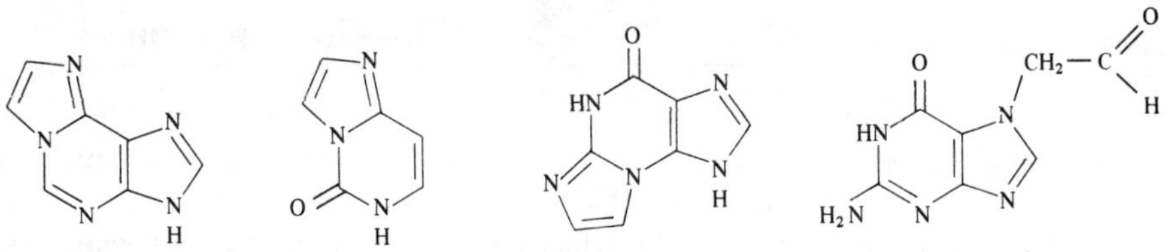

1-N^6-Ethenoadenine   3-N^6-Ethenocylosine N^6-3-Ethenoguanine   7,(2-Oxoethyl)guanine

The formation of the cyclised adducts has been explained by the following reaction sequence:

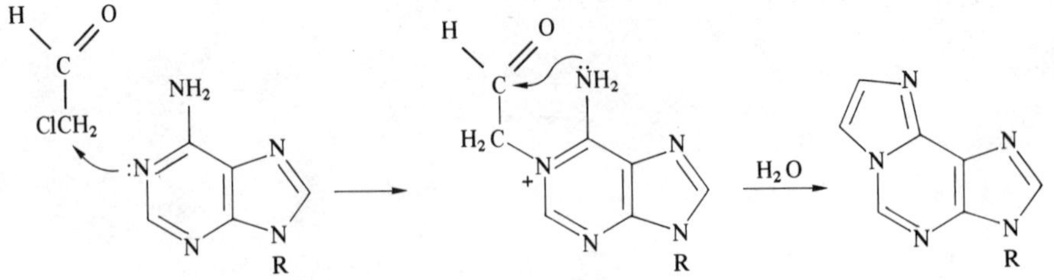

N^7-oxoethylguanine seems to be the major if not the only adduct formed under in vivo conditions (Laib et al., 1981).

In essence, the starting hypothesis of an oxidative attack by mono-oxygenation to form electrophilic epoxides, their rearrangement to compounds of lower energy state and the reaction of either epoxides or the rearrangement products or of both with low molecular weight nucleophiles, such as glutathione, has been found to account for the terminal (excretable) metabolites with one exception: trichloroethylene. This special case will be analysed in more detail on pp. 171-2.

IV. GENOTOXICITY: FIRST APPROACH

Although the study of bioactivation and degradation mechanisms indicates the formation of electrophilic intermediates, it does not provide information as to whether and to what extent these electrophiles will react with the genetic material as a first step in the carcinogenicity process. The quickest way to obtain this information is mutagenicity testing with primitive organisms. When we started our systematic experiments with the whole series of the 6-chlorinated ethenes, only vinyl chloride could be shown to exert mutagenic effects (Göthe et al., 1974; Barbin et al., 1975).

To cover all chloroethenes on a comparable basis, we selected a mutagenicity tester strain, E. coli K12, which was less sensitive to acute lethal effects than others (Greim et al., 1975). According to expectation, no compound exerted mutagenicity per se, that is without the addition of xenobiotic metabolising systems. After incubation with mouse liver microsomes, three of the compounds were definitely mutagenic (figure 7.4); vinyl chloride, vinylidene chloride and trichloroethylene, whereas tetra- and 1,2-dichloroethylenes were inactive in this sytem.

From these results, we extracted a tentative rule for the structure/activity relationships with regard to mutagenic potential, in view of the reactivity of the suspected electrophilic metabolites, the oxiranes (Henschler et al., 1976). This is shown in figure 7.5.

Symmetric chlorine substitution neutralises the electron withdrawing effect and renders the oxiranes relatively stable, which means less reactive; these are non-mutagenic (tetrachloroethylene, 1,2-dichloroethylenes cis and trans) whereas unsymmetric chlorine substitution results in an uneven electron distribution, thus inducing low stability (high reactivity), and provides mutagenic potential (vinyl chloride, vinylidene chloride, trichloroethylene). At the time when this tentative rule was established, it enjoyed satisfactory confirmation from the available carcinogenicity data: vinyl chloride was proven to be a carcinogen in animals (Maltoni and Lefemine, 1974) and humans (Creech and Johnson, 1974), vinylidene chloride was found to produce tumours in rodents (Lee et al., 1978) and trichloroethylene was claimed to induce hepatocellular carcinomas in one strain of mouse (NCI, 1976). Based on the information available at this stage, the rule could be taken as a valuable predictive tool.

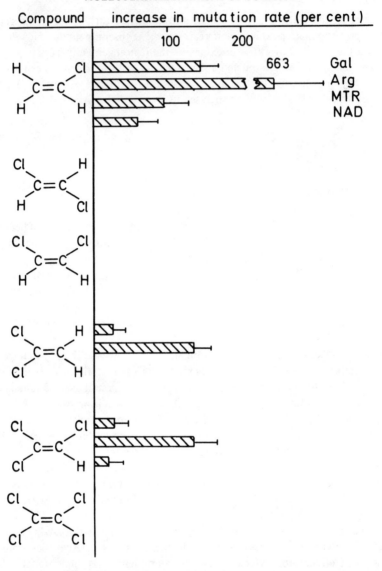

Figure 7.4 Mutagenicity testing of the 6 chlorinated ethenes in *E. coli* K12. The auxotrophic strain was tested, in a plate incorporation assay, for 3 backward mutations (galactose, arginine, NAD) and 1 forward mutation (methyltryptophan, MTR). 100% means the normal (back-) mutation rate. All compounds (at 1–10 mM) were pre-incubated in mouse liver microsome suspensions (5 mg protein/1.5 ml)

V. THE SPECIAL CASE: TRICHLOROETHYLENE

The early report of the carcinogenic potential of trichloroethylene (NCI, 1976) prompted concern from many directions because, for some years, the compound

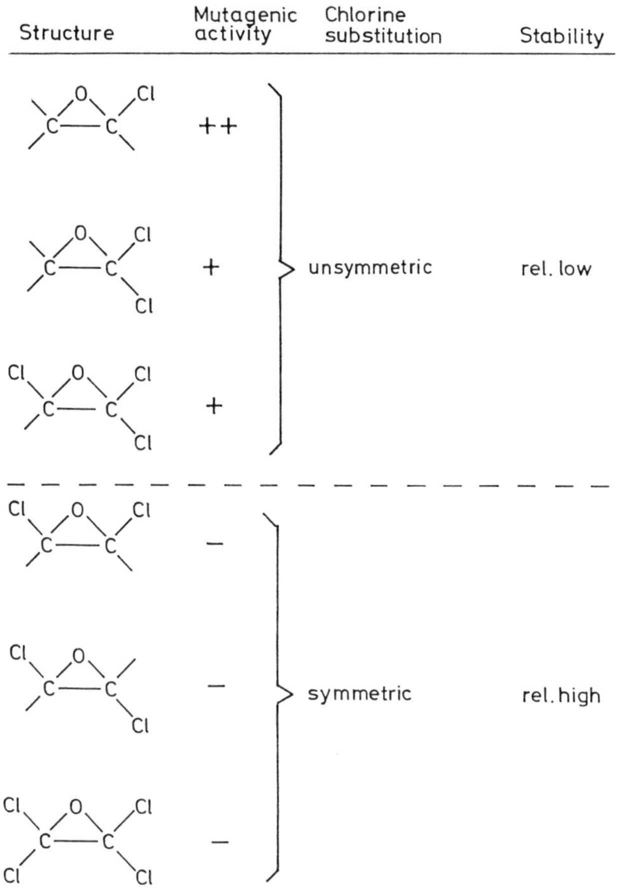

Structure	Mutagenic activity	Chlorine substitution	Stability
	++		
	+	unsymmetric	rel. low
	+		
	−		
	−	symmetric	rel. high
	−		

Figure 7.5 Tentative structure/activity relationship of the primary epoxide metabolites of chlorinated ethylenes, with regard to symmetry of substitution and relative stability (according to Henschler *et al.*, 1976)

had been used as a general anaesthetic particularly in England and, for several decades, as an analgesic in obstetrics without any evidence of a carcinogenic risk. Furthermore, worldwide large populations have been occupationally exposed to considerable concentrations, again producing no indication of a tumourigenic risk. In addition, it could soon be demonstrated that the samples of trichloroethylene used in the NCI study were of technical grade, and contained, according to a careful GC–MS analysis, besides several impurities, epichlorohydrin and epoxybutane which had been added as stabilisers; both compounds exerting a strong mutagenic activity (Henschler *et al.*, 1978). A re-evaluation of the above described tentative rule therefore seemed mandatory.

In doing so, we again started with a theoretical consideration of the chemical reactivity of the compounds and the possible biotransformation mechanisms. As outlined above, there is a discrepancy between the metabolites expected from the thermal rearrangement of trichlorooxirane (derivatives of dichloroacetyl chloride), and those found in *in vivo* experiments:

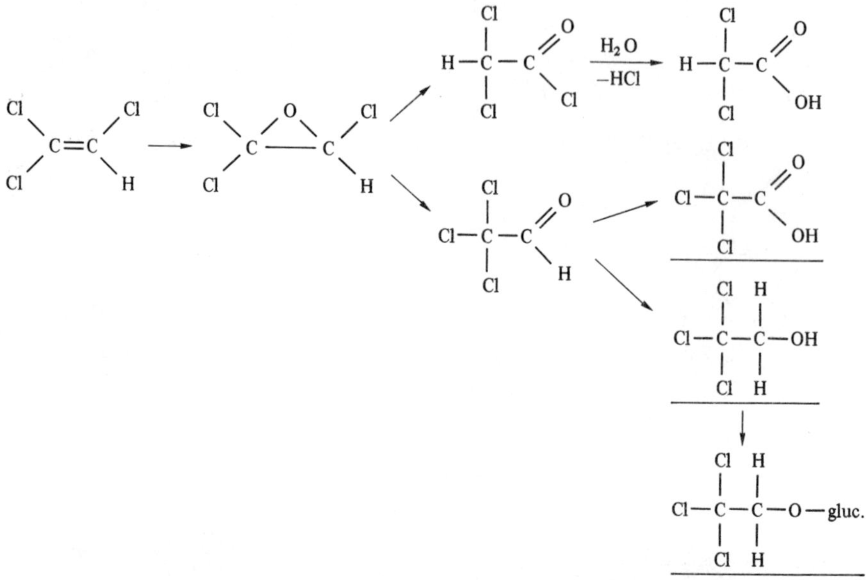

On a formal basis, there are in fact three possibilities of intramolecular rearrangement of trichlorooxirane: (1) simple hydride shift (which has low probability, McDonald and Schwab, 1963); (2) rearrangement without chlorine migration leading to dichloroacetyl chloride; and (3) with chlorine migration leading to 1,1,1-trichloroacetaldehyde (Bonse and Henschler, 1976). We have tried to analyse the molecular mechanisms of the last two possibilities making use of the existing knowledge that α-ketocarbonium ions should be expected as intermediates (Griesbaum *et al.*, 1975). There are two possibilities for C–O heterolysis as the initiating step:

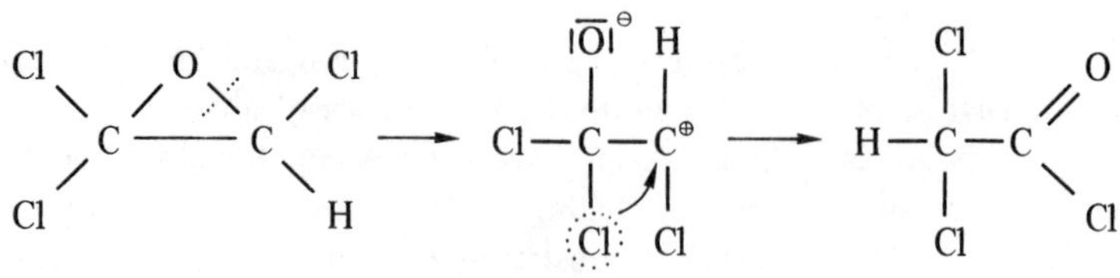

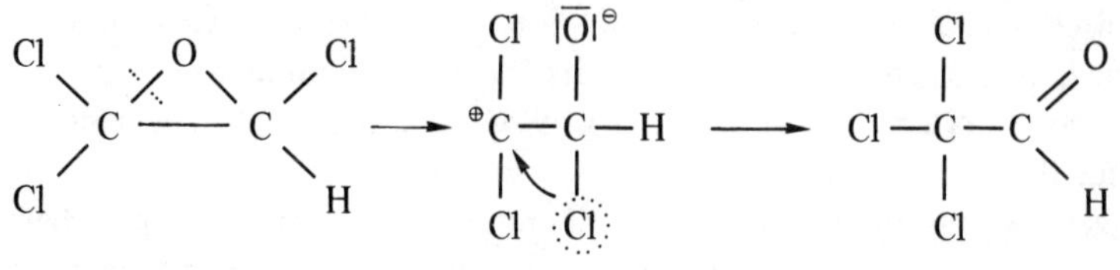

In case (A), the ionised carbon carries one chlorine residue, whereas in case (B) there are two chlorine substitutions resulting in the less stable form. Hence, (A) is preferred to (B) and dichloroacetyl chloride is found as the expected rearrangement product (see page 170). Route (B) can, however, be effected by means of Lewis acids, e.g. $FeCl_3$ (Bonse et al., 1975), whereby the attack of the Lewis acid is expected to occur at the nearest chlorine atom to the site of the steric opening of the oxirane and/or at the oxygen:

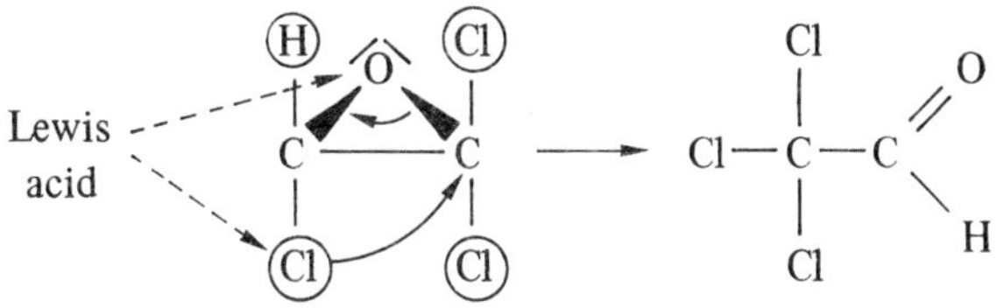

Such a mechanism is conceivable in the biological environment of the enzyme cytochrome P450, where the valency state of the haem iron changes, immediately after the transfer of the activated oxygen to the substrate, from II to III, thus accepting the property of a Lewis acid:

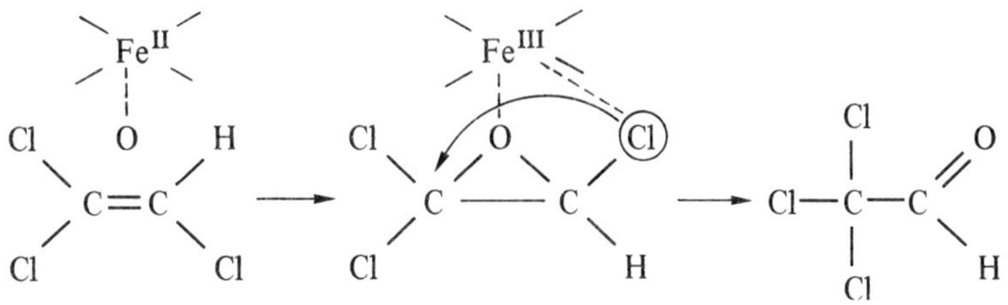

This would imply a two-step sequential reaction. An alternative one-step mechanism has been proposed (Miller and Guengerich, 1983), suggesting the formation of a complex of trichloroethylene ion or radical with iron of haem including activated oxygen:

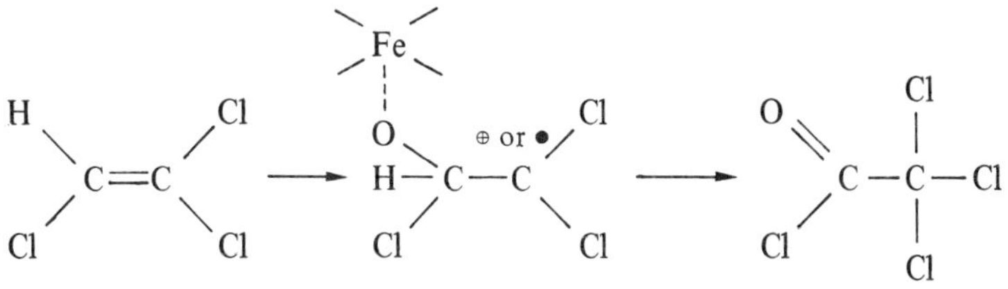

None of the suggested intermediates in this simultaneous mechanism has, however, been verified so far. The sequential, Lewis acid hypothesis has the advantage that the reactivity of the postulated intermediate, 2,2,3-trichlorooxirane, has been extensively studied, the results being compatible with biological findings (Henschler *et al.*, 1983). Trichlorooxirane decomposes rapidly in aqueous systems to form a variety of products, as outlined in figure 7.6. Both rearrangement products, chloral and dichloroacetic acid, are found, but in minor amounts only. The main products are carbon monoxide and formate, which indicates a C–C fission reaction occurring most probably at the stage of the vicinal diol formed through simple hydrolysis of the oxirane. Another ensuing product of this diol is, after three step dehydro-chlorination reactions, glyoxylic acid, a precursor of the potential final metabolite, oxalic acid (see page 173). No carbon monoxide formation has been found, how-ever, under *in vivo* metabolising conditions (Henschler and Hoos, 1982).

The following conclusion can be drawn from these data: mixed function oxidases form, from trichloroethylene, a highly reactive 2,2,3-trichlorooxirane which is effec-tiely transformed, immediately after its formation at the catalytic site of the oxidising enzyme, to the low or non-reactive chloral, before getting access to

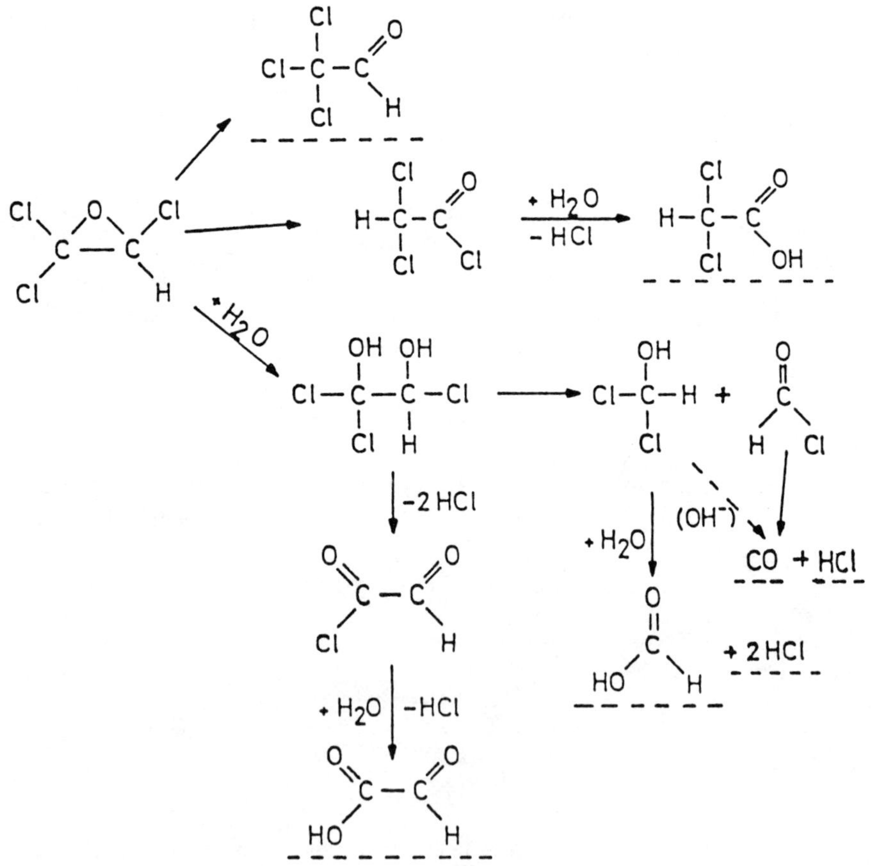

Figure 7.6   Decomposition of 2,2,3-trichlorooxirane in aqueous systems. Compounds analytic-ally identified and quantified are underlined.

the aqueous environment. Only after exaggerated doses, an overspill mechanism may come into play giving rise to the formation of dichloroacetic acid and other non-1,1,1-trichloro compounds (Hathway, 1980). In line with this is the finding that no noticeable binding of trichloroethylene metabolites to DNA or RNA of mouse liver can be verified (Parchman and Magee, 1980; Bergman, 1983), although distinct adducts with DNA can be found after reaction of 2,2,3-trichlorooxirane with model DNA *in vitro* (van Duuren and Banerjee, 1976). Thus, a very potent mechanism of deactivation of the oxirane intermediate, which protects the genetic structures from mutagenic effects, is operant in the case of trichloroethylene.

This hypothesis is supported by negative findings in many mutagenicity tests when highly purified samples of trichloroethylene, stabilised with non-mutagenic compounds, were used (for review, see Henschler 1985) and by the negative outcome of life-time inhalation studies in rats, mice and Syrian hamsters (Henschler *et al.*, 1980) and gavage studies in Swiss mice (Henschler *et al.*, 1984).

VI. TRICHLOROETHYLENE AND TETRACHLOROETHYLENE: AN ALTERNATIVE BIOACTIVATION MECHANISM

Recent carcinogenicity bioassays have shown that in male rats, with trichloroethylene as well as tetrachloroethylene under conditions of very high oral dosing by gavage an increase in renal tumours, benign as well as malignant, is observed (NTP, 1983, 1986). This surprising finding may be explained by a concomitant nephrotoxicity in these animals on the basis of which, through chronic inflammatory changes, tumour formation may be facilitated as an 'epigenetic' phenomenon. We have been able to offer, as a result of careful reinvestigations of the metabolism of the two chlorinated ethenes, an alternative mechanism which favours primary genotoxic events.

With trichloroethylene the formation of a mercapturic acid has been unequivocally demonstrated and this can only be explained by a primary conjugation of trichloroethylene with glutathione (Dekant *et al.*, 1986a):

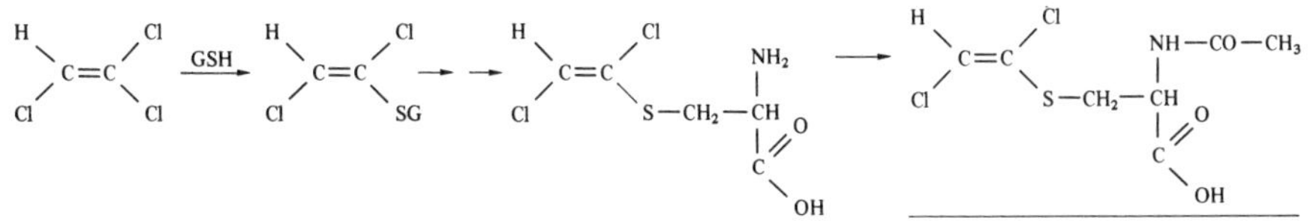

The mercapturic acid, N-acetyl-S-1,2-dichlorovinyl cysteine, is formed from the precursor, 1,2-dichlorovinyl cysteine, which itself is the product of well-known metabolic processing steps of glutathione adducts.

After dosing with tetrachloroethylene a similar mercapturic acid can be identified in rat urine, N-acetyl-S-1,1,2-trichlorovinyl cysteine (Dekant *et al.*, 1986b):

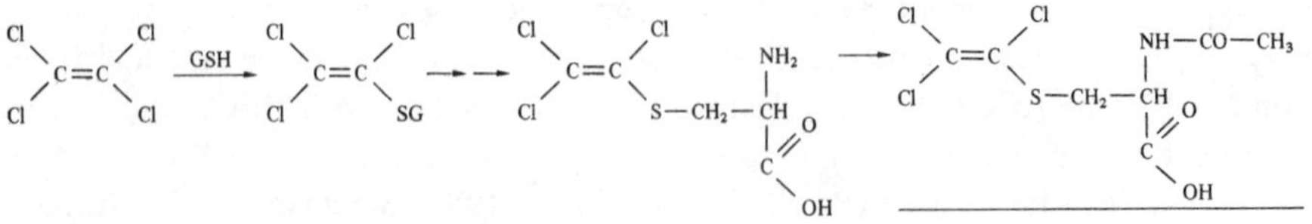

The di- or trichlorovinyl cysteines are well established nephrotoxic compounds (for review, see Anders and Pohl, 1985 and also chapter by Lock in this volume) and mutagens in *in vitro* systems (Green and Odum, 1985). The mutagenic potential may be attributed to products formed by an enzyme system which is specifically localised at high activity in the brush border of kidney tubular lining epithelial cells, β-lyase, which cleaves the sulphur from cysteine to produce the chlorovinyl residue:

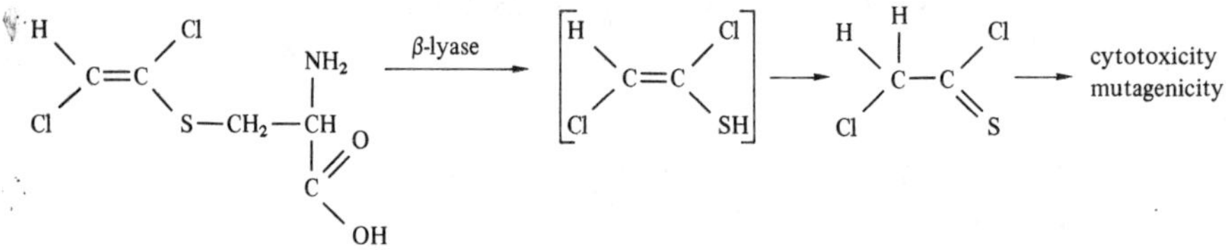

Although formed in small proportions only, these polychlorovinyl cysteine derivatives may well account for the cytotoxicity, as well as for the mutagenicity and carcinogenicity, in that the electrophilic sulphur bearing vinyl moiety may bind to DNA. Further experiments on DNA binding and identification of the adducts formed need to be performed to confirm or reject this hypothesis. Also, quantitative studies may well reveal that this minor pathway of metabolism will only be functional if very high doses lead to an overloading of the oxidative pathway involving the cytochrome P450 catalysed formation of the epoxides.

These recent studies have revealed a previously unexpected diversity of the metabolic conversion of these chlorinated ethenes. The complex pathways of activation and deactivation are outlined in figures 7.7 and 7.8.

VII. CHLORINATED ALLYLIC COMPOUNDS

The well established activation mechanism of chlorinated vinylic compounds, namely the oxidation of the double bond as outlined in pp. 158–65, has led some authors to the conclusion that this mechanism might also prevail with chlorinated propenes and butenes (van Duuren *et al.*, 1975). We have identified a completely different mechanism: direct alkylation through the formation of stable allylic cations (see page 175) via S_N1, S_N2 and S_N2' mechanisms (Eder *et al.*, 1980). The alkylating potency correlates well with direct mutagenicity in the Ames *S. typhimurium* test for a series of allylic compounds with various leaving groups, in which the strength of the leaving group determines the alkylating and likewise the direct

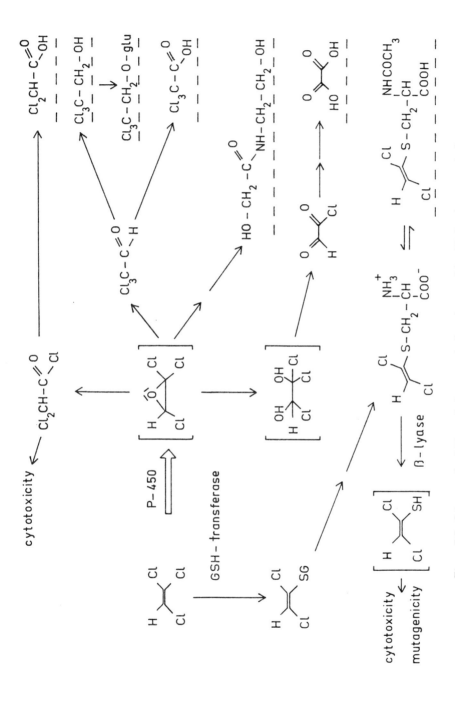

Figure 7.7 Scheme of trichloroethylene metabolism in rats. Identified urinary metabolites underlined

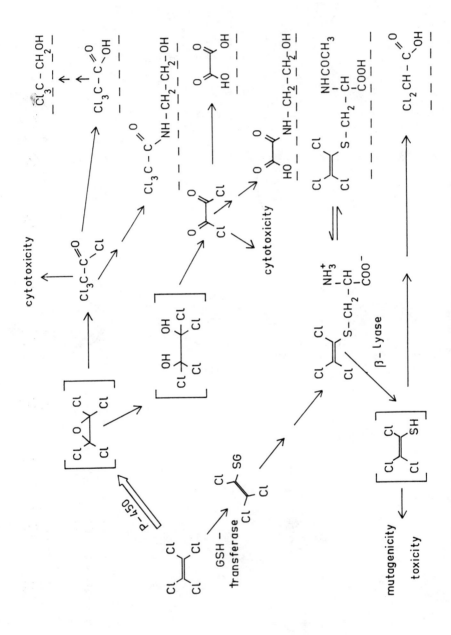

Figure 7.8 Scheme of tetrachloroethylene metabolism in rats. Identified urinary metabolites underlined

mutagenic activity: $OSO_3H > I > Br > Cl > NCS$. Benzyl chloride is one of the most potent direct mutagenic principles, due to a special resonance stabilisation of the benzyl cation in the aromatic system:

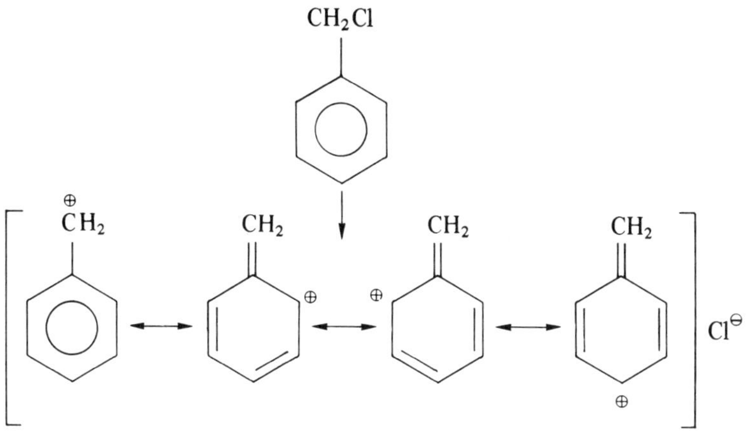

Further chlorine substitution in a chlorinated allylic moiety leads to an increase in the alkylating potential according to the strength of the negative inductive $(-I)$ effect (Neudecker *et al.*, 1980):

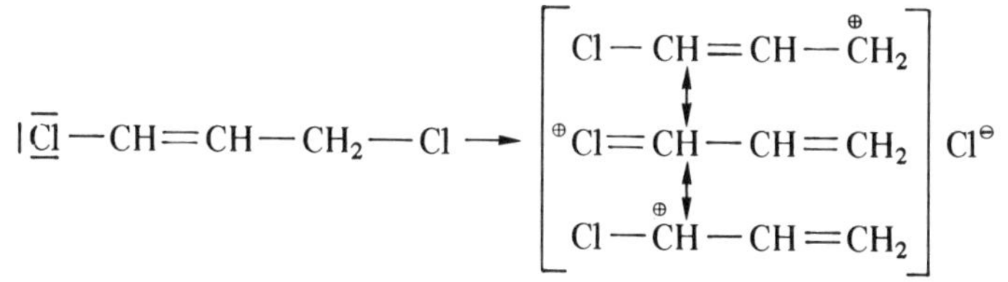

On the other hand, alkyl substitution in chlorinated allylic structures exerts a +M effect (hyperconjugation in the case of methyl) which again increases the polarity of the formed cation and thus also the alkylating potential:

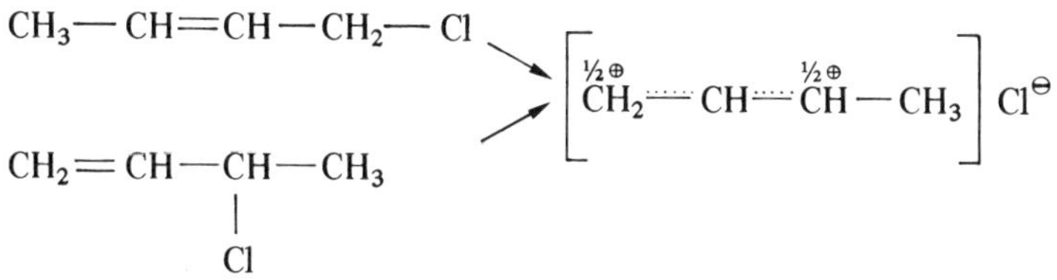

The systematic evaluation of structure/activity relationships in a series of 10 chlorine and/or methyl substituted derivatives of allyl chloride resulted in a very good correlation between alkylating potential and direct mutagenic activity (Eder *et al.*, 1982) as outlined in figure 7.9. One exception, 2,3-dichloro-1-propene can well be ex-

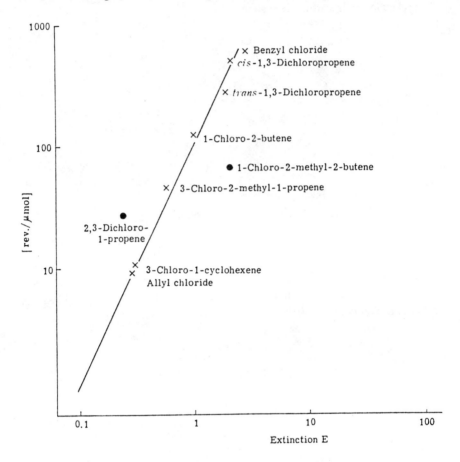

Figure 7.9   Correlation of alkylating and direct mutagenic potencies in a series of chlorinated propenes and butenes. Mutagenicity: Ames test with *S. typhimurium* TA100 (revertants per mole). Alkylating activity: nitrobenzyl-pyridine test.

plained by an interfering epoxidation either with ensuing intramolecular rearrangement, leading to the highly reactive and alkylating dichloroacetone:

or hydrolysis with subsequent hydrochloride elimination and formation of the like-wise very reactive chlorohydroxyacetone:

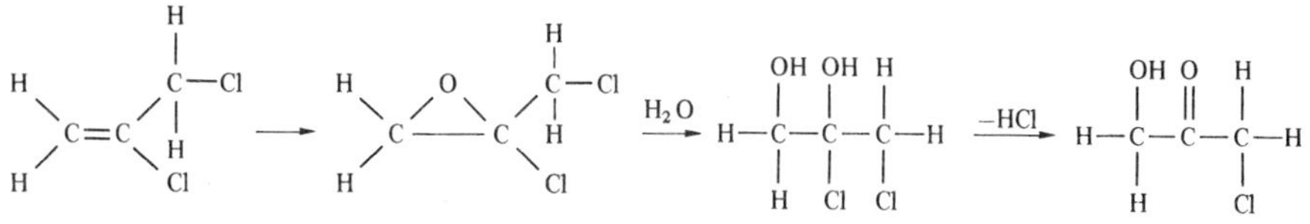

Allylic chlorinated compounds may also confer genotoxicity through another path-way which is in part non-enzymic: hydrolysis with formation of allylic alcohols which can easily be oxidised to α/β-unsaturated carbonyls:

$$CH_2{=}CH{-}CH_2{-}Cl \xrightarrow{H_2O} CH_2{=}CH{-}CH_2{-}OH \xrightarrow{ADH} CH_2{=}CH{-}C\overset{\displaystyle O}{\underset{\displaystyle H}{<}}$$

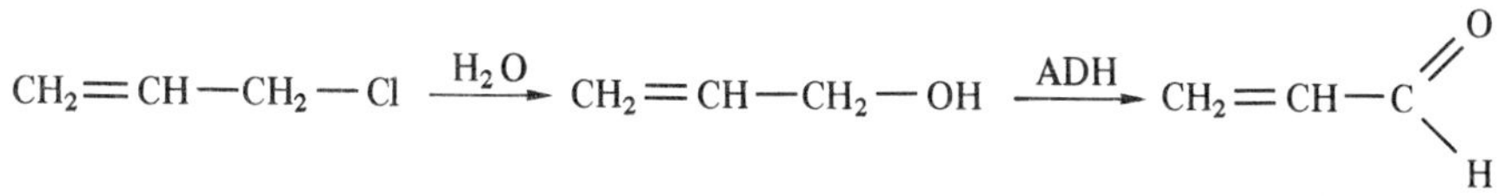

The acrolein derivatives formed are highly mutagenic (Lutz et al., 1982) and if substituted with a further chlorine atom in the C2-position the mutagenicity increases many fold (Rosen et al., 1980). The mechanism can be explained by an increase in polarity:

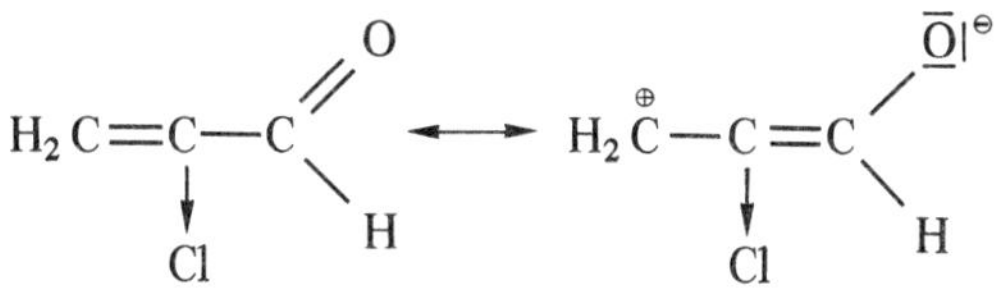

α/β-unsaturated carbonyls may react with nucleophilic sites in DNA either by Schiff's base formation, or by Michael addition. In the case of chlorinated acroleins, bifunctional agents, more complicated cross-linking reactions with DNA are con-ceivable.

More detailed studies on the reaction of all these electrophilic molecules with DNA are necessary to elucidate the final mechanisms of their genotoxicity. How-ever, knowledge of the basic reaction schemes will assist in identifying the DNA-adducts which may be subdivided into the following classes of expected products:

direct alkylation: $Base{-}O{-}CH_2{-}CH{=}CH_2$

$Base{-}\underset{\displaystyle |}{N}{-}CH_2{-}CH{=}CH_2$

indirect alkylation: $Base{-}O{-}CH_2{-}\underset{\displaystyle OH}{\underset{\displaystyle |}{CH}}{-}CH_2{-}Cl$
(through epoxide) $(-OH)$

hydrolysis and ensuing   Base $-$ O $-$ CH$_2$ $-$ CH$_2$ $-$ C $\diagdown$ $\overset{\displaystyle O}{\diagup}$
oxidation: (Michael addition)   H

Base $-$ N $=$ CH $-$ CH $=$ CH$_2$
(Schiff's base)

The activation mechanism of chlorinated allyl compounds through primary conjugation with glutathione, as outlined on page 172, has not yet been investigated but could easily constitute the major pathway and lead to DNA adducts different from those outlined above. Thus, a host of activation mechanisms must be considered in the chemically well defined class of chlorinated allylic hydrocarbons.

VIII. CONCLUDING REMARKS

Some decades ago the metabolism of chlorinated aliphatic compounds looked rather simple and the then known toxic effects, damage to parenchymal tissues and CNS, seemed to be explicable in terms of a few biochemical mechanisms. The disclosure of the mutagenic and carcinogenic properties which more recently have been observed with more and more members of this huge chemical family triggered more thorough mechanistic studies. The results of these, which represent just the first phase of the currently ongoing activities, may be characterised as an unexpectedly large variety of very different pathways of activation and molecular reactions with cellular constituents. At first glance, the scene seems to become rather more complicated than clear.

For the identification and evaluation of genotoxicity, however, the situation is much more favourable. Making proper use of the methods and approaches described in this paper, DNA-damage can easily be identified, and by establishing structure/activity relationships in closely related groups of chemicals and using knowledge of the carcinogenic activities of some member(s), one is in the position to make predictions of carcinogenic potentials and $-$ even more important for practical purposes $-$ to select certain compounds which are lacking a genotoxic potential.

Chlorinated aliphatics are many in number, enjoy large scale production and a broad scale of technical, medical or other applications and lead to considerably high exposure of widespread populations. In view of this practical significance as well as of the theoretical interest in this field, conventional strategies of collecting risk data in whole animal studies, particularly by long term carcinogenicity bioassays with great numbers of animals of different species, will not solve the problem within reasonable periods of time. To afford quicker risk assessment, alternative strategies such as have been described in this article may be useful and become even more important in view of the ever increasing number of compounds developed by chemical ingenuity and introduced for human use and into our environment.

REFERENCES

Anders, M. W. and Pohl, L. R. (1985). Halogenated alkanes. In: *Bioactivation of Foreign Compounds* (ed. M. W. Anders), Academic Press, New York, pp. 284–316

Barbin, A., Bresil, H., Croisy, A., Jacquignon, P., Malaveille, C. C., Montesano, R. and Bartsch, H. (1975). Liver microsome-mediated formation of alkylating agents from vinyl bromide and vinyl chloride. *Biochem. Biophys. Res. Commun.*, 67, 596

Bergman, K. (1983). Interactions of trichloroethylene with DNA in vitro and with RNA and DNA of various mouse tissues in vivo. *Arch. Toxicol.*, 54, 181–94

Bonse, G., Urban, T., Reichert, D. and Henschler, D. (1975). Chemical reactivity metabolic oxirane formation and biological reactivity of chlorinated ethylene in the isolated perfused liver preparation. *Biochem. Pharmacol.*, 24, 1829

Bonse, G. and Henschler, D. (1976). Chemical reactivity, biotransformation, and toxicity of polychlorinated aliphatic compounds. *CRC Crit. Rev. Toxicol.*, 5, 395

Creech, J. L. and Johnson, M. N. (1974). Angiosarcoma of liver in the manufacture of polyvinyl chloride. *J. Occup. Med.*, 16, 150

Dekant, W., Metzler, M. and Henschler, D. (1986a). Identification of S-1,2-dichloro-vinyl-N-acetyl-cysteine as a urinary metabolite of trichloroethylene: a possible explanation for its nephrocarcinogenicity in male rats. *Biochem. Pharmacol.*, 35, 2455–8

Dekant, W., Metzler, M. and Henschler, D. (1986b). Identification of S-1,1,2-tri-chlorovinyl-N-acetylcysteine as a urinary metabolite of tetrachloroethylene — bioactivation through glutathione conjugation may explain its nephrocarcino-genicity. *J. Biochem. Toxicol.*, 1, 57–72

Doerjer, G. and Oesch, F. (1981). Isolation of guanine derivatives in the reaction of chloroacetaldehyde with DNA in vitro. *J. Cancer Res. Clin. Oncol.*, 99, AZ4

Eder, E., Neudecker, T., Lutz, D. and Henschler, D. (1980). Mutagenic potential of allyl and allylic compounds. Structure–activity relationship as determined by alklyating and direct in vitro mutagenic properties. *Biochem. Pharmacol.*, 29, 993

Eder, E., Henschler, D. and Neudecker, T. (1982). Mutagenic properties of allylic and α,β-unsaturated compounds: Consideration of alkylating mechanisms. *Xenobiotica*, 12, 831–48

Göthe, R., Calleman, C. J., Ehrenberg, L. and Wachtmeister, C. A. (1974). Trapping with 3,4-dichlorobenzenethiol of reactive metabolites formed in vitro from the carcinogen vinyl chloride. *Ambio*, 3, 234

Green, T. and Hathway, D. E. (1975). The biological fate in rats of vinyl chloride in relation to its oncogenicity. *Chem.-Biol. Interact.*, 11, 545

Green, T. and Hathway, D. E. (1978). Interactions of vinyl chloride with rat liver DNA in vivo. *Chem.-Biol. Interact.*, 22, 211

Green, T. and Odum, J. (1985). Structure/activity studies of the nephrotoxic and mutagenic action of cysteine conjugates of chloro- and fluoroalkenes. *Chem.-Biol. Interact.*, 54, 15

Greim, H., Bonse, G., Radwan, Z., Reichert, D. and Henschler, D. (1975). Muta-genicity in vitro and potential carcinogenicity of chlorinated ethylenes as a function of metabolic oxirane formation. *Biochem. Pharmacol.*, 24, 2013

Griesbaum, G., Kibar, R. and Pfeffer, B. (1975). Synthese und Stabilität von 2,3-Dichloroxiranen. *Liebigs Ann. Chem.*, 2, 214

Hathway, D. E. (1980). Consideration of the evidence for mechanisms of 1,1,2-tri-chloroethylene metabolism, including new identification of its dichloroacetic acid and trichloroacetic metabolites in mice. *Cancer Lett.*, 8, 263

Hefner, R. E., Jr., Watanabe, P. G. and Gehring, P. J. (1975). Preliminary studies of the fate of inhaled vinyl chloride monomer (VCM) in rats. *Ann. N.Y. Acad. Sci.*, **246**, 135–48

Henschler, D., Bonse, G. and Greim, H. (1976). Carcinogenic potential of chlorinated ethylenes-tentative molecular rules. *Colloqu. Inst. Nat. Sante Rech. Med.*, **52**, 171–4

Henschler, D., Eder, E., Neudecker, T. and Metzler, M. (1977). Carcinogenicity of trichloroethylene: fact or artifact? *Arch. Toxicol.*, **37**, 233–6

Henschler, D., Romen, W., Elsässer, H. M., Reichert, D. and Radwan, Z. (1980). Carcinogenicity study of trichloroethylene by longterm inhalation in three animal species. *Arch. Toxicol.*, **43**, 237

Henschler, D. and Hoos, R. (1982). Metabolic activation and deactivation mechanisms of di-, tri-, and tetrachloroethylenes. In: *Biological Reactive Intermediates – II, Part A* (ed. R. Snyder *et al.*), Plenum Publishing Corporation, New York, pp. 659–66

Henschler, D., Bonse, G. and Dekant, W. (1983). Mechanisms of formation and reactions of electrophilic intermediates of halogenated olefins. *Proc. Int. Cancer Congr., 13th*, **1**, 175–83

Henschler, D., Elsässer, H. M., Romen, W. and Eder, E. (1984). Carcinogenicity study of trichloroethylene, with and without epoxide stabilisers, in mice. *J. Cancer Res. Clin. Oncol.*, **107**, 149–56

Henschler, D. (1985). Halogenated alkenes and alkynes. In: *Bioactivation of Foreign Compounds* (ed. M. W. Anders), Academic Press, New York, pp. 317–47

Jones, B. K. and Hathway, D. E. (1978). The biological fate of vinylidene chloride in rats. *Chem.-Biol. Interact.*, **20**, 27

Laib, R. J. and Bolt, H. M. (1977). Alkylation of RNA by vinyl chloride metabolites in vitro and in vivo: Formation of 1,N[6]-ethenoadenosine. *Toxicology*, **8**, 185

Laib, R. J. and Bolt, H. M. (1978). Formation of 2,N[4]-etheneocytidine moieties in RNA by vinyl chloride metabolites in vitro and in vivo. *Arch. Toxicol.*, **39**, 235

Laib, R. J., Gwinner, L. M. and Bolt, H. M. (1981). DNA alkylation by vinyl chloride metabolites: Etheno derivatives or 7-alkylation of guanine. *Chem.-Biol. Interact.*, **37**, 219

Lee, C. C., Bhanderi, J. C., Winston, J. M. and House, W. B. (1978). Carcinogenicity of vinyl chloride and vinylidene chloride. *J. Toxicol. Environ. Health*, **4**, 15

Lutz, D., Eder, E., Neudecker, T. and Henschler, D. (1982). Structure-mutagenicity relationship in α,β-unsaturated carbonylic compounds and their corresponding allylic alcohols. *Mutat. Res.*, **93**, 305–15

Maltoni, C. and Lefemine, G. (1974). Carcinogenicity bioassays of vinyl chloride. I. Research plans and early results. *Environ. Res.*, **7**, 387–405

McDonald, R. N. and Schwab, P. A. (1963). Molecular rearrangements II. Chlorine migrations in the epoxide-carbonyl rearrangement *J. Am. Chem. Soc.*, **85**, 4004–11

McKenna, M. I., Zempel, J. A., Madrid, E. O. and Braun, W. H. (1978). Metabolism and pharmacokinetic profile of vinylidene chloride in rats following oral administration. *Toxicol. appl. Pharmacol.*, **45**, 821

Miller, R. E. and Guengerich, F. P. (1983). Metabolism of trichloroethylene in isolated hepatocytes, microsomes, and reconstituted enzyme systems containing cytochrome P-450. *Cancer Res.*, **43**, 1145–52

NCI, National Cancer Institute (1976). Carcinogenesis bioassay of trichloroethylene. *Tech. Report Ser. No. 2*, DHEW Publ. No. 76–802, Washington, DC

NTP, National Toxicology Program (1983). Carcinogenesis Bioassay Technical Reports, Update No. 2

NTP National Toxicology Program Technical Report Series (1986) No. 311, Tetrachlorethylene. US Dept. Health & Human Services, *NIH – Publ.* No. 86–2567

Neudecker, T., Lutz, D., Eder, E. and Henschler, D. (1980). Structure–activity relationship in halogen and alkyl-substituted allyl and allylic compounds: Correlation of alkylating and mutagenic properties. *Biochem. Pharmacol.*, **29**, 2611

Osterman-Golkar, S., Hultmark, D., Segerbäck, D., Calleman, C. J., Gäthe, R. and Ehrenberg, C. A. (1977). Alkylation of DNA and proteins in mice exposed in vinyl chloride. *Biochem. Biophys. Res. Commun.*, **63**, 259

Parchman, L. G. and Magee, P. (1980). Production of $^{14}CO_2$ from trichloroethylene in rats and mice and a possible interaction of a trichloroethylene metabolite with DNA, *19th Society of Toxicology Meet. 1980 Abstr. No. 153*

Powell, J. F. (1945). Trichloroethylene: Absorption, elimination and metabolism. *Brit. J. ind. Med.*, **2**, 142

Reichert, D., Werner, H. W., Metzler, M. and Henschler, D. (1979). Molecular mechanism of 1,1-dichloroethylene toxicity: Excreted metabolites reveal different pathways of reactive intermediates. *Arch. Toxicol.*, **42**, 159

Rosen, J. D., Segall, Y. and Casida, J. E. (1980). Mutagenic potency of haloacroleins and related compounds. *Mutat. Res.*, **78**, 113–19

van Duuren, B. L. (1975). On the possible mechanism of carcinogenic action of vinyl chloride. *Ann. New York Acad. Sci.*, **246**, 258–67

van Duuren, B. L., Goldschmidt, B. M. and Seidman, J. (1975). Carcinogenicity activity of di- and trifunctional α-chloroethers and of 1,4-dichlorobutene-2 in ICR/ha Swiss mice. *Cancer Res.*, **35**, 2553

van Duuren, B. L. and Banerjee, S. (1976). Covalent interaction of metabolites of the carcinogen trichloroethylene in rat hepatic microsomes. *Cancer Res.*, **36**, 2419–22

Viola, P. W., Bigotti, A. and Caputo, A. (1971). Oncogenic response of rat skin, lungs, and bones to vinyl chloride. *Cancer Res.*, **31**, 517–19

8

Drugs as Suicide Substrates of Cytochrome P–450

F. De Matteis

INTRODUCTION

Interest in the toxicological significance of drug metabolism has increased enormously in the last 30 years, stimulated by the growing awareness that many potentially toxic chemicals are present in our environment; and also by the appreciation that drug-metabolising reactions are not only important in detoxifying chemicals, but in many cases can actually initiate toxic responses, by converting inert drugs into biologically reactive derivatives. The enzymes that have attracted most attention in this respect are the haemoproteins of the cytochrome P-450 group which are present in the endoplasmic reticulum of the hepatocyte and of other cell types and also in the membranes of certain other organelles. Extensive work carried out in many laboratories has established that this group of cytochromes is in fact a complex family of related but not identical haemoproteins. All members of this family contain, as the active prosthetic group, protohaem (the iron complex of protoporphyrin IX) bound to the apoprotein moiety through a thiolate anion (S^-) linkage from a cysteine residue, and all show the property of binding a lipid-like substrate in close proximity to the prosthetic group where the other reactant, molecular oxygen, can also bind in order to be activated (White and Coon, 1980). Oxygen activation is achieved by a stepwise addition of electrons (two per catalytic cycle) and these are donated by the satellite components of the electron transport system of the membrane (the flavoproteins and cytochrome b_5) and are presumably channelled through the apoprotein and the sulphur ligand on to the iron of the haem prosthetic group (figure 8.1). The net result is in most cases mono-oxygenation, that is the insertion of an atom of oxygen into the lipid-like substrate, so that this is rendered more reactive chemically and can therefore undergo a second reaction, this time a reaction of conjugation for example with glutathione, leading to increased

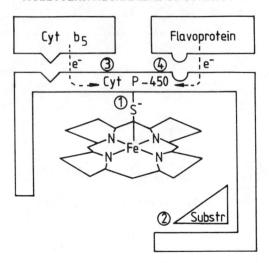

Figure 8.1 A simplified scheme of the interactions between the apoprotein of cytochrome P-450 and its haem prosthetic group (1); the substrate to be metabolised (2); the satellite components of the electron transport system [cytochrome b_5 (3) and the flavoprotein NADPH-cytochrome P-450 reductase (4)]. Potential sites of covalent binding of reactive metabolites are numbered and will be discussed in the text

water solubility and facilitated excretion. Instead of its more usual role of mono-oxygenase, with certain drugs cytochrome P-450 can function as a reductase or as an oxidase: in these cases no oxygen insertion reaction takes place, but only electron transfer between the haemoprotein and the drug substrate.

The active site of cytochrome P-450

There is now overwhelming evidence for the existence, even in the same organ, for example the liver, of many distinct types of cytochrome P-450 which differ in the properties of their respective protein moieties (or apoproteins). These are products of different genes and account for the differences in molecular weight, amino acid composition and antigenicity of the various cytochrome P-450 enzymes (Lu and West, 1980). The apoprotein provides the site of interaction with other components of the electron transport system (for example the ϵ amino group of a lysine residue, is apparently involved in electron transfer from NADPH-cytochrome P-450 reductase (Bernhardt *et al.*, 1984)) and there is evidence that different cytochromes P-450 may vary in their ability to interact and bind cytochrome b_5 (Miki *et al.*, 1980). But the most interesting variations between different apoproteins are probably those concerning the organisation of the active centre, particularly the binding site for the drug-substrate, which must be responsible for the different substrate specificities of the various enzymes. Although we are still very ignorant of the exact topology of the cytochrome P-450 active site, nevertheless the hypothetical model schematically represented in figure 8.2 will be briefly considered,

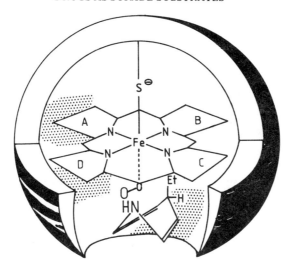

Figure 8.2 Schematic representation of cytochrome P-450 active centre, showing (a) the absolute orientation of the haem plane (with respect to its two axial ligands, O_2 and mercaptide, see Ortiz de Montellano *et al.*, 1983a); and (b) possible importance of the geometry of binding of a suicide substrate in determining which pyrrole nitrogen is alkylated. The orientation shown here for the dihydropyridine will make the nitrogen of pyrrole ring C more accessible to the reactive 4-ethyl group; with other cytochrome P-450 enzymes the drug may be bound in different orientations (see additional shaded areas) and pyrrole rings A or D may then be ethylated (see text)

in order to facilitate our understanding of the stereochemistry of covalent adduct formation, which will be discussed later in this paper. The first point to be made concerns the orientation of the haem plane in cytochrome P-450, with respect to each of its two axial ligands, oxygen and the mercaptide anion. Because of the asymmetric arrangement of the two vinyl substituents of the pyrrole rings A and B and of the two propionate substituents of rings C and D (figure 8.6), the two faces of the haem plane are not superimposable and can therefore be distinguished. Only one side of the haem plane, that bearing the oxygen ligand, will be facing the drug to be mono-oxygenated; this side will therefore be more likely to suffer attack from any resulting electrophilic metabolite. The second point to be discussed in connection with the model illustrated in figure 8.2 concerns the disposition of the drug to be metabolised with respect to the central iron of haem (and its bound oxygen) and also with respect to potential nucleophilic centres at the active site, such as the four pyrrole nitrogen atoms of the prosthetic group. It is probable that, whatever the cytochrome, a drug substrate will be bound in such a way as to ensure close proximity to the iron-bound oxygen of that particular region of the molecule where oxygen insertion (or electron transfer) is required. Nevertheless there may be slight differences according to the drug substrate or according to the particular enzyme in the exact geometry of drug binding, so that if a reactive metabolite is formed, a different pyrrole ring may be more accessible to attack than the other three. This is particularly true for drugs which suffer metabolic fragmentation (as the dihydro-pyridines) since in this case the reactive fragment may well be generated at some distance from the central iron of haem, as will be discussed later.

Suicide inactivation of cytochrome P-450

Once a metabolite of cytochrome P-450 has been produced, its ultimate fate depends largely on its chemical reactivity. Two extreme cases can be distinguished (figure 8.3): (1) the metabolite may possess only a low to medium chemical reactivity: it will then be sufficiently stable to leave the enzyme active site either to undergo conjugation (a detoxification pathway) or to interact covalently with nucleophilic centres elsewhere in the cell or in other organs and tissues (sometimes initiating in this way 'distal' toxic effects), but with the cytochrome P-450 enzyme remaining fully active and ready to start a new catalytic cycle. (2) Alternatively, the metabolite may be so extremely reactive that it will seek out and bind covalently nucleophilic centres within the cytochrome itself, modifying either the apoprotein or the haem prosthetic group and leading to irreversible inactivation of the enzyme. It is this second pathway, involving irreversible inactivation, that will be discussed in this paper. Although several alternative terminologies have been proposed (among these 'mechanism-based enzyme inhibitors' or 'enzyme-activated inhibitors')

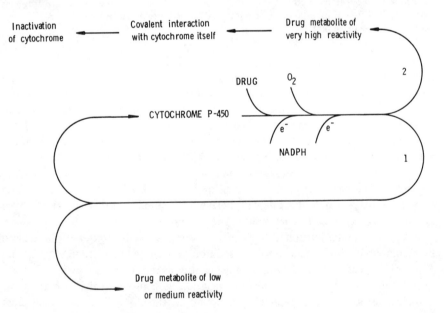

Figure 8.3 The two possible fates of a reactive metabolite produced by cytochrome P-450: only pathway 2 will be expected to lead to irreversible inactivation of the enzyme. In pathway 1 the metabolic product is instead released, leaving behind a fully active cytochrome, ready to initiate a new catalytic cycle

the expression suicide inhibitors (or substrates), though not ideal, is widely used in the field and will be followed here. It has the advantage of laying proper emphasis on the crucial features of the inactivation reaction (that is those of a self-inflicted, irreversible inhibition); and also the advantage of excluding other types of enzyme-activated inhibitors (for example those produced from isosafrole) where the metabolite acts as a high affinity ligand for the haem of cytochrome P-450, but the interaction is reversible and the inhibitor can be displaced by suitable displacer molecules (see for example Elcombe *et al.*, 1975).

With most suicide substrates inactivation of the enzyme is not observed invariably at every catalytic cycle, but every so often, for example, on average every 10 or 100 catalytic events, depending on the suicide substrate under study. Both pathways 1 and 2 (illustrated in figure 8.3) will therefore operate for the same drug in a given statistical ratio. This is either because the enzyme can metabolise the same drug in more than one way, only one of these leading to the suicidal event (Loosemore *et al.*, 1981), or because the potentially lethal, very reactive metabolite may also, to some extent, diffuse away and react with other target molecules.

As already mentioned, cytochrome P-450 can metabolise drugs by acting as a mono-oxygenase, as an oxidase or as a reductase. Suicide substrates are known for all three types of enzymatic mechanism and covalent modification of either the apoprotein moiety or of the haem prosthetic group is involved in all cases (table 8.1), even though the precise site and consequences of this interaction may vary. Compounds which attack preferentially the apocytochrome will first be discussed; then those where covalent modification of the haem prosthetic group is the main mechanism. A comprehensive coverage of all known suicide substrates of cytochrome P-450 is not possible in the relatively small space available for this article, but the reader is referred to the following papers for a discussion of carbon tetrachloride, cyclopropylamines and phenylhydrazine (De Groot and Haas, 1981; Hanzlik and Tullman, 1982; Macdonald *et al.*, 1982; Jonen *et al.*, 1982), the three classes of suicide inhibitors which will not be considered here.

COVALENT MODIFICATION OF THE APOPROTEIN

There are several possible sites within the polypeptide chain where covalent modification may be expected to produce inactivation of the enzyme and some of these are schematically illustrated in figure 8.1. Any bulky metabolite irreversibly bound in a region of the active centre intended for substrate binding may interfere with uptake of the substrate or with its proper orientation with respect to haem and result in loss of activity. Likewise enzyme inactivation might be expected from modifications of the apoprotein which lead to loss of affinity for the haem prosthetic group or in altered electron flow from the flavoprotein NADPH-cytochrome P-450 reductase, or from cytochrome b_5 (at least for those cytochromes P-450 which are strictly dependent on cytochrome b_5 for catalytic activity). Evidence for some of these selective mechanisms of inactivation is provided by the study of thionosulphur compounds and chloramphenicol, as will now be discussed.

Table 8.1 Modes of Enzymic Action of Cytochrome P-450 and Examples of Corresponding Suicide Substrates. (A self-inflicted irreversible inactivation of the enzyme is observed in all cases through covalent binding of the reactive metabolite (to either haem or the apoprotein moiety) as outlined at the bottom of the table)

Mode of enzyme action	Type of reaction	Suicide substrate	Main target within the cytochrome
Mono-oxygenase	Oxygen addition to: (1) a sulphur centre (2) an unsaturated side chain	Carbon disulphide Ethylene Acetylene	Apoprotein Haem
Oxidase	Electron transfer (from the drug to the haem)	3,5-diethoxycarbonyl-1,4-dihydrocollidine	Haem
Reductase	Electron transfer (from the haem to the drug)	Carbon tetrachloride	Haem

Drug ——→ Electrophilic reagent ——→ Covalent adduct ——→ Nucleophilic centres within the cytochrome

Carbon disulphide and other thionosulphur compounds

Among the first compounds to be suspected and partially characterised as a suicide substrate of cytochrome P-450 was carbon disulphide (CS_2). When CS_2 was administered to rats there was a reduction in the activity of drug-metabolising enzymes in the liver (Freundt and Dreher, 1969) and a loss of spectrally demonstrable cytochrome P-450 (Bond and De Matteis, 1969). These changes were too rapid in onset to be accounted for by inhibition of cytochrome P-450 synthesis and too persistent for a direct effect of CS_2 itself, since this chemical is volatile and rapidly eliminated. Rats pretreated with phenobarbitone in order to raise the concentration and activity of liver cytochrome P-450 showed a much greater loss of the cytochrome on dosing with CS_2 and this was accompanied, several hours later, by accumulation of water in the liver and by extensive hydropic degenerative changes in the centrilobular hepatocytes. CS_2 was partially metabolised in the intact rat to CO_2 and phenobarbitone pretreatment not only enhanced the loss of cytochrome P-450 due to CS_2, but also increased the extent of its oxidative conversion to CO_2. In addition, CS_2 caused destruction of cytochrome P-450 *in vitro* when liver microsomes were incubated aerobically in its presence, but NADPH, the cofactor essential for metabolism of drugs by cytochrome P-450, was required for maximal destruction. These findings all suggested that CS_2 required metabolic activation for its effects on cytochrome P-450 and therefore pointed to a suicidal mechanism of enzyme inactivation. Also, since a marked loss of spectrally demonstrable cytochrome P-450 was seen without an early loss of microsomal haem, the primary target was likely to be the apoprotein moiety (Bond and De Matteis, 1969; De Matteis and Seawright, 1973). More direct evidence for a suicidal mechanism involving covalent modification of the apoprotein of cytochrome P-450 is discussed below.

The conversion of CS_2 to CO_2 can be considered as a two-stage oxidative desulphuration reaction (figure 8.4) analogous to other desulphurations where either

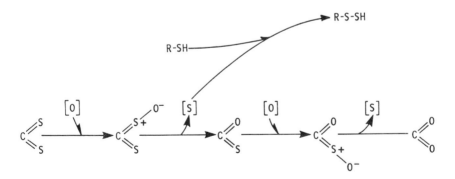

Figure 8.4 Oxidative metabolism of carbon disulphide involving two subsequent steps of mono-oxygenation, production of intermediary oxides and elimination of reactive elemental sulphur. The latter becomes bound to cysteine residues (R-SH) in apocytochrome P-450, generating hydrodisulphides (R-S-SH) (after De Matteis and Seawright, 1973; Catignani and Neal, 1975; and Neal, 1980). Note that both reactive sulphurs can give rise to hydrodisulphides

P=S is converted to P=O or C=S to C=O. By analogy with the mechanism proposed by Ptashne *et al.* (1971) for the oxidative metabolism of parathion, CS_2 could give rise to reactive elemental sulphur in two stages through the mono-oxygenated intermediate COS, and the reactive sulphur may become bound to the cytochrome, thereby inactivating it (De Matteis and Seawright, 1973; Dalvi *et al.*, 1974). Support for this mechanism is provided by the following evidence.

(1) When liver microsomes were incubated with either ^{14}C or ^{35}S-labelled CS_2 in the presence of NADPH (under conditions, that is, where loss of cytochrome P-450 was observed) labelled sulphur became covalently bound to the microsomes (Dalvi *et al.*, 1974; De Matteis, 1974). Although some increase in ^{14}C binding (over the values obtained on incubation without NADPH) was also observed, possibly indicating the production of reactive oxides (figure 8.4), the binding of ^{35}S was greatly in excess of that of ^{14}C, so sulphur itself must have become bound. (2) Other thionosulphur compounds (containing either P=S or C=S), among these parathion, were found to cause loss of cytochrome P-450 when added to microsomal incubations together with NADPH, whereas the oxygen containing analogues were all inactive. Similar effects have been reported *in vivo* (Neal, 1980). (3) Metabolic transfer of ^{35}S from parathion to microsomal proteins has also been demonstrated (Nakatsugawa *et al.*, 1968; Poore and Neal, 1972), and in experiments conducted with purified cytochrome P-450 and a reconstituted drug-metabolising system, the cytochrome was found to be the predominant (if not the only) protein attacked by atomic sulphur. Similar conclusions were reached using a partially purified antibody to the major phenobarbital-inducible form of rat liver cytochrome P-450 (Kamataki and Neal, 1976). (4) With both parathion and CS_2 nearly half of the total sulphur bound to the microsomes could be released as thiocyanate on incubation with cyanide (Catignani and Neal, 1975; Kamataki and Neal, 1976), suggesting that a portion of the sulphur liberated during the oxidative desulphuration of these compounds reacts with the sulphydryl groups of cysteine residues in the cytochrome P-450 apoprotein to form hydrodisulphides (figure 8.4).

The exact stoichiometry of binding (that is, how many atoms of sulphur are bound per molecule of inactivated enzyme) and the mechanism by which modification of the apoprotein leads to loss of activity have not yet been fully elucidated. In addition to the sulphur present as hydrodisulphides, evidence for sulphur binding to at least three other, as yet unidentified, amino acids has been obtained (Neal, 1980). As only a portion of the bound sulphur appears to be responsible for inactivation (Morelli and Nakatsugawa, 1978), it is still possible that a single critical amino acid is involved. The cysteine residue that donates a thiolate ligand to haem could be such a critical site (site 1, figure 8.1). This possibility is attractive as it would provide an explanation for the loss of the characteristic spectrum, for the increase in cytochrome P-420 that has been reported in some studies and also for the reduced affinity of the apoprotein for haem (see below). However this would probably require the reactive metabolite to migrate across the plane of haem (as it would be produced on the opposite side of the haem plane) and it is uncertain whether this would be possible.

Loss of microsomal haem has also been reported after administration of CS_2 and other sulphur-containing suicide substrates of cytochrome P-450 (Bond and De Matteis, 1969; Halpert et al., 1980; Menard et al., 1979). Accelerated conversion of haem to bile pigments and stimulation of the liver haem oxygenase activity have been described after CS_2 and other sulphur-containing chemicals, and also redistribution of haem radioactivity in the fractions of the liver homogenate, with apparent migration of haem from the microsomes into the cell sap. It was therefore suggested that the lesion of the apoprotein may result in reduced affinity for the prosthetic group and this in turn produces a dissociation of haem from the apoprotein and an increase in the size of the free (regulatory) haem pool, which will then act as a stimulus for induction of haem oxygenase (Järvisalo et al., 1978). In agreement with this interpretation Kikuchi et al. (1982) have reported that CS_2 increases considerably the haem saturation of tryptophan pyrrolase, an enzyme which has been widely used as an indicator of the concentration of free (exchangeable) haem in the liver. However with parathion and spironolactone the haem loss is probably too rapid to be accounted for by such an indirect mechanism and direct destruction of haem by reactive metabolites of these compounds has also been considered (Halpert et al., 1980; Menard et al., 1979) as a contributing factor.

Chloramphenicol as a suicide substrate of cytochrome P-450

The mechanism of cytochrome P-450 inactivation by chloramphenicol is more clearly defined, as in this case neither the amount nor the structure of the haem prosthetic group are affected and the loss of enzymic function is entirely due to covalent modification of important amino acid residues in the apoprotein moiety.

Following the demonstration that chloramphenicol inhibits drug-metabolism, when given in vivo to both humans and experimental animals (Adams et al., 1977) experiments with isolated liver microsomes showed that the antibiotic could inactivate drug-metabolism in vitro and was converted to reactive metabolites which bind covalently to microsomal protein (Pohl et al., 1978). More recent studies have been conducted with a reconstituted mono-oxygenase system, employing cytochrome P-450 purified from the liver microsomes of phenobarbital-treated rats. The inactivation of cytochrome P-450 was accompanied by the covalent binding of ^{14}C equivalent to 1.5 nmol of the labelled drug per nmol of cytochrome P-450, without any loss of either the characteristic carbon monoxide spectrum of cytochrome P-450 or of its haem prosthetic group, the latter as determined by the pyridine haemochrome reaction (Halpert and Neal, 1980). Several classes of covalent adducts were detected. (1) Approximately 50% of the bound chloramphenicol was present as an adduct of chloramphenicol oxamic acid to the ε-amino group of lysine residues in cytochrome P-450 (Halpert, 1981, 1982). The structure of this adduct is compatible with an oxamyl chloride reactive intermediate (Pohl et al., 1978; Pohl and Krishna, 1978), produced by cytochrome P-450 during the oxidative dechlorination of chloramphenicol (figure 8.5). (2) The remainder of the bound material was somewhat labile, appeared to originate from an active metabolite

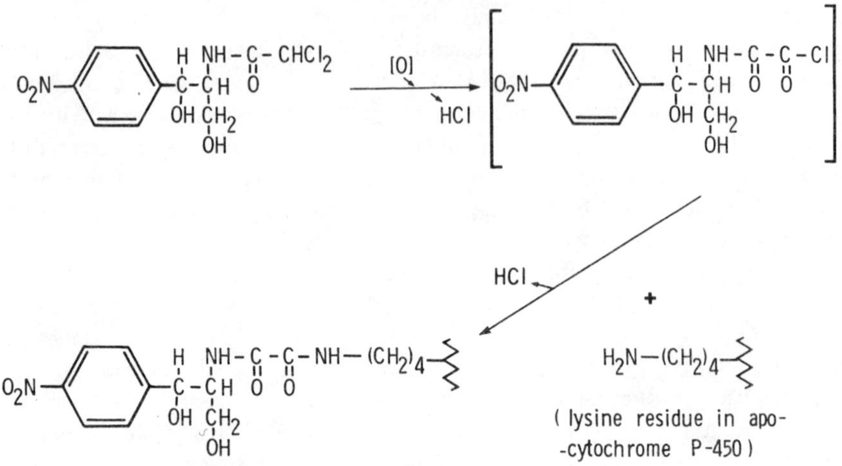

Figure 8.5 Oxidative dechlorination of chloramphenicol leading to an oxamyl chloride reactive intermediate, which then binds the ε-amino group of a lysine residue in apocytochrome P-450 (after Pohl *et al.*, 1978 and Halpert, 1981)

different from the acyl chloride responsible for the lysine adduct and, although not yet fully characterised, may also to some extent have been responsible for the inactivation of cytochrome P-450. This is suggested by the observation that on prolonged incubation of the inhibited cytochrome, some labile adduct was spontaneously liberated as oxalic acid and the cytochrome partially reactivated (Halpert, 1982).

After cytochrome P-450 had been inactivated by chloramphenicol, the NADPH-supported metabolism of drugs was strongly inhibited, as was the ability of NADPH to reduce the cytochrome. In contrast, cytochrome P-450 was still fully reduceable by a chemical reductant, dithionite, and its ability to oxidise drugs was unaffected when iodosobenzene was used to support drug metabolism. This agent acts as an oxygen donor *via* the haem of cytochrome P-450, but the normal reductive steps involved in the activation of molecular oxygen are not necessary. These findings all pointed to an inability of the chloramphenicol-inhibited cytochrome P-450 to undergo reduction by the flavoprotein NADPH-cytochrome P-450 reductase (Halpert *et al.*, 1985), either because of a steric hindrance by a covalently bound metabolite of the interaction of the cytochrome with the flavoprotein; or because some crucial amino acid residues have been modified, which are normally involved in the actual transfer of electrons to the haem iron (see site 4, figure 8.1). Other investigators have shown that lysine residues in the phenobarbital-inducible cytochrome P-450 may be important for the metabolism of at least some drug substrates (Kunz and Richter, 1983) and a lysine residue in the major phenobarbital-inducible cytochrome P-450 of the rabbit may be involved in electrostatic interactions with the reductase (Bernhardt *et al.*, 1984). As the main sites of covalent binding of chloramphenicol metabolites are, in fact, lysine residues of the apo-protein, these may well account for the main feature of the inhibitory process, namely the inability of the haem prosthetic group to be reduced by NADPH. More work is however necessary to elucidate the exact mechanisms involved in the enzyme inhibition and to clarify some additional properties of the inhibited enzyme, such as the inability to develop a type I spectral change with benzphetamine (Halpert *et al.*, 1985), for which no explanation has so far been offered.

COVALENT MODIFICATION OF THE HAEM PROSTHETIC GROUP

The best known examples of suicide substrates which modify sleectively the haem prosthetic group of cytochrome P-450, 2-allyl-2-isopropyl acetamide (AIA) and 3,5-diethoxycarbonyl-1,4-dihydrocollidine (DDC) (see figure 8.6), have both been extensively investigated in the past for their ability to produced in animals two types of hepatic porphyria, which are experimental models for certain hereditary human porphyrias. Both drugs are powerful inducers of the rate-limiting enzyme of haem biosynthesis, 5-aminolaevulinate synthase (ALA-S) and have therefore been used to stimulate ALA-S in the liver so that the induction of ALA-S and its regu lation by haem, the end product of the pathway, could be studied in detail. Abnor-mal porphyrins have been isolated from the liver of animals made porphyric with either drug and these have been characterised more recently as products of the

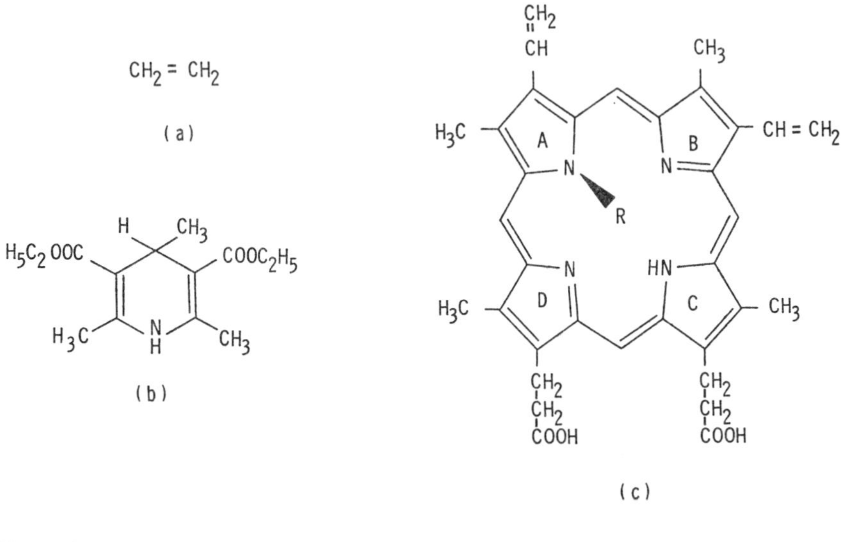

Figure 8.6 Structure of ethylene (a), 3,5-diethoxycarbonyl-1,4-dihydrocollidine, DDC (b) and general formula for the N-alkyl protoporphyrins (c) isolated from liver after treatment with these drugs. Four structural isomers of the porphyrins are possible, depending on which pyrrole nitrogen is alkylated, the isomer shown being N_A, where ring A is *N*-alkylated. The alkyl group present on the pyrrole nitrogen, as well as the isomeric type of the porphyrin vary according to the drug (see table 8.2)

suicidal inactivation of liver cytochrome P-450, arising in both cases from alkylation of the haem prosthetic group. It is now apparent that the irreversible modification of the structure of haem leads in both cases to a loss of its function as a feedback regulator of ALA-S; as a consequence ALA-S is markedly induced and hepatic porphyria becomes established. However, there are important differences between the two drugs in the mechanism of suicidal inactivation of the haem prosthetic group and in the biological properties of the corresponding alkylated porphyrins. This too has important implications for the biochemical picture of the resulting hepatic porphyria, as will now be discussed.

Effect of unsaturated compounds

The evidence that AIA inactivates liver cytochrome P-450 by modifying its haem prosthetic group can be traced back to important early findings in the literature, the significance of which has only recently become apparent. Schwartz and Ikeda (1955) had described a discoloration of the liver of rats and rabbits given AIA (or the related drug Sedormid) and had extracted certain ill-defined porphyrins or green pigments responsible for this abnormal colour. Wada *et al.* (1968) subsequently showed that the drug caused a decrease in the concentration of cytochrome P-450 in the liver and, shortly after, conclusive evidence was obtained for a rapid destruction of pre-existing cytochrome P-450 (rather than inhibition of its synthesis) with conversion of its haem prosthetic group in the Schwartz's green pigments (De Matteis, 1971). Additional findings (De Matteis, 1971; Levin *et al.*, 1973) suggested that metabolic activation of the allylic double bond was required before the haem moiety of the cytochrome could be converted into the abnormal porphyrins or green pigments. These results have since been extended to unsaturated compounds containing the acetylenic grouping ($-C\equiv C-$), including the ethynyl-substituted steroids which are components of the contraceptive pill (White and Muller-Eberhard, 1977; White, 1978, 1981). A comprehensive list of the unsaturated drugs capable of destroying cytochrome P-450 can be found in two recent reviews (Ortiz de Montellano and Correia, 1983; White, 1984). Since the simplest alkene and alkyne, ethylene and acetylene themselves, are active, it is clear that an unsaturated bond between two carbons is the only structural requirement for the effect. However, in more complex molecules, additional structural features are also important (see White, 1984), particularly the position of the unsaturated bond, which must be sterically unhindered for metabolic activation, that is, must be present at a terminal location in an accessible side chain. With both alkenes and alkynes the cytochrome inducible by phenobarbital was found to be particularly susceptible to drug-dependent destruction of the haem prosthetic group, probably because it could bind and activate the unsaturated drugs most effectively (Unseld and De Matteis, 1978; White, 1981).

Some of these early findings had therefore suggested that the unsaturated drugs may be acting as suicide substrates of cytochrome P-450. Conclusive evidence for this mechanism of inactivation has been obtained more recently by showing in reconstituted systems, containing purified cytochrome P-450, that the inactivation of the enzyme is in fact irreversible and does require metabolism of the unsaturated drug (Loosemore et al., 1981; Ortiz de Montellano and Mico, 1981). In addition, two recent findings have clarified the basic molecular mechanism for inactivation and opened the way to further important mechanistic studies in this field. Firstly, Ortiz de Montellano and collaborators (1978, 1979) have demonstrated that the green pigments represent a 1:1 covalent adduct of an activated drug (of either the alkene or alkyne series) and the protoporphyrin IX nucleus of haem. Secondly, it has been shown from the electronic absorption spectrum of the purified green pigments and from their titration behaviour with acid that the site of alkylation is one of the pyrrole nitrogens of the tetrapyrrolic system (De Matteis and Cantoni, 1979; De Matteis et al., 1980a). It can therefore be concluded that the unsaturated drugs are metabolised by cytochrome P-450 into reactive derivatives which alkylate one of the pyrrole nitrogens of its prosthetic group, giving rise to N-monosubstituted protoporphyrin derivatives (figure 8.6).

The detailed mechanism of the N-alkylation reaction and the nature of the alkylating metabolite have been explored by isolating and characterising the products of prosthetic haem alkylation. As originally reported for AIA the green pigments produced by treatment with unsaturated compounds of both classes contain iron in their native form (White, 1981; De Matteis et al., 1982a; White, 1982), are therefore present in the liver as alkylated haems, but readily lose iron on exposure to acids during the work-up procedure to generate the corresponding N-alkylated porphyrins. After such an acidic work-up procedure N-(2-hydroxyethyl) protoporphyrin IX has been isolated from the liver of rats given ethylene (De Matteis et al., 1980b) and N-(2-oxopropyl) protoporphyrin IX after propyne (Ortiz de Montellano and Kunze, 1981), suggesting a reactive mono-oxygenated intermediate for both drugs. Reactive cyclic oxides, oxiranes and oxirenes, are known to arise from mono-oxygenation of unsaturated double and triple carbon–carbon bonds, respectively; however the involvement of an oxirane (or epoxide) intermediate in haem alkylation by olefines has been specifically excluded (Ortiz de Montellano et al., 1983b). Instead Ortiz de Montellano et al. (1983b) propose that activation of an olefin may involve the formation of a common precursor, which can then proceed by independent mechanisms to either haem alkylation or to epoxide formation; the active haem alkylating species may be an acyclic mono-oxygenated intermediate (figure 8.7). Extensive and elegant nmr investigations by Ortiz de Montellano and collaborators have also established that the four pyrrole nitrogens of the haem prosthetic group of cytochrome P-450 are not randomly alkylated: on the contrary, different nitrogens are specifically substituted, depending on the suicide substrate under study; for example the nitrogen of pyrrole ring A after propyne and that of pyrrole ring D after ethylene (Ortiz de Montellano and Kunze, 1981; Ortiz de Montellano et al., 1981b). The main stages of cytochrome P-450 haem alkylation which have so far been discussed are summarised schematically in figure 8.7, where the native, iron-containing green pigment has been drawn as bearing the alkyl group on one pyrrole nitrogen, to account for the selectivity of pyrrole nitrogen alkylation, briefly referred to above. However, the exact structure of the native iron-containing alkylated pigment is still awaiting elucidation.

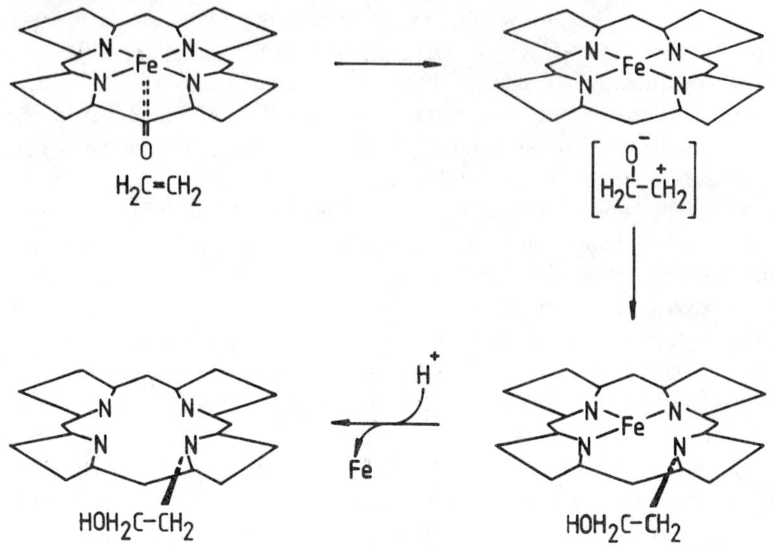

Figure 8.7 Possible reactions involved in activation of ethylene by cytochrome P-450 and consequent alkylation of one of its pyrrole nitrogens. (1) Ethylene is bound close to the active oxygen species in the cytochrome P-450 active centre; (2) a reactive intermediate, such as that proposed by Ortiz de Montellano *et al.*, 1983b, is formed; (3) this alkylates one of the pyrrole nitrogens, giving rise to an alkylated haem; (4) the latter then loses iron on exposure to strong acids to generate the corresponding porphyrin

Unsaturated drugs, belonging to either the alkene or the alkyne series, stimulate the formation of the intermediates of the pathway of haem biosynthesis in the liver and cause experimental hepatic porphyria. Several lines of evidence suggest that the drug-dependent destruction of liver haem may be responsible for porphyria by removing the feedback control that haem exercises on its own synthesis, through the following intermediary steps (De Matteis, 1978; Correia *et al.*, 1979). (1) The *N*-alkylated haem produced at the active site of cytochrome P-450, migrates from the endoplasmic reticulum into the cytosol, leaving empty the haem binding site of the apo-cytochrome. (2) Free haem can then be taken up to reconstitute a functional holo-cytochrome and to undergo fresh *N*-alkylation reaction. (3) The concentration of free haem will then decrease in the cell, leading to a reduced feedback control on ALA-S, so that this enzyme (the rate-limiting step in the pathway) will become stimulated. (4) The supply of haem precursors will then exceed the capacity of the subsequent enzymes of the pathway, and a mixture of porphyrins and early precursors will accumulate, giving rise to the biochemical picture of porphyria. It should be noticed that in this variety of porphyria the activity of ferrochelatase (the enzyme which converts protoporphyrin to haem) is not inhibited, so that the accumulation of protoporphyrin is only modest. An explanation for this is provided by the finding that the green pigments produced by unsaturated drugs – or at least the unsaturated drugs so far examined (De Matteis *et al.*, 1980d) – do not inhibit ferrochelatase. This contrasts with the effects of DDC and griseofulvin, where a powerful inhibitor of ferrochelatase is produced from haem alkylation, as will be discussed below.

Effect of substituted dihydropyridines and of griseofulvin

Griseofulvin, an antibiotic extensively used for treatment of fungal infections, and a substituted 4-methyl dihydropyridine, 3,5-diethoxycarbonyl-1,4-dihydrocollidine (DDC) both cause hepatic protoporphyria in mice (Cole and Marks, 1984) a porphyria, that is, characterised by marked accumulation of protoporphyrin and by pronounced inhibition of the enzyme ferrochelatase. Wada *et al.* (1968) had reported a loss of liver cytochrome P-450 after feeding either drug to mice and subsequent isotopic experiments had also shown that DDC increased liver haem degradation, with conversion of prelabelled haem into unidentified products (Abbritti and De Matteis, 1973). It is only recently that the product of cytochrome P-450 haem degradation has been isolated, identified, and shown to be responsible for the characteristic inhibition of ferrochelatase present in protoporphyria. Tephly *et al.* (1979) isolated from the liver of mice treated with DDC a modified porphyrin with strong inhibitory activity towards ferrochelatase *in vitro*. The inhibitor exhibited the characteristic spectrum of a *N*-alkylated protoporphyrin, but the spectral properties of its dication and zinc-complex derivatives suggested that the substituent on the pyrrole nitrogen must be small in size (De Matteis and Gibbs, 1980). Identification of the inhibitory porphyrin as *N*-methylprotoporphyrin was obtained by comparing its chromatographic, absorption and mass spectral properties with those of authentic synthetic *N*-methyl protoporphyrin, and by showing that the synthetic porphyrin was, like the biological product, a powerful inhibitor of ferrochelatase (De Matteis *et al.*, 1980b). Similar conclusions as to the identity of the DDC inhibitory porphyrin were reached by Tephly *et al.* (1981) and by Ortiz de Montellano *et al.* (1981d), who also resolved and fully characterised by nmr studies all four structural isomers of *N*-methyl protoporphyrin.

Subsequent work has shown that the methyl group on the pyrrole nitrogen of *N*-methyl protoporphyrin originates from the 4-methyl group of DDC itself, which is donated to haem during the process of haem alkylation. Mice given 3,5-diethoxycarbonyl-4-ethyl-1,4-dihydro-2,6-dimethyl pyridine (this analogue differs from DDC in having an ethyl group in the 4 position, instead of a methyl group) produced *N*-ethyl protoporphrin, instead of *N*-methyl protoporphyrin (De Matteis *et al.*, 1981). In addition, when the deuterated 4-CD$_3$-dihydropyridine was administered to mice, *N*-CD$_3$ protoporphyrin was isolated from their livers (De Matteis *et al.*, 1981), providing conclusive evidence that the 4-methyl group of DDC is transferred intact, that is with its full complement of hydrogen atoms. The conclusion that the *N*-alkyl group originates from the drug, also reached by Tephly *et al.* (1981) and by Ortiz de Montellano *et al.* (1981a), is entirely compatible with the finding (Cole *et al.*, 1981) that the inhibition of ferrochelatase caused *in vivo* by different dihydropyridines depends on the presence and nature of their 4-alkyl substituent.

The following evidence suggests that the porphyrin nucleus of the dihydro-pyridine green pigments originates from the haem prosthetic group of cytochrome P-450. (1) In isolated hepatocytes incubated with a series of DDC analogues (dif-fering in the size of the 4-alkyl group from a methyl to a propyl residue), the amount of alkylated porphyrin produced could be correlated with the loss of cyto-chrome P-450 (De Matteis *et al.*, 1982b). (2) The specific activity of the liver haem pool, from which the N-alkyl porphyrin originates, decayed with a half-life (De Matteis *et al.*, 1982b) similar to that reported by Levin and Kuntzmann (1969) for the rapidly turning over component of cytochrome P-450. (3) Destruction of cytochrome P-450 could also be demonstrated *in vitro* when isolated microsomes were incubated with a 4-alkyl dihydropyridine *in vitro*, provided that NADPH was also present (Augusto *et al.*, 1982; De Matteis *et al.*, 1982b; Marks *et al.*, 1985). (4) Finally, these N-alkylated porphyrins exhibited chiral properties (De Matteis *et al.*, 1982c; Ortiz de Montellano *et al.*, 1983a) and their structural isomerism was found to depend on the type of cytochrome P-450 predominating in the cell (De Matteis *et al.*, 1983); these findings, which also suggest that the alkylation of haem takes place at the cytochrome P-450 active site, will be considered in more detail later, in the discussion of the stereochemistry of prosthetic haem alkylation.

It can therefore be concluded that DDC and other 4-alkyl dihydropyridines inactivate cytochrome P-450 by alkylating one pyrrole nitrogen of the prosthetic haem group. However, unlike the unsaturated drugs which become themselves bound (together with an oxygen atom) to the pyrrole nitrogen, with the dihydro-pyridines only the 4-alkyl group is metabolically transferred, a reaction for which a precedent exists in chemical systems. Loev and Snader (1965) have shown that the 4-alkyl group of certain dihydropyridines may be eliminated during the oxidative process leading to aromatisation; and a similar oxidative mechanism, again involving concerted aromatisation of the dihydropyridine and elimination of its 4-alkyl group, has been suggested to take place with cytochrome P-450 (De Matteis *et al.*, 1981, 1982b; Augusto *et al.*, 1982; Marks *et al.*, 1985). In the enzymic mechanism, as in the chemical system, an initial oxidative attack at the dihydropyridine nitrogen can lead to aromatisation by one of two competing pathways (figure 8.8): (a) loss of the 4-alkyl group or, (b) loss of the 4-hydrogen atom. The first of these two pathways is favoured with leaving 4-alkyl groups of increased stability and under the influence of steric factors, for example when the substituents in the 3 and 5 posi-tions of the dihydropyridine are increased in size, as discussed (Loev and Snader, 1965; De Matteis *et al.*, 1982b). Augusto *et al.* (1982) have suggested that with cytochrome P-450 the first step is a one-electron oxidation of the dihydropyridine to the corresponding radical cation, leading to elimination of the 4-alkyl group as an alkyl radical.

A N-alkylated porphyrin with inhibitory properties towards ferrochelatase has also been isolated from the liver of mice given griseofulvin (De Matteis and Gibbs, 1980). Although the griseofulvin pigment has not yet been conclusively identified, nevertheless its spectral properties are identical to those of N-methyl protopor-phyrin. By analogy with the findings discussed above for DDC, the N-methyl group of this pigment could conceivably originate from griseofulvin, but this has not yet

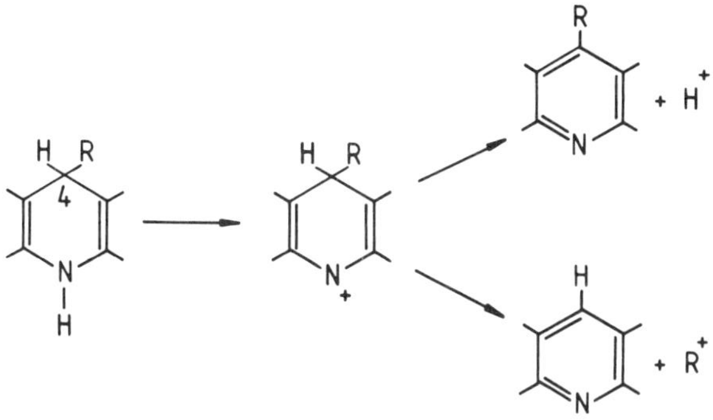

Figure 8.8 Oxidative dealkylation of dihydropyridines (according to Loev and Snader, 1965). An initial oxidative attack at the pyridine nitrogen leads to aromatisation either by loss of the 4-hydrogen atom, or by loss of the 4-alkyl group, the latter being eliminated in a reactive form

been established. The possibility that the drug may merely accelerate an alternative pathway of production of N-methyl protoporphyrin should also be considered as an N-alkylated pigment with inhibitory properties on ferrochelatase is present in trace amounts in the liver of control mice, that is in mice which have received no drug treatment (Tephly *et al.*, 1979, 1981).

The induction of porphyria by DDC can therefore be visualised as a multistage process, in which suicidal inactivation of cytochrome P-450 is apparently the first step. (1) The cytochrome transfers a methyl group from the drug to its own pros-thetic haem, giving rise to a powerful antimetabolite, N-methyl protoporphyrin. (2) The N-methyl protoporphyrin then migrates within the cell and crosses the mitochondrial membranes, so as to reach its ferrochelatase target, which is located on the matrix side of the mitochondrial inner membrane. (3) The inhibition of ferrochelatase is followed by a secondary stimulation of ALA-S, a compensatory response intended to overcome the enzymatic block. (4) As a result of the last two effects, protoporphyrin accumulates in the liver and hepatic protoporphyria becomes established. Support for this overall mechanism has been obtained by injecting mice with authentic N-methyl mesoporphyrin (a closely related analogue of N-methyl protoporphyrin) and by showing that inhibition of ferrochelatase, stimulation of ALA-S and accumulation of protoporphyrin (the main biochemical features of hepatic protoporphyria) all become demonstrable in their livers (De Matteis *et al.*, 1980c).

Stereochemistry of prosthetic haem alkylation

The N-alkylated porphyrins which have been isolated from the liver after treatment with drugs, all possess chiral configuration and also exhibit structural isomerism. From these properties, which will now be discussed in turn, important information has been derived, mostly from the laboratory of Ortiz de Montellano, on the orientation of haem in cytochrome P-450 and on the topology of the cytochrome P-450 active site.

As pointed out in the Introduction, in protoporphyrin IX the two faces of the porphyrin plane are not superimposable because of the asymmetric arrangement of the vinyl and propionate side chains. A *N*-alkylated protoporphyrin derivative may therefore exist in two chiral configurations, depending on whether the *N*-alkyl group lies above or below the porphyrin plane. Synthetic *N*-methyl protoporphyrin is optically inactive, as it is the racemic mixture of the two enantiomorphs. In contrast, the *N*-methyl protoporphyrin originating from DDC treatment and also the green pigments isolated from the liver of animals treated with propyne, ethylene, AIA and secobarbitone all exhibited chiral properties, as shown by a circular dichroism spectrum (Ortiz de Montellano and Kunze, 1981; De Matteis *et al.*, 1982c). The spectra obtained with these different pigments were also similar, suggesting that they may all possess the same configuration. These findings indicated that alkylation of the tetrapyrrolic macrocycle is stereospecific in cytochrome P-450 and takes place preferentially – if not exclusively – from one side of the porphyrin plane, most probably the oxygen binding side of haem, as this side will be facing the drugs to be metabolised and will therefore be directly exposed to the resulting electrophilic species. By establishing the absolute configuration of one such *N*-alkylated biological pigment it should therefore be possible to derive the orientation of the haem plane in cytochrome P-450, with respect to each of its two axial ligands, oxygen and the mercaptide anion (De Matteis *et al.*, 1982c).

Ortiz de Montellano *et al.* (1983a) have compared the chiral properties of (a) the *N*-ethyl protoporphyrin isolated from the liver of rats treated with the 4-ethyl analogue of DDC, and (b) the corresponding *N*-ethyl protoporphyrin obtained *in vitro* by reacting ethyl hydrazine with haemoglobin, a haemoprotein where the orientation of haem with respect to its axial ligands (oxygen and the proximal histidine) is known from X-ray crystallographic analysis (Fermi and Perutz, 1981) and, therefore, the exposed (or oxygen binding) side of the porphyrin plane is also known. Both *N*-ethyl protoporphyrins exhibited, as expected, chiral properties and their circular dichroism spectra were also identical, indicating that they must have possessed identical configuration. Ortiz de Montellano *et al.* (1983a) have therefore concluded that in cytochrome P-450 the orientation of haem is the same as in haemoglobin, with molecular oxygen binding from the same side of the porphyrin plane in both cases (the absolute configuration illustrated in figure 8.2), while the axial ligand on the opposite side of the haem plane is a mercaptide in cytochrome P-450 and a histidine residue in haemoglobin.

Another consequence of the asymmetrical arrangement of the vinyl and pro-pionate side chains in protoporphyrin IX is that four structural isomers of a *N*-monosubstituted protoporphyrin are possible, depending on which of the four pyrrole nitrogens has been alkylated (figure 8.6). *N*-methyl and *N*-ethyl proto-porphyrin obtained from chemical synthesis have both been shown to be a mixture of all four structural isomers. These have been fully characterised by nmr studies, and a hplc technique has been developed for their separation and quantitation (Ortiz de Montellano *et al.*, 1981a,d). Similar investigations carried out on the

Table 8.2 Regiospecificity of Prosthetic Haem Alkylation by Suicide Substrates of Cytochrome P-450. (Four structural or regio-isomers are possible for a N-monosubstituted protoporphyrin IX, depending on which pyrrole nitrogen is alkylated (see figure 8.6, where the pyrrole ring nomenclature is given))

Pretreatment of the rat *in vivo*	Suicide substrate	Alkylated protoporphyrin isolated from liver (only the substituent of the pyrrole nitrogen is given)	Main structural isomer (i.e. pyrrole ring with nitrogen alkylated)	References
Phenobarbitone	Ethylene	N-(2-hydroxyethyl)	D	
	Propene	N-(2-hydroxypropyl)	D	
Phenobarbitone	Octene	N-(2-hydroxyoctyl)	D	Kunze et al., 1983
Phenobarbitone	Propyne	N-(2-oxopropyl)	A	
	Octyne	N-(2-oxo-octyl)	A	
Phenobarbitone	DDC	N-methyl	A	Ortiz de Montellano et al., 1981d
None	4-Ethyl DDC	N-ethyl	C	
Phenobarbitone	4-Ethyl DDC	N-ethyl	A	De Matteis et al., 1983
β-Naphthoflavone	4-Ethyl DDC	N-ethyl	D	

N-alkylated porphyrins extracted from the liver of animals given DDC and other suicide substrates of cytochrome P-450 have shown that different pyrrole nitrogens are substituted, depending on the drug and also on the particular type of cytochrome P-450 enzyme predominating in the cell (see table 8.2).

In the experiments of Ortiz de Montellano and collaborators rats were all induced with phenobarbitone before being treated with different suicide substrates of cytochrome P-450. The predominant pyrrole nitrogen alkylated was that of ring A with propyne, octyne and other acetylenic compounds, while ring D was preferentially alkylated with ethylene, octene and other olefines. The differential ring specificity of the various drugs studied, as well as the almost complete lack of alkylation of the ring B nitrogen, led Kunze *et al.* (1983) to postulate a model for the active site of the phenobarbitone-inducible cytochrome P-450, as a region extending from the central haem iron to the areas overlooking rings A, C and D of the prosthetic group, but excluding the area corresponding to ring B, which they consider sterically hindered and therefore not accessible. They propose that the site of binding and of metabolic activation may be similar for both olefines and acetylenes, but that the terminal carbon of the postulated metabolite may reach out at a different angle in the two cases, thus leading to alkylation of different pyrrole nitrogens.

In an independent study (De Matteis *et al.*, 1983) differences in ring selectivity were also found when the same drug (the 4-ethyl analogue of DDC) was given to rats which had been pretreated with inducers of different cytochrome P-450 enzymes, suggesting a specific role for the various apocytochromes in directing alkylation on to different pyrrole nitrogens. This selectivity may be achieved through a change in orientation of the bound suicide substrate (with respect to the haem prosthetic group), so that in the various cytochromes P-450 a different pyrrole nitrogen may be more accessible to alkylation. Accordingly, if the dihydropyridine nitrogen (which is the likely site of oxidative interaction) is kept fixed at the central haem iron in all cases, the binding site for the drug may extend towards pyrrole ring A in the phenobarbitone-inducible cytochrome P-450 (the case illustrated in figure 8.2) or towards ring D in the enzyme inducible by β-naphthoflavone.

Although much more work is necessary to evaluate properly the significance of these findings, they nevertheless suggest that these classes of suicide substrate of cytochrome P-450 can be used as powerful molecular probes to investigate the stereochemistry of haem alkylation and also to gain an insight into the topology of the active centre of this important class of haemoproteins.

TARGETING OF SUICIDE SUBSTRATES ON SPECIFIC CYTOCHROME P-450 ENZYMES

A characteristic and essential feature of the suicidal inactivation reaction is that only those enzymes capable of binding and metabolising a given suicide substrate may be inactivated. This explains why the various suicide substrates discussed in this paper do not cause a total loss of cytochrome P-450 in the liver, but their effect is selective for certain enzyme types, as originally suspected in the whole animal (see for example Unseld and De Matteis, 1978) and now conclusively demon-strated in isolated purified systems (Ortiz de Montellano *et al.* 1981c; Waxman and Walsh, 1982). The factors which determine this selectivity are presumably related to the shape and size of the molecule to be metabolised (so that it can be accepted as a substrate at the enzyme active site) and also to the presence of a potentially reactive group in a specific position in the molecule, in close proximity to the haem iron, so that activation of this group may take place within the enzyme active centre. Attempts to 'target' suicide substrates to specific cytochrome P-450 enzymes have therefore been carried out by incorporating the potentially reactive acetylenic group in molecules which closely resemble the substrates for the enzyme and by placing the reactive group at, or near, the position in the molecule, where the normal substrate undergoes mono-oxygenation. Examples of these 'targeted' acetylenic suicide substrates are given in table 8.3. An additional example is pro-vided by spironolactone (Menard *et al.*, 1979) a sulphur-containing diuretic steroid, which directs the damaging potential of the sulphur centre to the cytochromes P-450 with progesterone 21- and 17-hydroxylase activities of testis and adrenals. This approach, which is now being actively pursued in several laboratories, has important implications not only for the study of the catalytic properties of specific cytochrome P-450 enzymes, but also for the design of selective inhibitors, which might prove useful in human therapy.

SUMMARY

The cytochromes of the P-450 group (a family of related haemoproteins with different substrate specificity) metabolise a large number of drugs and foreign chemicals, converting them in some cases to reactive and potentially toxic deriva-tives. The metabolites of certain drugs are so reactive that they become bound covalently at the very site of their production, within cytochrome P-450 itself, producing in this way a 'suicidal' irreversible inactivation of the cytochrome. Inactivation of the cytochrome can result from covalent modification of either the haem prosthetic group or the apoprotein moiety, but the consequences on cellular haem homoeostasis differ in the two cases.

With thionosulphur compounds (such as carbon disulphide and phosphoro-thionates) and chloramphenicol, the reactive metabolite binds covalently the *apoprotein*, indirectly modifying the binding of haem at the active site or its ability to undergo reduction during the catalytic cycle. These drugs do not cause stimulation of haem biosynthesis.

In contrast, with unsaturated drugs containing either allyl or ethynyl side chains (among these the ethynyl-substituted steroids of the contraceptive pill), the *haem* prosthetic group is directly attacked. A condition of cellular haem depletion and a compensatory stimulation of haem biosynthesis follow.

A special case is that provided by 3,5-diethoxycarbonyl-1,4-dihydrocollidine, which during oxidative metabolism, transfers a methyl group to the haem of cyto-chrome P-450. The product of haem alkylation, *N*-methylprotoporphyrin, is a

Table 8.3   Selective Suicide Inhibitors for Cytochrome P-450 Enzymes (Note the close similarity in chemical structure between the normal substrate and the corresponding suicide inhibitor

Enzyme	Prototype substrate	Suicide inhibitor	Reference
Hepatic Cytochrome P-450$_c$	Benzo[a]pyrene (arene oxidation)	1-ethynylpyrene	Gan et al., 1984
Hepatic lauric acid hydroxylase	Lauric acid (ω and ω-1 hydroxylation)	11-dodecynoic acid (terminal acetylenic analogue of substrate)	Ortiz de Montellano and Reich, 1984
Cytochrome P-450$_{scc}$	Cholesterol (side chain cleavage)	20-(1,5-hexadiynyl)-5-pregnen-3β-20α-diol	Nagahisa et al., 1983
Aromatase	Androst-4-ene-3,17-dione (sequential hydroxylations at 19-methyl)	19-propargyl analogue of substrate	Metcalf et al., 1981

selective and powerful inhibitor of the enzyme ferrochelatase, so that protoporphyrin accumulates in vast excess giving rise to hepatic protoporphyria.

Suicide substrates of cytochrome P-450 can therefore be used to explore the
mechanisms by which haem metabolism is regulated. Also, as these self-inflicted
lesions of cytochrome P-450 are directly related to the mechanism of enzyme
catalysis, information can be drawn on the mechanism of enzyme action. Finally,
the overall configuration of the drug appears to be important in targeting the
suicide substrate on to different cytochromes P-450 and this may be useful in
developing selective inhibitors for human therapy.

ACKNOWLEDGEMENT

I would like to thank Mrs Margaret Watts for much skill and patience in typing the
manuscript.

REFERENCES

Abbritti, G. and De Matteis, F. (1973). Effect of 3,5-diethoxycarbonyl-1,4-dihydro-
collidine on degradation of liver haem. *Enzyme*, **16**, 196–202

Adams, H. R., Isaacson, E. I. and Masters, B. S. S. (1977). Inhibition of hepatic
microsomal enzymes by chloramphenicol. *J. Pharmacol. exptl Ther.*, **203**,
388–96

Augusto, O., Beilan, H. S. and Ortiz de Montellano, P. R. (1982). The catalytic
mechanism of cytochrome P-450: spin-trapping evidence for one-electron substrate oxidation. *J. Biol. Chem.*, **257**, 11288–95

Bernhardt, R., Makower, A., Jänig, G-R. and Ruckpaul, K. (1984). Selective chemical modification of a functionally linked lysine in cytochrome P-450 LM_2. *Biochim. Biophys. Acta*, **785**, 186–90

Bond, E. J. and De Matteis, F. (1969). Biochemical changes in rat liver after administration of carbon disulphide, with particular reference to microsomal changes.
Biochem. Pharmacol., **18**, 2531–49

Catignani, G. L. and Neal, R. A. (1975). Evidence for the formation of a protein
bound hydrodisulfide resulting from the microsomal mixed function oxidase
catalyzed desulfuration of carbon disulfide. *Biochem. Biophys., Res. Commun.*,
65, 629–36

Cole, S. P. C. and Marks, G. S. (1984). Ferrochelatase and *N*-alkylated porphyrins.
Molec. Cell. Biochem., **64**, 127–37

Cole, S. P. C., Whitney, R. A. and Marks, G. S. (1981). Ferrochelatase-inhibitory
and porphyrin-inducing properties of 3,5-diethoxycarbonyl-1,4-dihydro-2,4,6-
trimethylpyridine and its analogues in chick embryo liver cells. *Molec. Pharmacol.*, **20**, 395–403

Correia, M. A., Farrell, G. C., Schmid, R., Ortiz de Montellano, P. R., Yost, G. S.
and Mico, B. A. (1979). Incorporation of exogenous heme into hepatic cytochrome P-450 *in vivo*. *J. Biol. Chem.*, **254**, 15–17

Dalvi, R. R., Poore, R. E. and Neal, R. A. (1974). Studies on the metabolism of
carbon disulfide by rat liver microsomes. *Life Sci.*, **14**, 1785–96

DeGroot, H. and Haas, W. (1981). Self-catalysed, O_2-independent inactivation of
NADPH or dithionite-reduced microsomal cytochrome P-450 by carbon tetrachloride. *Biochem. Pharmacol.*, **30**, 2343–7

De Matteis, F. (1971). Loss of haem in rat liver caused by the porphyrogenic agent 2-allyl-2-isopropylacetamide. *Biochem. J.*, **124**, 767–77

De Matteis, F. (1974). Covalent binding of sulfur to microsomes and loss of cytochrome P-450 during the oxidative desulfuration of several chemicals. *Molec. Pharmacol.*, **10**, 849–54

De Matteis, F. (1978). Hepatic porphyrias caused by 2-allyl-2-isopropylacetamide, 3,5-diethoxycarbonyl-1,4-dihydrocollidine, Griseofulvin and related compounds. *Handbook exptl Pharmacol.*, **44**, 129–55

De Matteis, F. and Cantoni, L. (1979). Alteration of the porphyrin nucleus of cytochrome P-450 caused in the liver by treatment with allyl-containing drugs. Is the modified porphyrin N-substituted? *Biochem. J.*, **183**, 99–103

De Matteis, F. and Gibbs, A. H. (1980). Drug-induced conversion of liver haem into modified porphyrins. Evidence for two classes of products. *Biochem. J.*, **187**, 285–8

De Matteis, F. and Seawright, A. A. S. (1973). Oxidative metabolism of carbon disulphide by the rat. Effect of treatments which modify the liver toxicity of carbon disulphide. *Chem. Biol. Interact.*, **7**, 375–88

De Matteis, F., Gibbs, A. H., Cantoni, L. and Francis, J. (1980a). Substrate-dependent irreversible inactivation of cytochrome P-450: conversion of its haem moiety into modified porphyrins. In: *Ciba Foundation 76* (New Series), Amsterdam, Excerpta Medica, pp. 119–31

De Matteis, F., Gibbs, A. H., Jackson, A. H. and Weerasinghe, S. (1980b). Conversion of liver haem into N-substituted porphyrins or green pigments. Nature of the substituent at the pyrrole nitrogen atom. *FEBS Lett.*, **119**, 109–12

De Matteis, F., Gibbs, A. H. and Smith, A. G. (1980c). Inhibition of protohaem ferro-lyase by N-substituted porphyrins. Structural requirements for the inhibitory effect. *Biochem. J.*, **189**, 645–8

De Matteis, F., Gibbs, A. H. and Tephly, T. R. (1980d). Inhibition of protohaem ferro-lyase in experimental porphyria. Isolation and partial characterization of a modified porphyrin inhibitor. *Biochem. J.*, **188**, 145–52

De Matteis, F., Gibbs, A. H., Farmer, P. B. and Lamb, J. H. (1981). Liver production of N-alkylated porphyrins caused in mice by treatment with substituted dihydropyridines. Evidence that the alkyl group on the pyrrole nitrogen atom originates from the drug. *FEBS Lett.*, **129**, 328–31

De Matteis, F., Gibbs, A. H. and Unseld, A. P. (1982a). Conversion of liver haem into N-substituted porphyrins or green pigments. Evidence for two distinct classes of products. In: *Biological Reactive Intermediates 2* (ed. R. Snyder), New York, Plenum Press, pp. 1319–34

De Matteis, F., Holland, C., Gibbs, A. H., De Sa, N. and Rizzardini, M. (1982b). Inactivation of cytochrome P-450 and production of N-alkylated porphyrins caused in isolated hepatocytes by substituted dihydropyridines. Structural requirements for loss of haem and alkylation of the pyrrole nitrogen atom. *FEBS Lett.*, **145**, 87–92

De Matteis, F., Jackson, A. H., Gibbs, A. H., Rao, K. R. N., Atton, J., Weerasinghe, S. and Hollands, C. (1982c). Structural isomerism and chirality of N-monosubstituted protoporphyrins. *FEBS Lett.*, **142**, 44–8

De Matteis, F., Gibbs, A. H. and Hollands, C. (1983). N-Alkylation of the haem moiety of cytochrome P-450 caused by substituted dihydropyridines. Preferential attack of different pyrrole nitrogen atoms after induction of various cytochrome P-450 isoenzymes. *Biochem. J.*, **211**, 455–61

Elcombe, C. R., Bridges, J. W., Gray, T. J. B., Nimmo-Smith, R. H. and Netter, K. J. (1975). Studies on the interaction of safrole with rat hepatic microsomes. *Biochem. Pharmacol.*, **24**, 1427–33

Fermi, G. and Perutz, M. (1981). *Atlas of Molecular Structures in Biology, Vol. 2, Hemoglobin and Myoglobin*, Oxford University Press, New York

Freundt, K. J. and Dreher, W. (1969). Inhibition of drug metabolism by small concentrations of carbon disulphide. *Naunym-Schmiedebergs Arch. Pharmakol. exp. Path.*, **263**, 208–9

Gan, L-S. L., Acebo, A. L. and Alworth, W. L. (1984). 1-ethynylpyrene, a suicide inhibitor of cytochrome P-450 dependent benz[*a*]pyrene hydroxylase activity in liver microsomes. *Biochemistry*, **23**, 3827–36

Halpert, J. (1981). Covalent modification of lysine during the suicide inactivation of rat liver cytochrome P-450 by chloramphenicol. *Biochem. Pharmacol.*, **30**, 875–81

Halpert, J. (1982). Further studies of the suicide inactivation of purified rat liver cytochrome P-450 by chloramphenicol. *Molec. Pharmacol.*, **21**, 166–72

Halpert, J. R. and Neal, R. A. (1980). Inactivation of purified rat liver cytochrome P-450 by chloramphenicol. *Molec. Pharmacol.*, **17**, 427–31

Halpert, J., Hammond, D. and Neal, R. A. (1980). Inactivation of purified rat liver cytochrome P-450 during metabolism of parathion (diethyl-p-nitrophenyl phosphorothionate). *J. Biol. Chem.*, **255**, 1080–9

Halpert, J. R., Miller, N. E. and Gorsky, L. D. (1985). On the mechanism of the inactivation of the major phenobarbital-inducible isozyme of rat liver cytochrome P-450 by chloramphenicol. *J. Biol. Chem.*, **260**, 8397–403

Hanzlik, R. P. and Tullman, R. H. (1982). Suicidal inactivation of cytochrome P-450 by cyclopropylamines. Evidence for cation-radical intermediates. *J. Am. chem. Soc.*, **104**, 2048–50

Järvisalo, J., Gibbs, A. H. and De Matteis, F. (1978). Accelerated conversion of heme to bile pigments caused in the liver by carbon disulfide and other sulfur-containing chemicals. *Molec. Pharmacol.*, **14**, 1099–106

Jonen, H. G., Werringloer, J., Prough, R. A. and Estabrook, R. W. (1982). The reaction of phenylhydrazine with microsomal cytochrome P-450. Catalysis of heme modification. *J. Biol. Chem.*, **257**, 4404–11

Kamataki, T. and Neal, R. A. (1976). Metabolism of diethyl *p*-nitrophenyl phosphorothionate (Parathion) by a reconstituted mixed-function oxidase enzyme system: studies of the covalent binding of the sulphur atom. *Molec. Pharmacol.*, **12**, 933–44

Kikuchi, G., Yoshida, T. and Ishizawa, S. (1982). Effect of drugs and metals on heme degradation by the heme oxygenase system. *Adv. Pharmacol. Ther. Proc. Int. Congr. 8th*, **5**, 121–30

Kunz, B. C. and Richter, C. (1983). Chemical modification of microsomal cytochrome P-450: role of lysyl residues in hydroxylation activity. *FEBS Lett.*, **161**, 311–14

Kunze, K. L., Mangold, B. L. K., Wheeler, C., Beilan, H. S. and Ortiz de Montellano, P. R. (1983). The cytochrome P-450 active site. Regiospecificity of prosthetic heme alkylation by Olefins and Acetylenes. *J. Biol. Chem.*, **258**, 4202–7

Levin, W. and Kuntzmann, R. (1969). Biphasic decrease of radioactive hemoprotein from liver microsomal CO-binding particles. Effect of 3-methylcholanthrene. *J. Biol. Chem.*, **244**, 3671–6

Levin, M., Jacobson, M., Sernatinger, E. and Kuntzman, R. (1973). Breakdown of cytochrome P-450 heme by secobarbital and other allyl-containing barbiturates. *Drug Metab. Dispos.*, **1**, 275–84

Loev, B. and Snader, K. M. (1965). The Hantzsch Reaction. I. Oxidative dealkylation of certain dihydropyridines. *J. Org. Chem.*, **30**, 1914–16

Loosemore, M. J., Wogan, G. N. and Walsh, C. (1981). Determination of partition ratios for allylisopropylacetamide during suicidal processing by a phenobarbitone-induced cytochrome P-450 isozyme from rat liver. *J. Biol. Chem.*, **256**, 8705–12

Lu, A. Y. H. and West, S. B. (1980). Multiplicity of mammalian microsomal cytocrome P-450. *Pharmacol. Rev.*, **31**, 277–95

Macdonald, T. L., Zirvi, K., Burka, L. T., Peyman, P. and Guengerich, F. P. (1982). Mechanism of cytochrome P-450 inhibition by cyclopropylamines. *J. Am. chem. Soc.*, **104**, 2050–2

Marks, G. S., Allen, D. T., Johnston, C. T., Sutherland, E. P., Nakatsu, K. and Whitney, R. A. (1985). Suicidal destruction of cytochrome P-450 and reduction of ferrochelatase activity by 3,5-diethoxycarbonyl-1,4-dihydro-2,4,6-trimethylpyridine and its analogues in chick embryo liver cells. *Molec. Pharmacol.*, **27**, 459–65

Menard, R. H., Guenthner, T. M., Kon, H. and Gillette, J. R. (1979). Studies on the destruction of adrenal and testicular cytochrome P-450 by spironolactone. Requirement for the 7α-thio group and evidence for the loss of heme and apoproteins of cytochrome P-450. *J. Biol. Chem.*, **254**, 1726–33

Metcalf, B. W., Wright, C. L., Burkhart, J. P. and Johnston, J. O. (1981). Substrate-induced inactivation of aromatase by allenic and acetylenic steroids. *J. Am. chem. Soc.*, **103**, 3221–2

Miki, N., Sugiyama, T. and Yamano, T. (1980). Purification and characterization of cytochrome P-450 with high affinity for cytochrome b_5. *J. Biochem.*, **88**, 307–16

Morelli, M. A. and Nakatsugawa, T. (1978). Inactivation *in vitro* of microsomal oxidases during parathion metabolism. *Biochem. Pharmacol.*, **27**, 293–9

Nagahisa, A., Spencer, R. W. and Orme-Johnson, W. H. (1983). Acetylenic mechanism-based inhibitors of cholesterol side chain cleavage by cytochrome P-450$_{scc}$. *J. Biol. Chem.*, **258**, 6721–3

Nakatsugawa, T., Tolman, N. M. and Dahm, P. A. (1968). Degradation and activation of parathion analogues by microsomal enzymes. *Biochem. Pharmacol.*, **17**, 1517–28

Neal, R. A. (1980). Microsomal metabolism of thiono-sulfur compounds: mechanisms and toxicological significance. *Rev. Biochem. Toxicol.*, **2**, 131–71

Ortiz de Montellano, P. R. and Correia, M. A. (1983). Suicidal destruction of cytochrome P-450 during oxidative drug metabolism. *Ann. Rev. Pharmacol. Toxicol.*, **23**, 481–503

Ortiz de Montellano, P. R. and Kunze, K. L. (1981). Cytochrome P-450 inactivation: Structure of the prosthetic heme adduct with propyne. *Biochemistry*, **20**, 7266–71

Ortiz de Montellano, P. R. and Mico, B. A. (1981). Destruction of cytochrome P-450 by allylisopropylacetamide is a suicidal process. *Arch. Biochem. Biophys.*, **206**, 43–50

Ortiz de Montellano, P. R. and Reich, N. O. (1984). Specific inactivation of hepatic fatty acid hydroxylases by acetylenic fatty acids. *J. Biol. Chem.*, **259**, 4136–41

Ortiz de Montellano, P. R., Mico, B. A. and Yost, G. S. (1978). Suicidal inactivation of cytochrome P-450. Formation of a heme-substrate covalent adduct. *Biochem. Biophys. Res. Commun.*, **83**, 132–7

Ortiz de Montellano, P. R., Kunze, K. L., Yost, G. S. and Mico, B. A. (1979). Self-catalyzed destruction of cytochrome P-450: Covalent binding of ethynyl sterols to prosthetic heme. *Proc. Nat. Acad. Sci. USA*, **76**, 746–9

Ortiz de Montellano, P. R., Beilan, H. S. and Kunze, K. L. (1981a). N-Alkylprotoporphyrin IX: Formation in 3,5-dicarbethoxy-1,4-dihydrocollidine-treated rats. Transfer of the alkyl groups from the substrate to the porphyrin. *J. Biol. Chem.*, **256**, 6708–13

Ortiz de Montellano, P. R., Beilan, H. S., Kunze, K. L. and Mico, B. A. (1981b). Destruction of cytochrome P-450 by ethylene. Structure of the resulting prosthetic heme adduct. *J. Biol. Chem.*, **256**, 4395–9

Ortiz de Montellano, P. R., Mico, B. A., Mathews, J. M., Kunze, K. L., Miwa, G. T. and Lu, A. Y. H. (1981c). Selective inactivation of cytochrome P-450 isoenzymes by suicide substrates. *Arch. Biochem. Biophys.*, **210**, 717–28

Ortiz de Montellano, P. R., Beilan, H. S. and Kunze, K. L. (1981d). *N*-Methylprotoporphyrin IX: Chemical synthesis and identification as the green pigment produced by 3,5-diethoxycarbonyl-1,4-dihydrocollidine treatment. *Proc. Nat. Acad. Sci. USA*, **78**, 1490–4

Ortiz de Montellano, P. R., Kunze, K. L. and Beilan, H. S. (1983a). Chiral orientation of prosthetic heme in the cytochrome P-450 active site. *J. Biol. Chem.*, **258**, 45–7

Ortiz de Montellano, P. R., Mangold, B. L. K., Wheeler, C., Kunze, K. L. and Riech, N. O. (1983b). Stereochemistry of cytochrome P-450-catalyzed epoxidation and prosthetic heme alkylation. *J. Biol. Chem.*, **258**, 4208–13

Pohl, L. R. and Krishna, G. (1978). Study of the mechanism of metabolic activation of chloramphenicol by rat liver microsomes. *Biochem. Pharmacol.*, **27**, 335–41

Pohl, L. R., Nelson, S. D. and Krishna, G. (1978). Investigation of the mechanism of the metabolic activation of chloramphenicol by rat liver microsomes. Identification of a new metabolite. *Biochem. Pharmacol.*, **27**, 491–6

Poore, R. E. and Neal, R. A. (1972). Evidence for extrahepatic metabolism of parathion. *Toxicol. appl. Pharmacol.*, **23**, 759–68

Ptashne, K. A., Wolcott, R. M. and Neal, R. A. (1971). Oxygen-18 studies on the chemical mechanisms of the mixed function oxidase catalysed desulfuration and dearylation reactions of parathion. *J. Pharmacol. exptl Ther.*, **179**, 380–5

Schwartz, S. and Ikeda, K. (1955). Studies of porphyrin synthesis and interconversion, with special reference to certain green porphyrins in animals with experimental hepatic porphyria. In: Ciba Foundation Symp: *Porphyrin Biosynthesis and Metabolism* (ed. G. E. W. Wolstenholme), J. & A. Churchill, London, pp. 209–26 ·

Tephly, T. R., Gibbs, A. H. and De Matteis, F. (1979). Studies on the mechanism of experimental porphyria produced by 3,5-diethoxycarbonyl-1,4-dihydrocollidine. Role of a porphyrin-like inhibitor of protohaem ferro-lyase. *Biochem. J.*, **180**, 241–4

Tephly, T. R., Coffman, B. L., Ingall, G., Abou Zeit-Har, M. S., Goff, H. M., Tabba, H. D. and Smith, K. M. (1981). Identification of *N*-methylprotoporphyrin IX in livers of untreated mice and mice treated with 3,5-diethoxycarbonyl-1,4-dihydrocollidine: source of the methyl group. *Arch. Biochem. Biophys.*, **212**, 120–6

Unseld, A. and De Matteis, F. (1978). Destruction of endogenous and exogenous haem by 2-allyl-2-isopropylacetamide: role of the liver cytochrome P-450 which is inducible by phenobarbitone. *Int. J. Biochem.*, **9**, 865–9

Wada, O., Yano, Y., Urata, G. and Nakao, K. (1968). Behaviour of hepatic microsomal cytochromes after treatment of mice with drugs known to disturb porphyrin metabolism in liver. *Biochem. Pharmacol.*, **17**, 595–603

Waxman, D. J. and Walsh, C. (1982). Phenobarbital-induced rat liver cytochrome P-450: purification and characterization of two closely related isozymic forms. *J. Biol. Chem.*, **257**, 10446–57

White, I. N. H. (1978). Metabolic activation of acetylenic substituents to derivatives in the rat causing the loss of hepatic cytochrome P-450 and haem. *Biochem. J.*, **174**, 853–61

White, I. N. H. (1981). Destruction of liver haem by norethindrone. Conversion into green pigments. *Biochem. J.*, **196**, 575–83

White, I. N. H. (1982). Biliary excretion of green pigments produced by norethindrone in the rat. *Biochem. Pharmacol.*, **31**, 1337–42

White, I. (1984). Suicidal destruction of cytochrome P-450 by ethynyl substituted compounds. *Pharmaceut. Res.*, 141–88

White, R. E. and Coon, M. J. (1980). Oxygen activation by cytochrome P-450. *Ann. Rev. Biochem.*, **49**, 315–56

White, I. N. H. and Muller-Eberhard, U. (1977). Decreased liver cytochrome P-450 in rats caused by norethindrone or ethynyloestradiol. *Biochem. J.*, **166**, 57–64

Part III

Human Aspects

9

Parkinsonian Syndrome Caused by 1-Methyl–4-Phenyl-1,2,3,6-tetrahydropyridine (MPTP) in Man and Animals

P. Jenner and C. D. Marsden

INTRODUCTION

In 1817 James Parkinson published his essay entitled 'The Shaking Palsy' in which he described a syndrome of paucity of movement, postural abnormalities and tremor which he had observed by casual observation of individuals from his window or by chance encounters in the street. Subsequently, Charcot re-named the disease Parkinson's disease since the limbs were not flaccid or paralysed, as the term palsy implied, but exhibited a marked rigidity. Since these early observations in the last century much has been learnt about Parkinson's disease. Idiopathic Parkinson's disease has an incidence of 1 in 1000 of the general population but affects 1 in 200 of those over the age of 50. Indeed, the increased incidence of Parkinson's disease with advancing age is the only known predisposing factor. There appears to be no difference in incidence between males or females and extensive twin studies have failed to show any hereditary link (Duvoisin et al., 1981). To date the only other factor found to influence Parkinson's disease is a negative correlation with cigarrette smoking (Bauman et al., 1980), the mechanism of which is not understood. Parkinson's disease is a progressive disease and, once diagnosed, patients have an average life expectancy of some fifteen years. Extensive research has described much of the brain pathology and biochemistry associated with Parkinson's disease and this is described in detail below.

PATHOLOGY, BIOCHEMISTRY AND TREATMENT OF PARKINSON'S DISEASE

Pathological changes in the brains of patients dying with Parkinson's disease were described in early investigations (Forno, 1982). The primary pathology appeared to involve a general loss of catecholamine containing pigmented brainstem nuclei, in particular cells within the zona compacta of substantia nigra, but other pigmented cell groups such as those of the locus coeruleus were also involved. Wherever pathological change was observed dense intracellular inclusions, termed Lewy bodies, were found. While the nature of the Lewy body remains unknown it appears to be the hallmark of pathological change in Parkinson's disease. The distribution of pathology in Parkinson's disease in pigmented brainstem nuclei led to the suggestion that there was an association between neuronal loss and the presence of the pigment neuromelanin. However, other areas of the brain which contain neither catecholamines nor neuromelanin also die in Parkinson's disease. These areas include the substantia innominata which contains cholinergic cell bodies ascending to cerebral cortex. Degenerating neurones in these regions also contain Lewy bodies. So, there is a widespread pathology in Parkinson's disease, but with a primary involvement of pigmented cells in substantia nigra.

When early pathological investigations of Parkinson's disease were undertaken, it was not known that dopamine was a neurotransmitter within brain. At that time dopamine was thought to be merely the precursor of noradrenaline. In the early 1960s, however, Hornykiewicz and colleagues discovered that the brains of patients dying from Parkinson's disease had exceptionally low concentrations of dopamine in the caudate-putamen (Ehringer and Hornykiewicz, 1960). With the subsequent discovery that the pigmented dopamine-containing cells of substantia nigra were dopaminergic cell bodies innervating this region, it became clear that the primary biochemical change in Parkinson's disease was a loss of brain dopamine content. Indeed, subsequent investigations have shown widespread loss of dopamine-containing neurones involving not only the nigro-striatal dopamine containing pathway, but also the mesolimbic and mesocortical dopamine containing pathways (Hornykiewicz, 1982).

Although brains from Parkinsonian patients show a generalised loss of dopamine, a variety of other biochemical changes are also observed (Hornykiewicz, 1982; Rinne, 1982). Alterations occur in brain noradrenaline content consistent with the destruction of noradrenaline-containing cell bodies in the locus coeruleus. Changes also occur in parameters associated with brain 5HT, acetylcholine and GABA function, although these appear not to be associated with the primary pathology of the disorder. More recently, selective changes in a variety of neuropeptides contained within the brain have been observed (Javoy-Agid et al., 1984). In particular, there are regional changes in the concentrations of met- and leu-enkephalin, substance P, neurotensin and cholecystokinin within basal ganglia. In addition, there appears to be a reduction of somatostatin in the cortex of those Parkinsonian patients who are also demented. So, overall, despite the primary involvement of brain dopamine function, there appears to be a whole variety of other biochemical changes occurring in the brains of patients dying with Parkinson's disease.

The primary involvement of a loss of brain dopamine function in Parkinson's disease is reflected by the treatment of the disorder. The mainstay of therapy remains the administration of the precursor amino acid of dopamine, namely L-3,4-dihydroxylphenylalanine (L-DOPA) in conjunction with a peripheral decarboxylase inhibitor such as carbidopa or benserazide. Synthetic dopamine agonist compounds, such as bromocriptine, pergolide, lisuride or lergotrile, are also employed in the treatment of Parkinson's disease. However, with the exception of anticholinergic drugs, which may be effective in the early stages of the disease, drugs acting on brain noradrenaline, 5-hydroxytryptamine (5HT) or γ-aminobutyric acid (GABA) systems generally appear ineffective in controlling the symptoms of Parkinson's disease (Jenner et al., 1983; Sheehy et al., 1981).

PROBLEMS IN PARKINSON'S DISEASE

Compared to many neurological diseases we know much about the pathology and biochemical changes occurring in Parkinson's disease. However, despite the wealth of information currently available a number of fundamental problems remain to be resolved. These are as follows:

1. The reason for dopamine cell death in Parkinson's disease is not known. It is not clear whether this is due to an accelerated loss of dopamine neurones occurring normally with age; or whether some toxic insult during life leads to a reduction in the number of dopamine neurones that then becomes evident during mid- and late life, as the natural loss of dopamine cells progresses. Whatever the cause, cell death appears closely linked to the appearance of Lewy bodies within the brains of Parkinsonian patients.
2. It is not known how biochemical changes in systems other than dopamine neurones contribute to the symptoms of Parkinson's disease or to the onset and progression of the disease; or whether they are a result of the prolonged drug treatment of the disorder.
3. While dopamine replacement therapy is effective in the treatment of Parkinson's disease for some 3-5 years, there is often a subsequent loss of drug efficacy associated with the onset of a variety of unwanted hyperkinetic motor disturbances (see Marsden et al., 1982). Why L-DOPA and other treatments cease to be effective is not known, but this may be related to pharmacokinetic or pharmacodynamic changes or to the progression of the disease process itself.

The lack of knowledge in these areas has severely hindered progress towards finding a cause or, indeed, even a cure for Parkinson's disease. However, a chance occurrence, namely the disovery that 1-methyl-4-phenyl-1,2,3-6-tetrahydropyridine (MPTP) can induce Parkinsonism in humans may have altered that situation.

THE DISCOVERY OF MPTP

In 1979 Davis and colleagues reported the case of a 23 year old chemistry graduate addicted to pethidine derivatives who apparently developed chronic Parkinsonism following the intravenous administration of 1-methyl-4-phenyl-4-propionoxy-piperidine (MPPP) (Davis *et al.*, 1979). The patient had access to a chemistry laboratory and was synthesising MPPP which he knew to be a potent pethidine derivative. He successfully manufactured and self-administered the material for some months. However, due to his haste to obtain this material he altered the reaction conditions by increasing temperature so as to decrease reaction time. Within a few days of self-administering this latest batch of material he was admitted to a psychiatric hospital mute and exhibiting rigidity, tremor and flat facial expression. Because of a prior history of behavioural disturbance he was diagnosed as a catatonic schizophrenic and treated with a course of haloperidol and electroconvulsive therapy (ECT). However, on examination by a neurologist the clear signs of Parkinsonism were recognised and the man was treated with standard anti-Parkinsonian therapy (L-DOPA plus benserazide and benztropine). This caused a marked reversal of his symptoms such that on subsequent examination he was found to be somewhat bradykinetic but otherwise no neurological deficits were noted. Indeed, a detailed neurological and psychiatric assessment failed to reveal any impairment apart from the persistent Parkinsonism. Removal of the anti-Parkinsonian medication caused a rapid reappearance of his initial symptomatology which again responded to anti-Parkinsonian medication. This patient therefore appeared to have many of the symptoms of Parkinson's disease itself as a result of his drug abuse.

The report of Davis and colleagues was published in a relatively new psychiatric journal and was largely overlooked. However, in 1983 Langston and colleagues reported on a further 4 young drug addicts who also had been abusing MPPP, which they used as a heroin substitute and who all subsequently became Parkinsonian (Langston *et al.*, 1983). All exhibited akinesia, rigidity, tremor, postural abnormalities and flat facial expression. In each case the symptoms responded to the administration of L-DOPA or to a synthetic dopamine agonist such as bromocriptine. Langston discovered that the original patient studied by Davis and colleagues had successfully abused pure MPPP for some months without ill effect. He obtained samples of the drugs taken by the four addicts and found that in addition to MPPP the material was contaminated with varying amounts of another substance, namely MPTP (figure 9.1). It appeared likely, therefore, that MPTP was the agent responsible for causing this chronic Parkinsonian syndrome.

The patient reported by Davis and colleagues in 1979 subsequently died from overdosage of another substance. On pathological examination of the brain it was found that there was a loss of dopamine-containing cell bodies in the zona compacta of substantia nigra. So, not only did this subject exhibit the symptoms of Parkinson's disease, but his brain also contained the major pathological change of this disorder. However, in contrast to Parkinson's disease the locus coeruleus, the source of ascending noradrenaline fibres, remained intact. At first it appeared that a single

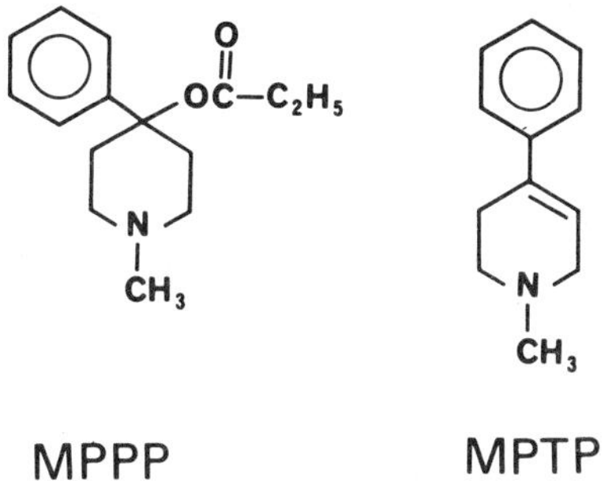

MPPP   MPTP

Figure 9.1   Chemical structures of MPPP and MPTP

intracellular eosinophilic body found in the substantia nigra was a Lewy body. However, this is now not thought to be the case.

Subsequently Langston and colleagues have identified a large group of individuals who were exposed to MPTP, some of whom have symptoms of Parkinsonism (Langston *et al.*, 1983; Langston and Ballard, 1984; Langston *et al.*, 1984c; Ballard *et al.*, 1985; Burns *et al.*, 1985b).

In addition to drug addicts abusing substances contaminated with MPTP, others may also have been exposed to its neurotoxic actions. MPTP was commonly utilised as an intermediate in organic chemistry for the synthesis of pethidine-type compounds. Indeed, a report has appeared of an organic chemist who utilised large quantities of MPTP over long periods and subsequently developed Parkinson's disease at an early age (Langston and Ballard, 1983). In addition, investigation of a group of workers at a factory where MPTP was manufactured has shown a correlation between the degree of exposure of the men to MPTP and the presence of motor deficits (Barbeau *et al.*, 1985a).

The conclusion from the human studies with MPTP seems to be that MPTP can induce a Parkinsonian state in man, which closely resembles that seen in idiopathic Parkinson's disease. This syndrome is associated with a selective loss of dopamine containing cells in zona compacta of substantia nigra but otherwise the pathology appears limited. However, it must be remembered that so far only one person exposed to MPTP has come to postmortem and the pathological picture may change on further investigation. Clearly MPTP is neurotoxic to dopamine cells in brain and the mechanism by which it produces its neurotoxicity may be of relevance to the mechanisms underlying cell death in Parkinson's disease itself. The discovery of MPTP-induced Parkinsonism in man has led to a flurry of investigations in animal species and these are described in detail in the following sections.

MPTP-NEUROTOXICITY IN RODENTS

In general, rodent species appear relatively insensitive to the pathological effects of systemic MPTP administration, and few motor deficits have been observed.

Rats

The rat, in particular, appears resistant to the actions of MPTP. In our own study, administration of MPTP 10 mg/kg ip for up to 16 days failed to alter motor activity in rats, during either MPTP administration or following its withdrawal (Boyce *et al.*, 1984) (table 9.1). Brain concentrations of dopamine and its metabolites were unchanged as were levels of ^{3}H-dopamine uptake into striatal synaptosomal preparations. These findings would appear to be in good accord with those of others, who have also found doses of MPTP in this range not to produce any biochemical, behavioural or pathological evidence of destruction of brain dopamine-containing neurones (Chiueh *et al.*, 1984; Saghal *et al.*, 1984). Higher doses of MPTP may, however, induce a persistent but partial depletion of dopamine in rat brain (Steranka *et al.*, 1983; Jarvis and Wagner, 1985a). However, even these doses did not induce motor deficits in the animals or provide any evidence for destruction of dopamine-containing cells in zona compacta of substantia nigra. The neurotoxic effects of MPTP in rats may be age dependent (Jarvis and Wagner, 1985b). Administration of MPTP (3 × 50 mg/kg) to young adult rats (120 days) caused a 65% loss of striatal dopamine content but neonates (7–10 days) receiving MPTP (8 × 50 mg/kg) showed no decrease in striatal dopamine levels.

Dopamine-containing cells may, however, be sensitive to the effects of MPTP if exposed to sufficiently high concentrations. Thus, Bradbury and colleagues (1986b) recently have shown that the direct unilateral or bilateral intranigral infusion of MPTP (1–10 µg/24 h for up to 13 days) caused persistent motor deficits in rats. The behavioural changes were accompanied by a fall in nigral dopamine and 3,4-dihydroxyphenyl acetic acid (DOPAC) concentrations but such changes were not observed in the striatum. Similar to the toxic actions of MPTP on direct infusion into rat brain, the exposure of explants of embryonic rat mesencephalon to MPTP results in the loss of dopamine cell bodies and fibre outgrowths (Mytilineou and Cohen, 1984).

Mice

Mice appear more susceptible to the effects of MPTP than rats, but high doses of MPTP are still required to induce neurotoxic actions. Heikkila and colleagues have shown that repeated administration of high doses of MPTP to mice causes a persistent loss in striatal dopamine homovanillic acid (HVA) and DOPAC content and ^{3}H-dopamine uptake and specific ^{3}H-mazindol binding (Heikkila *et al.*, 1984a,b,c; Heikkila *et al.*, 1985a; Sershen *et al.*, 1985a; Perry *et al.*, 1985a). Levels of dopamine can be reduced to less than 10% of those occurring in control animals and evidence has been provided that this loss is due to a destruction of nigral dopamine containing cells (Heikkila *et al.*, 1984b; Gupta *et al.*, 1984). Dopaminergic denervation by MPTP in mice is also suggested by electrophysiological data showing an increased spontaneous discharge rate of caudate neurones and a decreased ability of the indirect dopamine agonist phencyclidine to slow striatal neurone discharge (Jonsson *et al.*, 1985). Mesolimbic dopamine neurones may also be destroyed by MPTP in

Table 9.1 The Effect of Intraperitoneal (ip) Administration of MPTP (10 mg/kg/day ip) for 16 days Followed by 13–16 days Drug Withdrawal on Stereotyped Behaviour Induced by Subcutaneous (sc) Administration of Apomorphine (0.25 mg/kg sc) and Intraperitoneal (ip) Administration of Amphetamine (2.5 and 5 mg/kg ip) and on Striatal Dopamine, HVA and DOPAC Concentrations

Treatment group	Stereotypy			Striatal concentration			
	Amphetamine (mg/kg)		Apomorphine (mg/kg)	Dopamine (µg/g)	HVA (ng/g)	DOPAC (ng/g)	HVA/DOPAC ratio
	2.5	5.0	0.25				
Control	1.8 ± 0.2	2.7 ± 0.4	2.7 ± 0.2	8.34 ± 0.48	569 ± 70	746 ± 37	0.76 ± 0.07
MPTP	1.7 ± 0.2	2.0 ± 0	2.5 ± 0.3	8.47 ± 0.61	458 ± 23	778 ± 72	0.61 ± 0.03

Values are expressed as mean ± 1 SEM for 6–8 animals in each group.
No significant difference was found between control and MPTP groups. Student's t test for parametric data taken from Boyce et al. (1984).

mice, since persistent decreases in mesolimbic dopamine content occur (Melamed et al., 1985c). The effects of MPTP in mice may not, however, be limited to brain dopamine neurones. Evidence has been presented to suggest that MPTP treatment of mice also affects brain noradrenaline neurones as shown by decreased noradrenaline levels and reduced ^{3}H-nor-adrenaline uptake in a variety of areas, including the frontal and occiptal cortex, hippocampus and cerebellum (Hallman et al., 1984; Gupta et al., 1984; Wallace et al., 1984; Jonsson et al., 1985). However, despite the massive loss of brain dopamine content and of ^{3}H-dopamine uptake in the brain of mice treated with MPTP, until recently no report of persistent motor deficits had appeared. Duvoisin and colleagues (1986) have now produced severe dopamine depletion (> 90%) in mice and these animals show persistent bradykinesia associated with a festinant gait and kyphotic posture, which can be reversed by L-DOPA administration.

Considerable variability exists in the susceptibility of different mouse strains to MPTP. For example, C57 BL mice are more sensitive to its neurotoxic actions than Swiss-Webster mice (Duvoisin et al., 1986). But Swiss-Webster mice obtained from different suppliers also vary in sensitivity to MPTP (Heikkila, 1985). In addition, female and older mice appear more susceptible to MPTP than males and younger animals (Duvoisin et al., 1986).

The mouse and rat therefore appear more resistant to the effects of MPTP than would be expected from the human experience with this substance. The mouse may provide a useful model for detecting the toxicity of MPTP-like molecules and for investigating its mechanism of action. Similarly, disappointing results have been obtained in other rodent species, including the hamster and guinea pig (Chiueh et al., 1984; Heikkila et al., 1984a).

MPTP-INDUCED NEUROTOXICITY IN OTHER NON-PRIMATE SPECIES

With the initial difficulties of establishing an animal model of Parkinson's disease in rodents, attention has been turned to a variety of other species. In particular, two other non-primate mammals, namely the cat and dog, and two amphibian species, namely the frog and salamander, have been studied.

Like rodents, the cat appears refractory to the actions of MPTP and no clear evidence of neurotoxicity to brain dopamine neurones has been found (Schneider et al., 1985). In contrast, the beagle dog rapidly develops a gross motor syndrome in response to MPTP treatment which is accompanied by evidence for loss of brain dopamine content and selective destruction of nigro-striatal dopamine-containing neurones (Burns et al., 1985a). The motor deficits in the dog appear to improve somewhat after cessation of MPTP treatment, but the animals do not recover normal movement.

Recently, Barbeau and colleagues have proposed the use of the frog and salamander to investigate MPTP action (Barbeau et al., 1985a,b). The frog, in particular, offers the opportunity to investigate the effect of MPTP on pigmentation in melanin-bearing skin cells. Both the frog and salamander show motor deficits on administration of MPTP; in the frog, at least, these are accompanied by marked decrease in the brain concentration of dopamine, noradrenaline and adrenaline. However, although these species may be advantageous in terms of studying the effects of MPTP on pigmentation, it is difficult to extrapolate the motor deficits observed in those amphibians to those which might occur in humans or other primates as a result of MPTP-induced toxicity.

MPTP-NEUROTOXICITY IN NON-HUMAN PRIMATES

Since it is difficult to establish readily utilisable models of MPTP-induced Parkinsonism in lower animal species, many have turned their attention to the actions of MPTP in non-human primates. To date, MPTP has been shown to be neurotoxic in a variety of different primate species, including rhesus monkeys, squirrel monkeys, cynomologous monkeys and, as will be described in detail, the common marmoset.

Initial observations on the effect of MPTP in primates were made simultaneously by Langston and colleagues (1984a) and Burns and co-workers (1983) using rhesus and squirrel monkeys. After the second and subsequent doses of MPTP, an *acute behavioural syndrome* was observed in which the animals showed a decrease in movement accompanied by drooping of the eyelids, so that the animal appeared to be falling asleep. After three or more doses of MPTP other *persistent motor deficits* became apparent. Animals became increasingly akinetic and bradykinetic showing a flexed posture, increased rigidity of the limbs and decreased vocalisation. The animals showed some postural tremor and were generally clumsy in their movements, at times exhibiting freezing episodes. Some behavioural recovery might occur over the following week, but animals remained obviously Parkinsonian (Burns *et al.*, 1986). There is some indication that the susceptibility of monkeys to the effects of MPTP may increase with increasing age (Burns *et al.*, 1986) but this issue has not been resolved. All of these persistent behavioural effects could be reversed by the administration of L-DOPA plus carbidopa, or bromocriptine.

Initial biochemical studies reported that the motor deficits induced by MPTP were associated with a persistent severe decrease in content of dopamine and HVA in the caudate nucleus and putamen with no change in the nucleus accumbens (Burns *et al.*, 1983). Some transient alterations were seen in noradrenaline and 5HT parameters but these did not persist. Histological analysis verified these findings (Burns *et al.*, 1983; Langston *et al.*, 1984a). Light microscopic and immunocytochemical analysis showed a reduction in tyrosine hydroxylase-containing cells in zona compacta of substantia nigra, with no change in the immediately adjacent ventral tegmental area. The locus coeruleus also appeared to be intact. However, MPTP treatment of cynomologous monkeys has recently shown more widespread effects (Mitchell *et al.*, 1985). There were dramatic decreases in the dopamine content of the caudate nucleus, putamen and nucleus accumbens and in the noradrenaline content of the cortex. Histological examination revealed cell loss in both the pars compacta of substantia nigra and the ventral tegmental area as well as damage to the locus coeruleus.

These studies showed the sensitivity of non-human primate species to the actions of MPTP. However, it is difficult in large primates of this kind to carry out the type of detailed biochemical and histopathological examination required to evaluate the full effects of MPTP treatment. For this reason we have turned our attention to a commonly available laboratory-bred primate species, namely the common marmoset (Jenner *et al.*, 1984).

NEUROTOXICITY OF MPTP IN THE COMMON MARMOSET

Initial attempts to treat common marmosets with MPTP in fixed dose regimes, utilising 1–4 mg/kg ip per day for 4 days, showed that the individual susceptibility of animals varied greatly. Thus, at any one fixed dose level some animals would be unaffected by MPTP treatment, others would show moderate toxicity, while some animals would be so severely affected as to subsequently die. For these reasons a variable dosage regime has been employed in the experiments to be described. Routinely animals were given 2 mg/kg ip MPTP on day 1, but subsequently doses of between 1 and 4 mg/kg ip were administered, the dose and time course of drug administration being varied according to effect. The object was to obtain animals which were moderately affected by MPTP treatment yet were not so severely affected as to be unable to maintain themselves. Usually this involved a cumulative dose of MPTP of between 7 and 10 mg/kg ip being administered over time courses of 3–5 days.

Motor effects of MPTP

Alterations in motor behaviour produced by MPTP can be divided into three distinct phases (Jenner *et al.*, 1984, 1986a; Rose *et al.*, unpublished observations; Nomoto *et al.*, unpublished observation). As previously described for higher primates, *acute* actions of MPTP became evident following the second and subsequent doses of the drug. Animals lost their sense of balance, rocking backwards and forwards on the perch with their eyes closing and head drooping in a manner reminiscent of falling asleep. This caused them to fall from their perch to the floor of the cage where they remained prostrate, showing torsion of the neck and extension of the limbs sometimes accompanied by curvature of the tail. The animals' eyes remained open with a vacant gaze, but they could be temporarily roused from this state by tactile or auditory stimuli. Such acute effects lasted for between 30 and 60 min following each injection of MPTP.

After 2 or 3 doses of MPTP more persistent *subacute* motor deficits became apparent. Animals exhibited varying degrees of akinesia and bradykinesia accompanied by rigidity of the limbs, postural abnormality, loss of vocalisation and blink reflex; in some a postural tremor appeared, particularly of the hindquarters. This state was maintained for 10 days following the start of MPTP treatment. However, over the next weeks animals showed varying degrees of behavioural recovery from the subacute effects of MPTP treatment. Thus, at 4–6 weeks following cessation of

MPTP intake, the animals were no longer grossly akinetic or rigid and could freely move about the home cage particularly when challenged.

However, by then the animals exhibited a residual stable *chronic* motor deficit. They showed fewer movements over a smaller area in the home cage and tasks such as running, climbing and jumping from perch to perch were executed abnormally. Such movements appeared clumsy and poorly coordinated. All animals remained obviously affected 4-6 weeks after MPTP treatment and these deficits appeared to be maintained for at least 6-7 months.

From these results it appears that the common marmoset does not maintain the subacute gross Parkinsonian syndrome induced by MPTP treatment tailored to produce moderate disability; partial behavioural recovery can subsequently occur. This raises the question of whether MPTP in this species produces loss of dopaminergic neurones, as occurs in higher primates, or whether there are other reasons to explain the reversal of the subacute Parkinsonism.

Alterations in nigro-striatal dopaminergic parameters induced by MPTP treatment

To assess damage to the nigro-striatal tract caused by the administration of MPTP to the common marmoset, a number of different dopaminergic parameters were measured at 10 days and at 4-6 weeks following cessation of MPTP intake, and were compared to values obtained for control marmosets (Jenner *et al.*, 1984; Rose *et al.*, unpublished observation) (table 9.2).

At 10 days a marked fall in ^{3}H-dopamine uptake into synaptosomal preparations of caudate-putamen was observed; this effect was maintained or increased at the 4-6 week time period.

These results indicate a persistent loss of dopamine neuronal terminals in this area following MPTP treatment, despite the change in motor state of the animals between the two different time points. Similarly, measurement of caudate-putamen dopamine concentration showed a 90% or greater loss at both 10 days and 4-6 weeks. Marked falls in the concentrations of the dopamine metabolites HVA and DOPAC were also observed at 10 days, but by 4-6 weeks the levels of HVA and DOPAC were higher than those found at 10 days, although they were still reduced compared to control values. This latter data suggests that one reason for the behavioural recovery of the animals is that remaining dopaminergic neurones increased synthesis and turnover of dopamine in an attempt to compensate for the neuronal destruction occurring as a result of MPTP treatment.

Surprisingly, no changes were found in the number of specific binding sites for ^{3}H-spiperone in the caudate-putamen of these animals at either 10 days or 4-6 weeks (table 9.2). Considering the degree of loss of dopaminergic innervation to this area it might have been expected that increased numbers of binding sites would have been observed. The reason for this is unclear, but may relate to regional changes in innervation within the caudate-putamen which are not detected by the *in vitro* homogenate ligand binding technique employed.

Overall, these findings support the idea that in the common marmoset, as in other primate species, MPTP can produce a persistent destruction of nigro-striatal

Table 9.2 Alterations in Neurochemical Parameters in the Caudate-Putamen at 10 days and 4–6 weeks Induced by Acute MPTP Treatment of Common Marmoset

	Controls	MPTP	
		10 days	4–6 weeks
[3]H-dopamine uptake (pmoles/mg protein/h)	228 ± 47	77 ± 10*	34 ± 12*
Dopamine (μg/g)	8.9 ± 0.6	0.35 ± 0.20*	0.89 ± 0.32*
HVA (μg/g)	5.6 ± 0.6	0.26 ± 0.03*	1.4 ± 0.4*[+]
DOPAC (μg/g)	5.2 ± 0.5	0.28 ± 0.08*	0.87 ± 0.17*[+]
[3]H-spiperone (Bmax; pmoles/g)[a]	17.2 ± 1.1	19.2 ± 1.5	18.9 ± 0.9
5HT (μg/g)	0.16 ± 0.04	0.19 ± 0.07	0.26 ± 0.04
5HIAA (μg/g)	0.47 ± 0.10	0.20 ± 0.05	0.88 ± 0.13*
Noradrenaline (μg/g)	0.60 ± 0.12	0.16 ± 0.02*	0.99 ± 0.08*
[3]H-glutamate uptake (pmoles/mg protein/h)	138 ± 24	114 ± 9	155 ± 20

Mean ± SEM; n = 6–10.
*$p < 0.05$ Student's t test compared to controls.
[+]$p < 0.05$ Student's t test compared to animals at 10 days.
[a]Number of specific binding sites.

dopaminergic neurones. In a recent experiment we have compared the effects of MPTP treatment in the marmoset on dopamine content of the caudate-putamen and nucleus accumbens 10 days and 3–4 months following MPTP treatment. At 10 days a decrease in dopamine, HVA and DOPAC is observed in both areas (table 9.2). However, by 3–4 months the decreases initially observed in the nucleus accumbens are largely reversed while those in the caudate-putamen persist (table 9.3). So the persistent neurotoxic effects of MPTP in the marmoset appear selective for the nigro-striatal system.

The effect of MPTP treatment on other neurotransmitter systems

To determine the selectivity of effect of MPTP we have determined the effects of MPTP treatment in the common marmoset on a variety of other neuronal transmitter systems using both the 10 day and 4–6 week time points.

At 10 days changes in regional concentrations of noradrenaline, 5HT and 5-hydroxyindole acetic acid (5HIAA) were observed, but by 4–6 weeks these changes were largely reversed and no consistent deficits in 5HT or noradrenaline parameters were observed (Rose et al., unpublished observation). Similarly, at 10 days no change was observed in pallidal or thalamic GAD activity, but observations have not been made at the later time points.

Table 9.3 Alterations in Dopamine, HVA and DOPAC Content of Putamen and Nucleus Accumbens, at 10 days and 3-4 months Following MPTP Treatment of the Common Marmoset

	Dopamine	HVA	DOPAC
	Putamen concentrations (μg/g)		
Control	13.0 ± 0.2	10.8 ± 1.0	1.8 ± 0.2
10 days	0.17 ± 0.06*	0.01 ± 0.01*	0.16 ± 0.03*
Control	15.2 ± 1.6	6.1 ± 0.8	0.99 ± 0.28
3-4 months	2.8 ± 1.4*[+]	1.7 ± 1.1*	0.20 ± 0.08*
	Nucleus Accumbens concentrations (μg/g)		
Control	10.4 ± 1.1	7.7 ± 2.1	1.4 ± 0.2
10 days	0.82 ± 0.40*	0.17 ± 0.12*	0.04 ± 0.03*
Control	10.1 ± 0.8	8.3 ± 0.4	2.3 ± 0.3
3-4 months	7.4 ± 0.8*[+]	4.6 ± 1.5[+]	1.2 ± 0.2[+]

*$p < 0.05$ compared to controls.
+$p < 0.05$ 10 days versus 3-4 months.

Cortical, pallidal and thalamic choline acetyltransferase activity and ^{3}H-quinuclidinyl benzilate (^{3}H-QNB) binding to muscarinic receptors were unaltered at 10 days after cessation of MPTP treatment (Garvey *et al.*, 1986) (table 9.4). No changes were observed in cortical cholinergic markers at 4-6 weeks, but by then there was a decrease in choline acetyltransferase activity in the palladium with a corresponding increase in the number of ^{3}H-QNB binding sites; similar changes tended to occur in the thalamus. The late onset of these changes suggests that they occur secondary to the primary loss of nigro-striatal dopamine function.

Measurements of neuropeptide concentrations in a variety of brain regions have also been made 10 days following the start of MPTP treatment (Jenner *et al.*, 1986) (table 9.5). However, no changes in the levels of *met-* or *leu*-enkephalin, neurotensin or cholecystokinin (CCK-8) were found in any basal ganglia region, and only substance P content was decreased in the frontal cortex of these animals. Recently, Allen *et al.*, (1986) have reported changes in basal ganglia peptides following MPTP treatment for 4 days, the animals being killed on day 5. In the substantia nigra, substance P concentrations were increased while vasoactive intestinal peptide and neuropeptide Y were reduced. There was no change reported in the nigral content of neurotensin, CCK-8 or somatostatin. In caudate-putamen the content of neuropeptide Y was reduced but otherwise there was no effect on the levels of other peptides. Whether the changes reported reflect the neurotoxic action of MPTP or its acute actions (see below) remains in doubt because of the short time after MPTP administration when these observations were made. However, some long-term persistent changes in neuropeptides are induced by MPTP. Thus, in rhesus monkeys treated with MPTP 1-5 months previously *met*-enkephalin

Table 9.4 Alterations in Cholineacetyltransferase (CAT) Activity and Specific ^{3}H-QNB Binding in Frontal Cortex, Thalamus and Pallidum in Marmosets at 10 days and 4–6 weeks Following Acute MPTP Treatment

Treatment group and time period	CAT (nmoles acetylcholine/ h/mg protein)	^{3}H-QNB (B_{max}; fmoles/mg protein)
10 days		
Thalamus		
Control	23.1 ± 0.7	572 ± 13
MPTP	25.9 ± 2.2	576 ± 5
Globus Pallidus		
Control	21.5 ± 2.1	712 ± 74
MPTP	25.6 ± 3.7	715 ± 53
Frontal cortex		
Control	11.4 ± 0.9	1561 ± 156
MPTP	13.3 ± 0.7	1469 ± 53
4–6 weeks		
Thalamus		
Control	27.0 ± 3.8	873 ± 18
MPTP	20.7 ± 2.8	1164 ± 89
Globus Pallidus		
Control	35.0 ± 7.3	206 ⊥ 45
MPTP	20.5 ± 2.5*	538 ± 14*
Frontal cortex		
Control	7.6 ± 1.0	1634 ± 128
MPTP	8.6 ± 0.5	1333 ± 131

Mean ± 1 SEM; n = 3–6.
*$p < 0.05$ Student's t test compared to controls.

concentrations were reduced in substantia nigra while other peptides derived from either proenkephalin A or B were not changed (Zamir *et al.*, 1984). In the caudate dynorphin B concentration was reduced while in the putamen peptides derived from both proenkephalin A and B were decreased. Substance P and somatostatin levels were not changed in any brain area examined.

All these results contrast with the distribution of selective regional changes in the concentration of these peptide substances observed in idiopathic Parkinson's disease (Javoy-Agid *et al.*, 1984).

Histological changes induced by MPTP treatment

The brains from MPTP treated animals taken up to 6 weeks following the start of MPTP treatment have been the subject of histological examination using both light

Table 9.5 Regional Peptide Concentrations in the Brains of MPTP-treated and Control Marmosets 10 days Following Acute MPTP Treatment (pmoles/g tissue)

Brain	met-enkephalin		leu-enkephalin		Substance P		CCK-8	
	Control	MPTP	Control	MPTP	Control	MPTP	Control	MPTP
Caudate	1538 ± 192	1578 ± 131	244 ± 21	232 ± 25	126 ± 17	126 ± 9	27 ± 5	24 ± 4
Putamen	1618 ± 193	2043 ± 275	187 ± 23	234 ± 56	91 ± 9	96 ± 7	23 ± 4	27 ± 3
Substantia nigra	1021 ± 329	1352 ± 369	509 ± 111	583 ± 143	1138 ± 341	1234 ± 282	12 ± 3	14 ± 1
Nucleus accumbens	1765 ± 209	3034 ± 603	406 ± 43	485 ± 56	176 ± 21	180 ± 30	33 ± 4	27 ± 4
External pallidum	6121 ± 813	9545 ± 1716	740 ± 79	509 ± 99	153 ± 28	186 ± 56	7 ± 1	5 ± 1
Internal pallidum	4301 ± 782	3560 ± 912	522 ± 92	446 ± 102	359 ± 79	303 ± 21	5 ± 2	6 ± 2
Hippocampus	259 ± 29	241 ± 34	95 ± 15	88 ± 4	151 ± 24	120 ± 15	43 ± 6	39 ± 6
Frontal cortex	47 ± 8	42 ± 4	32 ± 5	38 ± 5	36 ± 3	28 ± 2*	45 ± 7	44 ± 6

Mean ± 1 SEM; $n = 6$.
*$p < 0.05$ Student's t test compared to controls.

microscopical and immunocytochemical techniques (Gaspar *et al.*, 1986; Walters *et al.*, unpublished observation; Gibb *et al.*, unpublished observations).

There was a marked loss of tyrosine hydroxylase immunoreactive cells in the zona compacta of the substantia nigra. Interestingly, other cells not staining for tyrosine hydroxylase were also destroyed by the actions of MPTP. The nature of this cell population is not clear. Cell loss extended into the ventral tegmental area where varying degrees of loss of tyrosine hydroxylase immunoreactive cells were observed. The loss in this area was not as extensive as that observed in the substantia nigra zona compacta. There was no evidence of any significant loss of tyrosine hydroxylase immunoreactive cells in the locus coeruleus. Some loss of cells was also observed in the median eminence and arcuate nucleus complex of the hypothalamus. Immunohistochemical localisation of substance P, *met*-enkephalin, dynorphin (1-17) and neurotensin showed no alteration as a result of MPTP treatment. Autoradiographic analysis showed a substantial loss of neurotensin binding sites and ^{3}H-spiperone binding sites in the zona compacta of the substantia nigra, with smaller reductions in the substantia zona pars reticulata and ventral tegmental area. In the striatum there was again no loss of neurotensin binding sites but a regional increase in the number of ^{3}H-spiperone binding sites was observed.

No histological evidence of loss of cells in the substantia innominata was found and this result, coupled with the failure to find any change in cortical choline acetyltransferase activity or ^{3}H-QNB binding, suggests that this cortical acetylcholine neuronal projection remains intact following MPTP treatment. This contrasts with idiopathic Parkinson's disease where degeneration of this area is observed.

Also in contrast to idiopathic Parkinson's disease, no evidence has been found in the histological studies for the presence of Lewy bodies in any of the areas where cell degeneration has been seen to occur.

Relevance of the MPTP-treated marmoset as an animal model of Parkinson's disease

The administration of MPTP to the common marmoset results in the production of a Parkinsonian syndrome from which the animal shows some recovery. However, persistent motor deficits exist in this species over a period of many months following cessation of MPTP treatment. The behavioural syndrome is accompanied by evidence that MPTP acts as a selective nigro-striatal toxin, although some damage to the mesolimbic dopaminergic system also may occur. Biochemical changes would also indicate that MPTP affects primarily brain dopamine systems in the brain of the common marmoset, with no direct evidence of neurotoxic actions on other neuronal systems.

In these respects, MPTP treatment of the common marmoset only produces a partial model of Parkinson's disease. The pathology observed is more limited than that observed in human postmortem brain for patients with Parkinson's disease, as are the biochemical changes. MPTP treatment of the marmoset produces an acute lesion of nigro-striatal systems: it may be that at longer time intervals following MPTP treatment more extensive biochemical and pathological changes may occur which are secondary to the initial loss of nigro-striatal fibres. Despite only providing a partial model of Parkinson's disease, the MPTP-treated marmoset provides an exciting experimental system in which to investigate mechanisms by which dopamine containing neurones of the zona compacta of the substantia nigra degenerate, and insights into its mechanism of action may be a vital clue to the cause of idiopathic Parkinson's disease.

MECHANISM OF ACTION OF MPTP

Although the identification of MPTP as a selective nigro-striatal toxin has occurred only recently, a number of important advances have been made in understanding its mechanism of action. Initially it is necessary to differentiate between the acute and chronic effects of MPTP, for the drug does produce acute behavioural syndromes in animals as well as the more persistent neurotoxic actions.

Acute actions of MPTP

Comparisons have been made between the acute effects of MPTP and 5HT syndromes which can be induced in animals by the administration of 5HT agonists and hallucinogens (Chiueh et al., 1984). Thus, the acute administration of MPTP has been associated with the occurrence of prostration, limb extension, head weaving and Straub tail phenomenon. No detailed investigation of the acute MPTP syndrome has been made. However, in in vitro experiments MPTP in micromolar concentrations appears to alter the release and uptake of ^{3}H-dopamine, ^{3}H-5HT and ^{3}H-noradrenaline (Denton and Howard, 1984; Schmidt et al., 1984; Kula et al., 1984). The acute actions of MPTP on brain dopamine neurones have been investigated in more detail (Pileblad et al., 1984, 1985). Acute administration of MPTP produced a puzzling sequence of dramatic changes in striatal dopamine synthesis and metabolism during the first few hours. Initially there was an increase in DOPA synthesis at 15 min rapidly followed by a marked inhibition of DOPA formation. Within the first hour DOPAC formation was decreased but without any similar change in the level of dopamine. Between 60 and 75 min, dramatic changes took place with a decrease in dopamine content and an increase in 3-methoxytyramine. Subsequently, there was a slow further depletion of dopamine accompanied by a decrease in 3-methoxytyramine and sustained high levels of HVA for several hours. DOPAC levels showed some irregularities which could not be explained. Finally, after 6 h, all levels of dopamine and its metabolites reached sub-normal values leading to a picture similar to that seen two weeks after MPTP administration to mice. Obviously such data are complex and may relate to various phases of MPTP action linked with its effect on metabolic enzymes and its own metabolism (see below). Perhaps the data in the latter period of even this acute experiment reflects the neurotoxic process but the relationship between the early changes and neurotoxic activity as well as the mechanisms underlying such actions remain to be determined.

Accumulation of MPP^+ in brain

An important initial observation was the finding that following MPTP admini-stration to primate species another substance, namely MPP^+ (figure 9.2), was present in high concentrations in brain (Markey et al., 1984; Langston et al., 1984b). Indeed, MPTP appeared to be rapidly cleared from primate brain while MPP^+ accumulated and persisted over many days (Johannesen et al., 1985). Although MPP^+ appeared to accumulate initially in a number of brain areas, the concentration in the substantia nigra increased during the first 72 h reaching the highest concentration of any brain area studied (Irwin and Langston, 1985). In contrast, the concentration of MPP^+ in other brain areas decreased over the same period. The situation in primates differed from that found in the rodent species studied in which MPTP and MPP^+ were rapidly cleared from brain. The results suggest that MPP^+ may be trapped intraneuronally in primate brain and that it is this accumulation of MPP^+ which leads to neurotoxic effects.

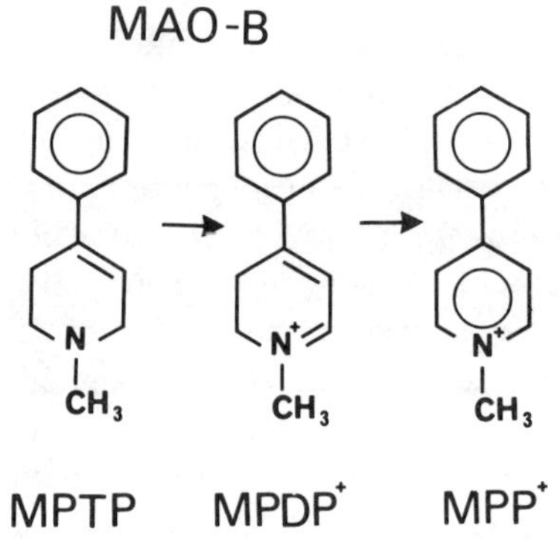

Figure 9.2 Proposed metabolic pathway for the formation of MPP^+ from MPTP by mono-amine oxidase B.

The effect of monoamine oxidase inhibitors on the accumulation of MPP^+ and the neurotoxic actions of MPTP

Pretreatment of primates with the monoamine oxidase inhibitor pargyline caused a dramatic reduction in the accumulation of MPP^+ in brain tissue (Markey et al., 1984; Langston et al., 1984b). Pretreatment with pargyline also inhibited the neurotoxic actions of MPTP preventing the decrease in caudate-putamen dopamine content and ^{3}H-dopamine uptake as well as damage to cells in zona compacta of substantia nigra (Cohen et al., 1985) (table 9.6). Interestingly, the selective mono-amine oxidase B inhibitor, deprenyl, also prevents biochemical changes associated with MPTP neurotoxicity suggesting the involvement of this form of monoamine oxidase.

Table 9.6   The Effect of Pretreatment with Monoamine Oxidase Inhibitors on MPTP-induced Change in Caudate Dopamine Neuronal Markers in the Monkey

Treatment (mg/kg)	Dopamine (μg/g)	HVA (μg/g)	^{3}H-dopamine uptake (pmol/mg tissue)
Control	11.4 ± 1.0	9.1 ± 0.7	0.53 ± 0.14
MPTP (0.35)	0.2 ± 0.2*	0.2*	0.03 ± 0.02*
Pargyline (10) + MPTP	17.9 ± 1.5	3.4 ± 0.5	0.76 ± 0.26
Deprenyl (10)	11.4 ± 1.4	6.3 ± 3.8	0.53 ± 0.13

$n = 2$–3.
*$p < 0.05$ compared to control values.
Data taken from Cohen *et al.* (1985).

In addition to these findings a variety of other evidence has accumulated to suggest a relationship between formation of MPP^+, MPTP-induced neurotoxicity and monoamine oxidase activity. Thus, monoamine oxidase inhibitors (MAOI), including selective MAOI B inhibitors, prevent the toxicity of MPTP to nigro-striatal dopamine systems in mice (Heikkila *et al.*, 1984c) and the toxicity of MPTP to rat embryo mesencephalon in culture (Cohen and Mytilineou, 1985). Recently, Melamed and Youdim (1985) have shown the toxicity of MPTP in mice to be prevented by combined treatment with phenylethylamine, a naturally occurring specific substrate of monoamine oxidase B.

Similarity between ^{3}H-MPTP binding sites in brain and monoamine oxidase

Identification of a specific binding site for ^{3}H-MPTP in *in vitro* brain slices or homogenate preparations suggests that there is a strong resemblance between such sites and those occupied by ligands identifying monoamine oxidase. Initially, Wieczorek *et al.* (1984) showed a saturable specific binding site of high affinity for ^{3}H-MPTP to slices of rat brain. ^{3}H-MPTP binding sites showed a regional distribution not obviously linked to the anatomy of a previously described neurotrans-mitter system or its receptors. In these rat studies the highest amount of binding occurred in the arcuate nucleus of the hypothalamus, the dorsal raphe nucleus, the locus coeruleus and the interpeduncular nucleus. There was only a low level of specific ^{3}H-MPTP binding sites in the caudate-putamen or the substantia nigra. In contrast, autoradiographic studies on human brain showed very high receptor densities in the caudate nucleus, substantia nigra and locus coeruleus (Javitch *et al.*, 1984). Such differences in localisation may relate to the differential toxicity of MPTP in the two species. Subsequently, Parsons and Rainbow (1984) demonstrated that specific binding of MPTP to brain slices could be displaced by incorporation of the monoamine oxidase inhibitor, pargyline. There was also a highly significant correlation between the concentration of ^{3}H-MPTP binding sites in a variety of brain regions with the known activity of monoamine oxidase in these areas. Simi-larly, there were striking similarities between the autoradiographs of ^{3}H-MPTP binding sites and of monoamine oxidase as judged using ^{3}H-pargyline as a ligand. A similar distribution of ^{3}H-MPTP binding sites and monoamine oxidase was also found by others (Del Zompo et al., 1984; Bocchetta et al., 1985). Interestingly, the pharmacological specificity of ^{3}H-MPTP binding indicated that in rat brain it was more selective for monoamine oxidase A than for monoamine oxidase B (Rainbow et al., 1985; Del Zompo et al., 1984); although this may merely reflect the relative distribution and predominance of the isoenzymes in this species. Recently, Reznikoff et al. (1985) showed that ^{3}H-MPTP labelled both MAO A and MAO B, with a slight preference for MAO B, in human brain tissue. The density of ^{3}H-MPTP and ^{3}H-pargyline binding sites was unaltered in human substantia nigra when comparing control subjects with those dying of Parkinson's disease (Uhl et al., 1985). This latter finding would suggest an extra-neuronal location for MPTP binding sites in human substantia nigra.

MPTP metabolism by monoamine oxidase B

The connection between MPTP toxicity, the formation of MPP$^+$ and monoamine oxidase activity became clear with the discovery that MPTP was an unexpected substrate for monoamine oxidase B. MPTP is oxidised by brain mitochondrial preparations to an intermediate, MPDP$^+$, which is then converted to MPP$^+$ (Chiba et al., 1984; Salach et al., 1984) (figure 9.2). Recent results suggest that MPTP might be a suicide inhibitor for MAO B (Kinemuchi et al., 1985). The metabolic sequence between MPTP and MPDP$^+$ is inhibited by non-selective monoamine oxidase inhibitors, such as pargyline, and by selective monoamine oxidase B inhibitors, such as deprenyl, but only weakly by monoamine oxidase A inhibitors, such as chlorgyline. In contrast, the oxidation of MPDP$^+$ to MPP$^+$ is not inhibited by pargyline. MPDP$^+$ is unstable and rapidly undergoes a disproportionation into MPTP and MPP$^+$ (Castagnoli et al., 1985). Recent studies would also suggest that the monoamine oxidase catalysed bioactivation of MPTP leads to the formation of a variety of reactive molecules that are potentially cytotoxic to nigro-striatal cells due to the disproportionation of MPDP$^+$ caused by inherent chemical instability (Peterson et al., 1985). The oxidation of MPTP by monoamine oxidase B occurs more rapidly than for many of its analogues even those with relatively minor structural changes (Heikkila et al., 1985d).

In addition to its metabolism by monoamine oxidase B, MPTP is also metabolised by rabbit liver microsomal preparations. Two principal products are formed, namely the N-desmethyl compound 4-phenyl-1,2,3,6-tetrahydropyridine together with 1-methyl-4-phenyl-1,2,3,6-tetrahydropyridine-N-oxide. In contrast to metabolism by monoamine oxidase B, which also occurs in hepatic mitochondrial preparations, these pathways can be looked upon as resulting in detoxification, since the secondary amine product is devoid of neurotoxic effect (Weissman et al., 1985).

Uptake of MPP$^+$ into dopamine neurones

One further piece of evidence which helps explain the apparent persistence of MPP$^+$ within some areas of brain is that MPP$^+$, but not MPTP, is a substrate for the dopamine uptake mechanism and that MPP$^+$ is taken up at a rate equivalent to that of dopamine itself (Javitch and Snyder, 1985; Javitch et al., 1985). Selective use of monoamine reuptake blockers has shown that those blocking dopamine uptake prevent access of MPP$^+$ into rat striatal synaptosomes. Similar experiments in rat cortical synaptosomes, where noradrenaline uptake mechanisms predominate, show little uptake of MPP$^+$ to occur. MPTP itself and MPP$^+$ can inhibit the uptake of ^{3}H-dopamine and ^{3}H-5HT into synaptosomal preparations (Heikkila et al., 1985b; Kula et al., 1984). So, although MPTP itself does not appear to be taken up into dopamine neurones it may interfere with such uptake processes.

The involvement of dopamine uptake mechanisms suggests another level at which the toxic actions of MPTP or MPP$^+$ may be limited. Indeed, it has been demonstrated that pretreatment of mice with the dopamine reuptake blocker, mazindol, can prevent the occurrence of MPTP-induced toxicity (Heikkila et al., 1985b). Recently a variety of other compounds interfering with dopamine uptake mechanisms, including nomifensine, amfonelic acid, benztropine, bupropion, budipine, GBR 13098 and amphetamine, all inhibited the persistent reductions in striatal dopamine content produced by MPTP administration to rodents (Melamed et al., 1985a,b; Ricaurte et al., 1985; Przuntek et al., 1985; Pileblad and Carlsson, 1985; Sundstrom and Jonsson, 1985).

Interestingly, in mice, where MPTP also causes a depletion of brain noradrenaline, noradrenaline uptake inhibitors such as desipramine, nortryptiline and maprotiline, selectively protected against this loss. This would implicate the uptake of MPP$^+$ (or indeed MPTP itself) in the toxicity to noradrenaline neurones in the mouse (Pileblad and Carlsson, 1985; Sundstrom and Jonsson, 1985).

Are 5HT neurones involved in the biotransformation of MPTP?

Recently Shen et al. (1985) have suggested that non-dopamine neurones, particularly 5HT neurones, may be involved in the metabolism of MPTP. They showed that rat brain synaptosomes have a greater affinity for uptake of MPP$^+$ than for MPTP and that MPP$^+$ is more likely to accumulate in the striatum than in the hypothalamus where the uptake of MPTP and MPP$^+$ is equivalent. In the striatum uptake of MPP$^+$ and MPTP was blocked by nomifensine and dopamine, but in the hypothalamus uptake of these substances was inhibited by desipramine, imipramine, noradrenaline and 5HT. They suggest that since the hypothalamus is rich in 5HT neurones or other terminals which contain monoamine oxidase B, MPTP may be converted to MPP$^+$ via MPDP$^+$ in these neurones. MPP$^+$ or MPDP$^+$ may then be released from 5HT neurones into the interneuronal space and MPP$^+$ is specifically accumulated in dopaminergic neurones in striatum where it induces neurotoxicity. Once in the striatum MPP$^+$ and MPTP could inhibit monoamine oxidase A activity and thus elevate dopamine to neurotoxic levels although other toxic mechanisms could also account for the striatal cell destruction observed.

Working hypothesis of MPTP action

These pieces of information taken together provide an overall working scheme for MPTP toxicity (figure 9.3). The lipophilic MPTP molecule enters into the brain where it is selectively metabolised by monoamine oxidase B located in mitochondria

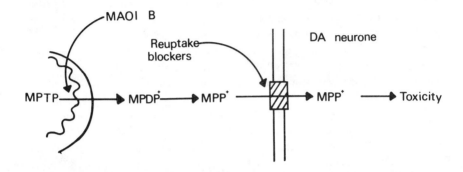

Figure 9.3 Current working hypothesis to explain the selective toxicity of MPTP to nigral dopamine neurones. The lipophilic MPTP enters the brain where it is transformed to MPP$^+$ by MAO B located at an extraneuronal site in close proximity to nigral dopamine neurones. MPP$^+$ is then actually taken up by nigral dopamine neurones where it accumulates causing cell death by an unknown mechanism. MPTP toxicity can be presented either by blockade of MAO B, using compounds such as deprenyl, or by inhibiting reuptake mechanisms, using drugs such as mazindol.

extraneuronally, possibly in glia, or by monoamine oxidase located within non-dopamine neurones, particularly 5HT neurones. The MPDP$^+$ so formed is then converted extraneuronally into MPP$^+$, which is then actively taken up into dopamine neurones by the uptake mechanism. How MPP$^+$ exerts its toxic effects once it has entered into dopamine neurones is not established. While such a scheme seems to explain the actions of MPTP it does, however, leave a number of questions unanswered. For example, the scheme envisaged does not explain the following:

1. If MPP$^+$ is accumulated into dopamine neurones via the dopamine uptake mechanism, why does this only affect nigro-striatal neurones and not meso-limbic and mesocortical dopamine containing neurones?
2. Autoradiographic studies suggest MPP$^+$ accumulated in areas other than the substantia nigra and in regions which contain noradrenaline and 5HT-containing neurones. Why are these neurones not killed by the actions of MPP$^+$?
3. The uptake of MPP$^+$ into dopamine neurones has mainly been demonstrated using rat synaptosomal preparations. However, present evidence would sug-

gest that MPTP and MPP$^+$ are relatively non-toxic in this species. Why does MPP$^+$ uptake into nigro-striatal neurones in the rat not destroy this pathway?

Perhaps a better understanding of the toxicity of MPTP would be gained by an insight into the mechanism of toxicity itself. Already some evidence is accumulating on the mechanism of MPP$^+$ and this will be discussed in the following sections.

INVESTIGATIONS INTO THE MECHANISM UNDERLYING MPTP AND MPP$^+$ TOXICITY

Present interest in the toxic mechanisms underlying MPTP destruction of nigral dopamine-containing cells centres on the effects of the metabolite MPP$^+$. Since this species accumulates within brain, neurotoxicity of MPTP has been attributed to its actions. Indeed, MPTP as a pyridinium ion is capable of redox cycling to induce free radical mechanisms and cellular toxicity. However, it is not proven that MPP$^+$ is itself the toxic moiety or that other components of the MPTP metabolic pathway do not contribute to its toxicity. Only now is evidence starting to appear on the mechanisms by which MPTP and MPP$^+$ might exert neurotoxic effects on dopamine neurones and the ability of close analogues of these compounds to elicit similar effects.

Is MPP$^+$ neurotoxic?

Although inhibition of MPTP metabolism by monoamine oxidase B and the uptake of MPP$^+$ into dopamine neurones has been shown to be associated with a reduction of neurotoxicity, until recently there was no direct evidence that MPP$^+$ itself was neurotoxic. A major difficulty in examining MPP$^+$ neurotoxicity is its high polarity and poor penetration into the brain. Indeed, Perry et al. (1985a) administered MPP$^+$ subcutaneously to mice and found evidence for the accumulation of MPP$^+$ in mouse striatum. However, the levels achieved were far below the levels found after administration of MPTP itself. For this reason the toxicity of MPP$^+$ has been examined by direct intracerebral injection.

In our own study (Bradbury et al., 1986a) we infused both MPTP and MPP$^+$ directly into the dopaminergic cell body group in the substantia nigra of the rat. Infusion of MPTP (10 μg/24 h) produced no loss of striatal dopamine or its metabolites and there was a small but non-persistent fall in ^{3}H-dopamine uptake. In contrast, MPP$^+$ infused into rat substantia nigra was markedly neurotoxic to dopamine function. There was a dramatic decrease in striatal dopamine HVA and DOPAC levels with no change in levels of 5HT or 5HIAA. Infusion of MPP$^+$ caused a large decrease in ^{3}H-dopamine uptake both 1 day and 1 month post-infusion. MPP$^+$ also caused a profound change in motor behaviour characterised by a reduction in locomotion, a loss of ability to coordinate movements with both front- and hindlimbs, and the development of rigidity in forelimbs, hindlimbs and trunk. In similar studies the stereotaxic injection of MPP$^+$ into the medial forebrain bundle of rats or the intracerebroventricular injection in mice resulted in significant losses of dopamine and its metabolites in striatum (Cavalla *et al.*, 1985; Heikkila *et al.*, 1985c). All these results are consistent with the idea that MPP$^+$ may at least be partially responsible for the toxicity observed after MPTP administration. MPP$^+$ is also toxic to mesencephalic dopamine neurones in culture, like MPTP, causing a decrease in ^{3}H-dopamine uptake by the cultures and a decrease in endogenous levels of dopamine and HVA (Mytilineou *et al.*, 1985). Catecholamine histofluorescence demonstrated the loss of fluorescing fibres after exposure to MPP$^+$. Strangely, deprenyl protects these neurons from the actions of MPP$^+$ (Mytilineou and Cohen, 1985).

Involvement of neuromelanin in the mechanism of MPTP and MPP$^+$ toxicity

In the substantia nigra of man and other primate species neuromelanin accumulates within dopamine-containing cells. In contrast, nigral dopamine-containing cells in rodent species do not contain neuromelanin. This difference between species reflects the differences in toxicity of MPTP observed and has led to the idea that neuromelanin may be a key to understanding MPTP neurotoxic actions. Indeed, *in vitro* MPTP binds with micromolar affinity to melanin (Lyden *et al.*, 1983). Recent autoradiographic studies of the distribution of MPTP in the mouse have shown a high level of radioactivity in the pigmented structures of the eye. At 4 and 16 days after the administration of MPTP when most of the drug was eliminated, high levels persisted in this area. However, high levels of radioactivity also persisted within the adrenal medulla. In the albino mouse a low level of radioactivity was found in the tissues corresponding to the pigmented ones (Lyden *et al.*, 1985). So in some areas the persistence of MPTP (or products derived from this substance) may persist due to the presence of neuromelanin. An alternative idea is that MPP$^+$ might react with neuromelanin to generate free radical species which are then neurotoxic (Kopin *et al.*, 1986).

In dogs the dopamine-containing cells of zone compacta of substantia nigra, the ventral tegmental area and the locus coeruleus all contain neuromelanin. In this species MPTP administration causes damage to all three neuromelanin-containing areas. This again would seem to support the neuromelanin hypothesis. However, in primate species and in man there are pigmented brainstem cell groupings which are unaffected by MPTP administration despite the fact that they contain neuromelanin and despite the fact that MPP$^+$ has been shown to accumulate there. At present the role of neuromelanin is uncertain. Although the evidence is not strongly in support of the role of neuromelanin, it is still possible that it may play some part in either the accumulation of MPP$^+$ or in the mechanism of its neurotoxic actions.

Inhibition of MPTP toxicity by agents preventing oxidative free radical attack

The redox cycling of MPP$^+$ can potentially induce free radical mechanisms leading to neuronal cell death (see review by Kopin *et al.*, 1986). Recently, three reports have indicated that ascorbic acid administration to mice protects against the neurotoxic actions of MPTP as judged by lack of change in striatal dopamine content and in ^{3}H-mazindol binding (Sershen et al., 1985b; Perry et al., 1985b; Wagner et al., 1985). In addition, α-tocopherol, β-carotene and N-acetylcysteine all decreased striatal dopamine loss and α-tocopherol prevented neuronal loss in the substantia nigra. All these findings would suggest that antioxidants can prevent the neuro-toxicity of MPTP or MPP$^+$ by interfering with free radical mechanisms.

Are other MPTP-like molecules neurotoxic?

It remains to be determined what portion of the MPTP or MPP$^+$ molecule imparts neurotoxicity and whether other chemically related substances may also exert neurotoxic actions on nigro-striatal systems. The importance of the '4–5' double bond has previously been demonstrated (Langston et al., 1984d). In a recent study we have compared the effects of MPTP, MPP$^+$ and three analogues of MPTP lacking an N-methyl moiety, namely 4-phenylpiperidine, 4-phenyl-1,2,3,6 tetrahydro-pyridine, and 4-phenylpyridine. These substances were infused continuously for a period of 4 days into the substantia nigra of the rat. Within 12 h of commencing the bilateral infusion of MPTP or MPP$^+$, rats showed marked motor deficits with reduction in locomotor activity, loss of ability to move forelimbs and grip with the forepaws; following MPP$^+$ infusions similar loss of movement in hindlimbs occurred associated with development of limb and body rigidity. These motor deficits were not induced by the three analogues of MPTP on infusion into the substantia nigra. After 4 days of infusion motor deficits caused by MPTP, and in particular MPP$^+$ were still marked, and for MPP$^+$ these correlated with a marked loss of striatal dopamine, DOPAC and HVA (table 9.7). 4-Phenyl-1,2,3,6-tetrahydropyridine

Table 9.7 Changes in Striatal Dopamine and DOPAC Concentrations Following the Infusion of MPTP, MPP$^+$ and Analogues of MPTP into Rat Substantia Nigra

Drug treatment	Dopamine (ng/mg)	DOPAC (ng/mg)
Vehicle	9.0 ± 0.2	679 ± 28
MPTP	8.8 ± 0.4	740 ± 15
MPP$^+$	5.7 ± 0.3*	337 ± 19*
Vehicle	11.0 ± 0.9	776 ± 19
4-phenylpiperidine	10.3 ± 0.6	821 ± 53
4-phenyl-1,2,3,6-tetrahydropyridine	8.2 ± 0.6*	625 ± 57*
4-phenylpyridine	11.0 ± 0.8	956 ± 82

Mean ± 1 SEM: $n = 5$.
*$p < 0.05$ Student's t test compared to vehicle.
All compounds were infused bilaterally into the substantia nigra (10 µg/24 h) and animals were killed on the 4th day.

caused a small loss in striatal dopamine and DOPAC while the other analogues failed to modify the striatal content of dopamine or its metabolites.

Clearly small alterations of chemical structure related to MPTP and its metabolite can critically alter the ability to induce behavioural and neurochemical changes reflecting neurotoxicity on the nigro-striatal dopamine system. Removal of the N-methyl group is such a change. The compound 4-phenyl-1,2,3,6-tetrahydropyridine is interesting in this respect since it is dramatically less toxic than MPTP, although still causing a small loss of striatal dopamine and DOPAC content. This suggests that N-methylation *in vivo* does not occur to any significant extent and that metabolism by monoamine oxidase, if occurring at all, results in the production of metabolites with only limited toxicity. That 4-phenylpyridine is not toxic is an indication of the absence of any notable cerebral N-methylation. Clearly the presence of a pyridinium ion is important in imparting neurotoxic potential. Overall, it appears that an N-methyl group and partial unsaturation of the alicyclic moiety plays a critical role in the toxicity of MPTP. All available evidence points to a quaternary cation incorporated into a biphenyl-like aromatic system as the toxophore responsible for MPP$^+$ activity.

Since quaternary nitrogen appears important for the action of MPP$^+$ we determined whether a number of other quaternary phenylpyridine derivatives could also exert neurotoxic actions similar to those produced by MPP$^+$ (Bradbury *et al.*, 1986, unpublished observations). In particular, MPP$^+$ bears a strong structural resemblance to the herbicide paraquat which is known to exhibit pronounced toxic actions on peripheral organs. Therefore, we have used continuous bilateral infusion into the substantia nigra to compare the potential behavioural and neurochemical consequences of the neurotoxic actions of MPP$^+$, paraquat and 1-(4-pyridyl) pyridine on the nigro-striatal system (table 9.8). As shown previously, MPP$^+$ produced marked motor deficit and losses of dopamine, HVA and DOPAC in striatum or substantia nigra. Similar intranigral infusion of paraquat (10 μg) caused

Table 9.8 Changes in Striatal Dopamine, HVA or DOPAC Concentrations. Following the Infusion of MPP$^+$ and Pyridinium Ion Analogues into Rat Substantia Nigra

Drug treatment (dose μg/24 h)	Dopamine (ng/g)	DOPAC (pg/g)	HVA (pg/g)
Vehicle	9.6 ± 0.5	862 ± 70	650 ± 6
MPP$^+$ (10), 4 days	4.2 ± 0.14*	393 ± 25*	220 ± 25*
Paraquat (10), 1 day	17.5 ± 2.3$^+$	3088 ± 54$^+$	4517 ± 103$^+$
Paraquat (1), 4 days	9.5 ± 0.6	1506 ± 210$^+$	1398 ± 229$^+$
1-(4-pyridyl)-pyridinium chloride (10), 4 days	8.3 ± 0.4	718 ± 144	719 ± 62

Mean ± 1 SEM; n = 5.
*$p < 0.05$ Student's t test; decreased compared to control.
+$p < 0.05$ Student's t test; increased compared to control.
All animals were killed immediately following cessation of the infusions.

seizure and barrel rotation after 24 h. A lower dose of paraquat (1 μg) caused no behavioural change. The high dose of paraquat produced marked increases in dopamine, HVA and DOPAC concentrations in the striatum; HVA and DOPAC concentrations in substantia nigra were also increased, although dopamine levels were reduced. The lower dose of paraquat also increased the striatal HVA and DOPAC concentrations, although dopamine levels were unaltered. However, in the substantia nigra a decrease in dopamine content was maintained although DOPAC concentrations were unaffected. Intranigral infusion of 1-(4-pyridyl)pyridine did not alter motor behaviour or the concentrations of dopamine, HVA or DOPAC in the striatum. In substantia nigra the dopamine content was again reduced but levels of HVA and DOPAC were unaffected. It appears that quaternary nitrogen compounds closely related to MPP$^+$ do not mimic its neurotoxic action in substantia nigra. This may relate to their failure to be taken up into dopamine neurones and exert neurotoxic effects.

Others have also examined a variety of MPTP analogues for toxicity. For example, the n-propyl analogue and derivatives with a p-chloro- or fluoro-moiety were examined in rodents but found not to show neurotoxic effects (Duvoisin *et al.*, 1986; Fuller *et al.*, 1985). Similarly, administration of cinnamaldehyde, N,N-dimethylcinnamylamine, arecoline and 2-methyl-1,2,3,4-tetrahydroisoquinolinediol did not alter striatal dopamine content in mice (Perry *et al.*, 1985b).

Strict structural requirements for MPTP-like neurotoxicity are perhaps not surprising. The compound must be capable of entering dopamine neurones either passively or by active uptake and there exert a neurotoxic action. Also prior metabolism by MAO B may be required. Such complexities are illustrated by 1-methyl-4-benzyl-1,2,3,6-tetrahydropyridine (MBTP): this was a better substrate for MAO B than MPTP, but the resulting pyridine species had low affinity for dopamine uptake mechanisms and *in vivo* produced no reduction in mouse brain dopamine content (Youngster and Heikkila, 1986).

Recently, however, two neurotoxic derivatives of MPTP have been described. In mice 1-methyl-4-(2-thienyl)-1,2,3,6-tetrahydropyridine (MTTP) did produce striatal dopamine loss but was one-fourth as potent as MPTP (Fuller *et al.*, 1986). So replacement of the phenyl ring by a heterocycle can lead to some retention of toxicity. Another derivative, 1-methyl-4-(1'-methylphenyl)-1,2,3,6-tetrahydropyridine (2'-CH$_3$ MPTP) also is toxic in mice, as judged by striatal dopamine depletion, decreased ^{3}H-dopamine uptake and nigral cell loss (Youngster *et al.*, 1986). In mice this derivative is approximately ten times more potent than MPTP, although in primates its toxicity appears less than that of MPTP (Nomoto *et al.*, 1986, unpublished data).

RELEVANCE OF THE MPTP MODEL TO THE CAUSE OF IDIOPATHIC PARKINSON'S DISEASE

Few clues have emerged as to the cause of idiopathic Parkinson's disease. The excitement caused by the discovery of MPTP as a selective nigro-striatal toxin active on peripheral administration to humans and other non-human primate species must be tempered by a discussion of its relevance to idiopathic Parkinson's disease. The administration of MPTP to primates produces a motor syndrome which closely resembles that of Parkinson's disease and which responds to drug treatment in a similar manner. However, the pathological and biochemical changes of MPTP-induced Parkinsonism are clearly limited compared to the extensive changes in brain pathology and biochemistry occurring in Parkinsonian patients. So can the mechanisms by which MPTP destroys nigro-striatal dopamine neurones be of any relevance to those processes which underlie the changes occurring in Parkinson's disease? Certainly as far as the hallmark of Parkinson's disease, namely the Lewy body, is concerned there is no evidence to date that MPTP administration results in the appearance of these inclusion bodies. Since the Lewy body is found in all areas of brain degenerating in Parkinson's disease different mechanisms may be operative. Indeed, while loss of the cholinergic cells of substantia innominata occurs in Parkinson's disease accompanied by the appearance of Lewy bodies, MPTP does not cause degeneration in this area as judged by the lack of change in cortical choline acetyl-transferase activity. However, it must be remembered that MPTP-induced Parkinsonism has only been studied acutely or sub-acutely, whereas idiopathic Patkinson's disease may develop over many years. The mechanisms underlying cell death in Parkinson's disease may continue after the disease first appears, whereas MPTP treatment is discontinued and compensatory mechanisms in the brain may help to counter some of the secondary changes which would otherwise occur. At present MPTP appears to be an interesting neurotoxin, which only partially mimics the characteristics of idiopathic Parkinson's disease. There may, however, be much to be learnt from a study of its mechanism of action, since we may discover why the cells of the nigro-striatal dopamine containing system are especially sensitive to its actions and why such cells may be among the first to degenerate in Parkinson's disease.

The ability of MPTP to induce Parkinsonism raises the question of whether MPTP or MPP^+-like molecules may be involved in the production of the idiopathic disease itself. It could be that aberrant metabolic pathways in brain give rise to endogenous MPTP or MPP^+-like molecules which exert a neurotoxic action over many years. We, and others, have postulated as to the type of compounds which might be involved but so far there is no evidence of such processes occurring (Ramsden and Williams, 1985; Fellman and Nutt, 1985; Ohkuba et al., 1985; Collins and Neafsey, 1985; Testa et al., 1985). The alternative hypothesis would be that MPTP or MPP^+-like molecules exist in the environment and that at least some cases of Parkinson's disease have an exogenous environmental cause. Indeed, it has been recently speculated that those groups of the population exposed to herbicides, fungicides and pesticides may show a higher incidence of Parkinson's disease than is observed in the general population (Barbeau and Roy, 1985; Barbeau et al., 1985d). This has relevance to the MPTP story since MPP^+, otherwise known as cyperquat, is itself a herbicide closely related to paraquat. But, to date such ideas are purely speculative and require further detailed study. Indeed, in the United Kingdom the incidence of Parkinson's disease as recorded by death certificates has not increased dramatically since the 1920s, and there is little other evidence to point to an environmental cause of Parkinson's disease.

SUMMARY

The incidence of Parkinson's disease increases with advancing age and is associated with a primary loss of brain dopamine neurones although other pathological and biochemical changes also occur. Why dopamine cells die in Parkinson's disease is not known but the discovery that 1-methyl-4-phenyl-1,2,3,6-tetrahydropyridine (MPTP) can destroy dopamine cells in brain and induce Parkinsonism in man and other non-human primates may provide a clue to its cause.

MPTP is relatively ineffective in causing dopamine cell loss in rodents. In primate species MPTP induces a selective loss of dopamine-containing cells in the zona compacta of the substantia nigra. Other dopamine-containing cell bodies in the brain generally appear to be spared. In primates MPTP does not induce changes in markers of 5HT, noradrenaline, GABA, acetylcholine or peptide neurones. In this respect the pathological and biochemical changes produced by MPTP only partially resemble those observed in idiopathic Parkinson's disease.

The toxicity of MPTP appears related to its selective conversion to the corresponding pyridinium species (MPP^+) by monoamine oxidase B. MPP^+ appears to accumulate within catecholamine-containing neurones of brain. The formation of MPP^+, its accumulation in brain and the toxicity of MPTP itself can be prevented by selective monoamine oxidase B inhibitors such as deprenyl. MPP^+ may enter dopamine neurones by acting as a substrate for the dopamine reuptake system. The toxicity of MPTP can be prevented by administration of dopamine reuptake blockers such as mazindol. Focal injection of MPP^+ into substantia nigra shows this substance to be neurotoxic but the mechanism of cell death remains unclear. MPP^+ may undergo redox cycling leading to the generation of free radicals. MPTP provides a model of nigral dopamine cell death and the toxic actions of this substance may have relevance to an environmental cause of Parkinson's disease.

ACKNOWLEDGEMENTS

This study was supported by the Parkinson's Disease Society, the Medical Research Council, the Wellcome Trust and the Research Funds of the Bethlem Royal and Maudsley Hospitals and King's College Hospital.

REFERENCES

Allen, J. M., Cross, A. J., Yeats, J. C., Ghatei, M. A., McGregor, G. P., Close, S. P., Pay, S., Marriott, A. S., Tyers, M. B., Crow, T. J. and Bloom, S. R. (1986). Neuropeptides and dopamine in the marmoset: Effect of treatment with 1-methyl-4-phenyl-1,2,3,6-tetrahydropyridine (MPTP) a animal model for Parkinson's Disease? *Brain*, **109**, 143–57

Ballard, P. A., Tetrud, J. W. and Langston, J. W. (1985). Permanent human parkinsonism due to 1-methyl-4-phenyl-1,2,3,6-tetrahydropyridine (MPTP): Seven cases. *Neurology*, **35**, 949–56

Barbeau, A. and Roy, M. (1985). Genetic susceptibility, environmental factors and Parkinson's disease. Presented at VIII. International Symposium on Parkinson's disease, New York, 1985

Barbeau, A., Dallaire, L., Buu, N. T., Veilleux, F., de Boyer, H., Lanney, L. E., Irwin, I., Langston, E. B. and Langston, J. W. (1985a). New amphibian models for the study of 1-methyl-4-phenyl-1,2,3,6-tetrahydropyridine (MPTP). *Life Sci.*, **36**, 1125–34

Barbeau, A., Dallaire, L., Buu, N. T., Poirier, J. and Rucinska, E. (1985b). Comparative behavioural, biochemical and pigmentary effects of MPTP, MPP$^+$ and paraquat in rana pipens. *Life Sci.*, **37**, 1529–38

Barbeau, A., Roy, M. and Langston, J. W. (1985c). Neurological consequence of industrial exposure to 1-methyl-4-phenyl-1,2,3,6-tetrahydropyridine. *Lancet*, **1**, 747

Barbeau, A., Roy, M., Paris, S., Cloutier, T., Plasse, L. and Poirier, J. (1985d). Ecogenetics of Parkinson's disease: 4-hydroxylation of debrisoquine. *Lancet*, **2**, 1213–16

Bauman, R. J., Jameson, H. D., Weisberg, L. H., McKean, H. E. and Hack, D. G. (1980). Cigarette smoking and Parkinson's disease. *Neurology*, **30**, 839–43

Bocchetta, A., Piccardi, M. P., del Zompo, M., Pintus, S. and Corsini, S. (1985). 1-methyl-4-phenyl-1,2,3,6-tetrahydropyridine: Correspondence of its binding sites to monoamine oxidase in rat brain and inhibition of dopamine oxidative deamination *in vivo* and *in vitro*. *J. Neurochem.*, **45**, 673–6

Boyce, S., Kelly, E., Reavil, C., Jenner, P. and Marsden, C. D. (1984). Repeated administration of N-methyl-4-phenyl-1,2,3,6-tetrahydropyridine to rats is not toxic to striatal dopamine neurones. *Biochem. Pharmac.*, **23**, 1747–52

Bradbury, A. J., Costall, B., Domeney, A. M., Testa, B., Jenner, P., Marsden, C. D. and Naylor, R. J. (1985). The toxic action of MPTP and its metabolite MPP$^+$ are not mimicked by analogues of MPTP lacking an N-methyl moiety. *Neurosci. Lett.*, **61**, 121–6

Bradbury, A. J., Costall, B., Domeney, A. M., Jenner, P., Kelly, M. E., Marsden, C. D. and Naylor, R. J. (1986a). 1-methyl-4-phenylpyridine is neurotoxic to the nigrostriatal dopamine pathway. *Nature, Lond.*, **319**, 56–7

Bradbury, A. J., Costall, B., Domeney, A. M., Jenner, P., Marsden, C. D., and Naylor, R. J. (1986b). MPTP infusion into rat substantia nigra causes hypokinesia and bradykinesia, which are reversed by L-DOPA treatment (in press)

Burns, R. S., Chiueh, C. C., Markey, S. P., Ebert, M. H., Jacobowitz, D. M. and Kopin, I. J. (1983). A primate model of parkinsonism: selective destruction of dopaminergic neurones in the pars compacta of the substantia nigra by N-methyl-4-phenyl-1,2,3,6-tetrahydropyridine. *Proc. Nat. Acad. Sci. USA*, **80**, 4546–50

Burns, R. S., Chiueh, C. C., Paris, J. and Kopin, I. J. (1985a). Neuromelanin accumulation and the mechanisms of toxicity of MPTP. Presented at Symposium on MPTP: A parkinsonism syndrome producing neurotoxin, Bethesda, Maryland

Burns, R. S., LeWitt, P. A., Ebert, M. H., Pakkenberg, H. and Kopin, I. J. (1985b). The clinical syndrome of striatal dopamine deficiency. Parkinsonism induced by 1-methyl-4-phenyl-1,2,3,6-tetrahydropyridine. *New Engl. J. Med.*, **312**, 1418–21

Burns, R. S., Chiueh, C. C., Paris, J., Markey, S. and Kopin, I. J. (1986). Biochemical and pathological effects of MPTP in the Rhesus monkey. In: *Recent Developments in Parkinson's Disease* (ed. S. Fahn, C. D. Marsden, P. Jenner and P. Teychenne), Raven Press, New York, pp. 127–36

Castagnoli, N., Chiba, K. and Trevor, A. J. (1985). Potential bioactivation pathways for the neurotoxin 1-methyl-4-phenyl-1,2,3,6-tetrahydropyridine (MPTP). *Life Sci.*, **36**, 225–30

Cavalla, D., Hadjiconstantinou, M., Laird, H. E. and Neff, N. H. (1985). Intracerebroventricular administration of 1-methyl-4-phenyl-1,2,3,6-tetrahydropyridine (MPTP) and its metabolite 1-methyl-4-phenylpyridine ion (MPP$^+$) decrease dopamine and increase acetylcholine in the mouse neostriatum. *Neuropharmacology*, **24**, 585–6

Chiba, K., Trevor, A. and Castagnoli, N. (1984). Metabolism of the neurotoxic tertiary amine, MPTP, by brain monoamine oxidase. *Biochem. Biophys. Res. Comm.*, **120**, 574–8

Chiueh, C. C., Markey, S. P., Burns, R. S., Johannessen, J. N., Pert, A. and Kopin, I. J. (1984). Neurochemical and behavioural effects of systemic and intranigral administration of N-methyl-4-phenyl-1,2,3,6-tetrahydropyridine in the rat. *Eur. J. Pharmacol.*, **100**, 189–94

Cohen, G., Pasik, P., Cohen, B., Leist, A., Mytilineou, C. and Yahr, M. D. (1985). Pargyline and deprenyl prevent the neurotoxicity of 1-methyl-4-phenyl-1,2,3,6-tetrahydropyridine (MPTP) in monkeys. *Eur. J. Pharmacol.*, **106**, 209–10

Cohen, G. and Mytilineou, C. (1985). Studies on the mechanism of action of 1-methyl-4-phenyl-1,2,3,6-tetrahydropyridine (MPTP). *Life Sci.*, **35**, 237–42

Collins, M. A. and Neafsey, E. J. (1985). β-carboline analogues of N-methyl-4-phenyl-1,2,3,6-tetrahydropyridine (MPTP): Endogenous factors underlying idiopathic parkinsonism. *Neurosci. Lett.*, **55**, 179–84

Davis, G. C., Williams, A. C., Markey, S. P., Ebert, M. H., Caine, E. D., Reichert, C. M. and Kopin, I. J. (1979). Chronic parkinsonism secondary to intravenous injection of mepiridine analogues. *Psychiat. Res.*, **1**, 249–54

Del Zompo, M., Bocchetta, A., Piccardi, M. P., Pintus, S. and Corsini, G. U. (1984). Inhibition of ^{3}H-MPTP binding to rat brain by pargyline. *Biochem. Pharmac.*, **33**, 4105–7

Denton, T. and Howard, B. D. (1984). Inhibition of dopamine uptake by N-methyl-4-phenyl-1,2,3,6-tetrahydropyridine, a cause of parkinsonism. *Biochem. Biophys. Res. Comm.*, **119**, 1186–90

Duvoisin, R. C., Eldridge, R., Williams, A., Nutt, J. and Calne, D. (1981). Twin study of Parkinson's disease. *Neurology*, **31**, 77–80

Duvoisin, R. C., Heikkila, R. E., Nicklas, W. J. and Hess, A. (1986). Dopaminergic neurotoxicity of MPTP in the mouse: A model of Parkinsonism. In: *Recent Developments in Parkinson's Disease* (ed. S. Fahn, C. D. Marsden, P. Jenner and P. Teychenne), Raven Press, New York, pp. 147–54

Ehringer, H. and Hornykiewicz, O. (1960). Verteilung von Noradrenalin und Dopamin (3-hydroxytyramin) im gehirn des menschene und ihr verhalten bei erkrankungen des extrapyramidalen systems. *Klin. Wochensch.*, **38**, 1238–9

Fellman, J. H. and Nutt, J. N. (1985). MPTP-like molecules and Parkinson's disease. *Lancet*, **1**, 924

Forno, L. S. (1982). Pathology of Parkinson's disease. In: *Movement Disorders* (ed. C. D. Marsden and S. Fahn), Butterworths, London, pp. 25–40

Fuller, R. W., Hemrich-Leucke, S. K. and Robertson, D. W. (1985). Comparison of 1-methyl-4-(p-chlorophenyl)-1,2,3,6-tetrahydropyridine 1-methyl-4-phenyl-1,2,3,6-tetrahydropyridine (MPTP) and perchloroamphetamine as monoamine depletors. *Chem. Path. Res. Comm.*, **50**, 57–65

Fuller, R. W., Robertson, D. W. and Hemrich-Luecke, S. K. (1986). Persistent depletion of striatal dopamine in mice by 1-methyl-4-(2-thienyl)-1,2,3,6-tetrahydropyridine (MTTP). *Biochem. Pharmac.*, **35**, 143–4

Garvey, J., Petersen, M., Walters, C., Rose, S., Hunt, S., Briggs, R., Jenner, P. and Marsden, C. D. (1986). Administration of MPTP to the common marmoset does not alter cortical cholinergic function. *J. Movement Disorders.* (in press)

Gaspar, P., Berger, B., Jenner, P. and Marsden, C. D. (1986). Subacute histopathological changes in the brain of marmosets treated with MPTP. *Neuropath. appl. Neurobiol.* (in press)

Gupta, M., Felten, D. L. and Gash, D. M. (1984). MPTP alters central catecholamine neurons in addition to the nigrostriatal system. *Brain Res. Bull.*, **13**, 737–42

Hallman, H., Olson, L. and Jonsson, G. (1984). Neurotoxicity of the meperidine analogue N-methyl-4-phenyl-1,2,3,6-tetrahydropyridine on brain catecholamine neurons in the mouse. *Eur. J. Pharmacol.*, **97**, 133–6

Heikkila, R. E. (1985). Differential neurotoxicity of 1-methyl-4-phenyl-1,2,3,6-tetrahydropyridine (MPTP) in Swiss Webster mice from different sources. *Eur. J. Pharmac.*, **117**, 131–3

Heikkila, R. E., Cabbat, F. S., Manzino, L. and Duvoisin, R. C. (1984a). Effects of 1-methyl-4-phenyl-1,2,3,6-tetrahydropyridine on neostriatal dopamine in mice. *Neuropharmacology*, **3**, 711–13

Heikkila, R. E., Hess, A. and Duvoisin, R. C. (1984b). Dopaminergic neurotoxicity of 1-methyl-4-phenyl-1,2,3,6-tetrahydropyridine in mice. *Science, N.Y.*, **224**, 1451–3

Heikkila, R. E., Manzino, L., Cabbat, F. S. and Duvoisin, R. C. (1984c). Protection against the dopaminergic neurotoxicity of 1-methyl-4-phenyl-1,2,3,6-tetrahydropyridine by monoamine oxidase inhibitors. *Nature, Lond.*, **311**, 467–9

Heikkila, R. E., Hess, A. and Duvoisin, R. C. (1985a). Dopaminergic neurotoxicity of 1-methyl-4-phenyl-1,2,3,6-tetrahydropyridine (MPTP) in the mouse: Relationship between monoamine oxidase, MPTP metabolism and neurotoxicity. *Life Sci.*, **36**, 231–6

Heikkila, R. E., Youngster, S. K., Manzino, L., Cabbat, F. S. and Duvoisin, R. C. (1985b). Effects of 1-methyl-4-phenyl-1,2,3,6-tetrahydropyridine and related compounds on the uptake of ^{3}H-3,4-dihydroxyphenylethylamine and ^{3}H-5-hydroxytryptamine in neostriatal synaptosomal preparations. *J. Neurochem.*, **44**, 310–13

Heikkila, R. E., Nicklas, W. J., Manzino, L. and Duvoisin, R. C. (1985c). Dopaminergic toxicity after the stereotaxic administration of the 1-methyl-4-phenyl pyridinium ion (MPP[+]) to rats. *Neurosci. Lett.* (in press)

Heikkila, R. E., Manzino, L., Cabbat, F. S. and Duvoisin, R. C. (1985d). Studies on the oxidation of the dopaminergic neurotoxin 1-methyl-4-phenyl-1,2,3,6-tetrahydropyridine by monoamine oxidase B. *J. Neurochem.*, **45**, 1049–54

Hornykiewicz, O. (1982). Brain neurotransmitter changes in Parkinson's disease. In: *Movement Disorders* (ed. C. D. Marsden and S. Fahn), Butterworths, London, pp. 41–58

Irwin, I. and Langston, J. W. (1985). Selective accumulation of MPP[+] in the substantia nigra: A key to neurotoxicity? *Life Sci.*, **36**, 207–12

Jarvis, M. F. and Wagner, G. C. (1985a). Neurochemical and functional consequences following 1-methyl-4-phenyl-1,2,3,6-tetrahydropyridine (MPTP) and methamphetamine. *Life Sci.*, **36**, 249–54

Jarvis, M. F. and Wagner, G. C. (1985b). Age-dependent effects of 1-methyl-4-phenyl-1,2,3,6-tetrahydropyridine (MPTP). *Neuropharmacology*, **24**, 581–3

Javitch, J. A. and Snyder, S. H. (1985). Uptake of MPP$^+$ by dopamine neurons explain selectivity of parkinsonism inducing neurotoxin MPTP. *Eur. J. Pharmacol.*, **106**, 455–6

Javitch, J. A., Uhl, G. R. and Snyder, S. H. (1984). Parkinsonism-induced neurotoxin, N-methyl-4-phenyl-1,2,3,6-tetrahydropyridine: characteristics and localization of receptor binding sites in rat and human brain. *Proc. Nat. Acad. Sci. U.S.A.*, **81**, 4591–5

Javitch, J. A., d'Amato, R. J., Strittmatter, S. M. and Snyder, S. H. (1985). Parkinsonism inducing neurotoxin, N-methyl-4-phenyl-1,2,3,6-tetrahydropyridine: uptake of the metabolite N-methyl-4-phenylpyridine by dopamine neurons explain selective toxicity. *Proc. Nat. Acad. Sci. U.S.A.*, **82**, 2173–7

Javoy-Agid, F., Taquet, H., Cesselin, F., Epelbaum, J., Grouselle, D., Mauborgne, A., Studler, J. M. and Agid, Y. (1984). Neuropeptide in Parkinson's disease. In: *Catecholamines: Part C Neuropharmacology and Central Nervous System – Therapeutic Aspects* (ed. E. Usdin, A. Carlsson, A. Dablstum and J. Engel), Alan R. Liss, New York, p. 35

Jenner, P., Sheehy, M. and Marsden, C. D. (1983). Noradrenaline and 5-hydroxytryptamine modulation for brain dopamine function: Implications for the treatment of Parkinson's disease. *Brit. J. Clin. Pharmac.*, **15**, 277S–289S

Jenner, P., Rupniak, N. M. J., Rose, S., Kelly, E., Kilpatrick, G., Lees, A. and Marsden, C. D. (1984). 1-methyl-4-phenyl-1,2,3,6-tetrahydropyridine-induced parkinsonism in the common marmoset. *Neurosci. Lett.*, **50**, 85–90

Jenner, P., Rose, S., Boyce, S., Kelly, E., Kilpatrick, G., Rupniak, N. M. J., Briggs, R. and Marsden, C. D. (1986a). Induction of Parkinsonism in the common marmoset by administration of 1-methyl-4-phenyl-1,2,3,6-tetrahydropyridine. In: *Recent Development in Parkinson's Disease* (ed. S. Fahn, C. D. Marsden, P. Jenner and P. Teychenne), Raven Press, New York, pp. 137–46

Jenner, P., Taquet, H., Mauborgne, A., Benoliel, J. T., Cesselin, F., Rose, S., Javoy-Agid, F., Agid, Y. and Marsden, C. D. (1986b). Lack of change in basal ganglia neuropeptide content following subacute MPTP treatment of the common marmoset. *J. Neurochem.* (in press)

Johannesen, J. N., Chiueh, C. C., Burns, R. S. and Markey, S. P. (1985). Differences in the metabolism of MPTP in the rodent and primate parallel differences in sensitivity to the neurotoxic effects. *Life Sci.*, **36**, 219–24

Jonsson, G., Sundstrom, E., Mefford, I., Olson, L., Johnson, S., Freedman, R. and Hoffer, B. (1985). Electrophysiological and neurochemical correlates of the neurotoxic effects of 1-methyl-4-phenyl-1,2,3,6-tetrahydropyridine (MPTP) on central catecholamine neurons in the mouse. *Naunyn-Schmied. Arch. Pharmac.*, **331**, 1–6

Kinemuchi, H., Arai, Y. and Toyoshima, Y. (1985). Participation of brain and monoamine oxidase B form in the neurotoxicity of 1-methyl-4-phenyl-1,2,3,6-tetrahydropyridine: Relationship between the enzyme inhibition and the neurotoxicity. *Neurosci. Lett.*, **58**, 195–200

Kopin, I. J., Markey, S. P., Burns, R. S., Johannessen, J. N. and Chiueh, C. C. (1986). Mechanisms of neurotoxicity of MPTP. In: *Recent Developments in Parkinson's Disease* (ed. S. Fahn, C. D. Marsden, P. Jenner and P. Teychenne), Raven Press, New York, pp. 165–73

Kula, N. S., Baldessarini, R. J., Campbell, A., Finklestein, S., Ram, V. J. and Neumeyer, J. L. (1984). Effects of N-substituted phenyltetrahydropyridines in cerebral high-affinity synaptosomal uptake of dopamine and other monoamines in several mammalian species. *Life Sci.*, **34**, 2567–75

Langston, J. W. and Ballard, P. (1983). Parkinson's disease in a chemist working with 1-methyl-4-phenyl-1,2,3,6-tetrahydropyridine. *New Engl. J. Med.*, **309**, 310

Langston, J. W. and Ballard, P. (1984). Parkinsonism induced by 1-methyl-4-phenyl-1,2,3,6-tetrahydropyridine (MPTP): Implications for the treatment and pathogenesis of Parkinson's disease. *Can. J. Neurol. Sci.*, ii (suppl), 160–5

Langston, J. W., Ballard, P., Tetrud, J. W. and Irwin, I. (1983). Chronic parkinsonism in humans due to a product of meperidine-analog synthesis. *Science, N.Y.*, **219**, 979–80

Langston, J. W., Forno, L. S., Rebert, C. S. and Irwin, I. (1984a). Selective nigral toxicity after systemic administration of 1-methyl-4-phenyl-1,2,3,6-tetrahydropyridine (MPTP) in the squirrel monkey. *Brain Res.*, **292**, 390–4

Langston, J. W., Irwin, I., Langston, E. B. and Forno, L. S. (1984b). Pargyline prevents MPTP-induced parkinsonism in primates. *Science, N.Y.*, **225**, 1480–2

Langston, J. W., Langston, E. B. and Irwin, I. (1984c). MPTP-induced parkinsonism in human and non-human primates – clinical and experimental aspects. *Acta Neurol. Scand.*, **70** (suppl. 100), 49–54

Langston, J. W., Irwin, I., Langston, E. B. and Forno, L. S. (1984d). The importance of the '4–5' double bond for neurotoxicity in primates of the pyridine derivative MPTP. *Neurosci. Lett.*, **50**, 289–94

Lyden, A., Bondesson, U., Larsson, B. S. and Lindquist, N. G. (1983). Melanin affinity of 1-methyl-4-phenyl-1,2,3,6-tetrahydropyridine, an inducer of chronic Parkinsonism in humans. *Acta Pharmacol. Toxicol.*, **53**, 429–32

Lyden, A., Bondesson, U., Larsson, B. S., Lindquist, N. G. and Olson, L. I. (1985). Autoradiography of 1-methyl-4-phenyl-1,2,3,6-tetrahydropyridine (MPTP): Uptake in the monoaminergic pathways and in melanin containing tissues. *Acta Pharmac. Toxicol.*, **57**, 130–5

Markey, S. P., Johannessen, J. N., Chiueh, C. C., Burns, R. S. and Herkinbaum, M. A. (1984). Intraneuronal generation of a pyridinium metabolite may cause drug-induced parkinsonism. *Nature, Lond.*, **311**, 464–7

Marsden, C. D., Parkes, J. D. and Quinn, N. (1982). Fluctuations of disability in Parkinson's disease – clinical aspects. In: *Movement Disorders* (ed. C. D. Marsden and S. Fahn), Butterworths, London, pp. 96–122

Melamed, E. and Youdim, M. B. H. (1985). Prevention of dopaminergic toxicity of MPTP in mice by phenylethylamine, a specific substrate of type B monoamine oxidase. *Brit. J. Pharmac.*, **86**, 529–31

Melamed, E., Rosenthal, J., Cohen, O., Uzzan, A. and Globus, M. (1985a). Amphetamine, but not reserpine, protects mice against dopaminergic neurotoxicity of MPTP. *Neuropharmacology*, **24**, 923–5

Melamed, E., Rosenthal, J., Globus, M., Cohen, O. and Uzzan, A. (1985b). Suppression of MPTP-induced dopaminergic neurotoxicity in mice by nomifensine and L-DOPA. *Brain Res.*, **342**, 401–4

Melamed, E., Rosenthal, J., Globus, M., Cohen, O., Frucht, Y. and Uzzan, A. (1985c). Mesolimbic dopamine neurons are not spared by MPTP neurotoxicity in mice. *Eur. J. Pharmac.*, **114**, 97–100

Mitchell, I. J., Cross, A. J., Sambrook, M. A. and Crossman, A. R. (1985). Sites of the neurotoxic action of 1-methyl-4-phenyl-1,2,3,6-tetrahydropyridine in the macaque monkey include the ventral tegmental area and the locus coeruleus. *Neurosci. Lett.*, **61**, 195–200

Mytilineou, C. and Cohen, G. (1984). 1-methyl-4-phenyl-1,2,3,6-tetrahydropyridine destroys dopamine neurons in explants of rat embryo mesencephalon. *Science, N.Y.*, **225**, 529–31

Mytilineou, C. and Cohen, G. (1985). Deprenyl protects dopamine neurons from the neurotoxic effects of 1-methyl-4-phenyl-pyridinium ion. *J. Neurochem.*, **45**, 1951–3

Mytilineou, C., Cohen, G. and Heikkila, R. E. (1985). 1-Methyl-4-phenylpyridine (MPP$^+$) is toxic to mesencephalic dopamine neurones in culture. *Neurosci. Lett.*, **57**, 19–24

Ohkuba, S., Hirano, T. and Oka, K. (1985). Methyltetrahydro-carboline and Parkinson's disease. *Lancet*, **i**, 1273

Parsons, B. and Rainbow, T. C. (1984). High-affinity binding sites for ^{3}H-MPTP may correspond to monoamine oxidase. *Eur. J. Pharmacol.*, **102**, 375–7

Perry, T. L., Yong, V. W., Jones, K., Wall, R. A., Clavier, R. M., Foulks, J. G. and Wright, J. M. (1985a). Effects of N-methyl-4-phenyl-1,2,3,6-tetrahydropyridine and its metabolite N-methyl-4-phenylpyridinium ion on dopaminergic nigrostriatal neurons in the mouse. *Neurosci. Lett.*, **58**, 321–6

Perry, T. L., Yong, V. W., Clavier, R. M., Jones, K., Wright, J. M., Foulks, J. G. and Wall, R. A. (1985b). Partial protection from the dopaminergic neurotoxin N-methyl-4-phenyl-1,2,3,6-tetrahydropyridine by four different antioxidants in the mouse. *Neurosci. Lett.*, **60**, 109–14

Peterson, L. A., Caldera, P. S., Trevor, A., Chiba, K. and Castagnoli, N. Jr (1985). Studies on the 1-methyl-4-phenyl-2,3-dihydropyridinium species 2,3-MPDP$^+$, the monoamine oxidase catalysed oxidation product of the nigro-striatal toxin 1-methyl-4-phenyl-1,2,3,6-tetrahydropyridine (MPTP). *J. Med. Chem.*, **28**, 1432–6

Pileblad, E. and Carlsson, A. (1985). Catecholamine-uptake inhibitors present the neurotoxicity of 1-methyl-4-phenyl-1,2,3,6-tetrahydropyridine (MPTP) in mouse brain. *Neuropharmacology*, **24**, 689–92

Pileblad, E., Nissbrandt, H. and Carlsson, A. (1984). Biochemical and functional evidence for a marked dopamine releasing action of N-methyl-4-phenyl-1,2,3,6-tetrahydropyridine (NMPTP) in mouse brain. *J. Neurol. Trans.*, **60**, 199–203

Pileblad, E., Fornstedt, B., Clark, D. and Carlsson, A. (1985). Acute effects of 1-methyl-4-phenyl-1,2,3,6-tetrahydropyridine on dopamine metabolism in mouse and rat striatum. *J. Pharm. Pharmac.*, **37**, 707–12

Przuntek, H., Russ, H., Henning, K. and Pindur, U. (1985). The protective effect of 1-tetrabutyl-4,4-diphenylpiperidine against the nigro-striatal neurodegeneration caused by 1-methyl-4-phenyl-1,2,3,6-tetrahydropyridine. *Life Sci.*, 1195–200

Rainbow, T. C., Parsons, B., Wieczorek, C. M. and Manaker, J. (1985). Localization in rat brain of binding sites for parkinsonism toxin MPTP. Similarities with ^{3}H-pargyline binding to monoamine oxidase. *Brain Res.*, **330**, 337–42

Ramsden, D. B. and Williams, A. C. (1985). Production in nature of compounds resembling methylphenyltetrahydropyridine, a possible cause of Parkinson's disease. *Lancet*, **i**, 215–16

Reznikoff, G., Manaker, S., Parsons, B., Rhodes, C. H. and Rainbow, T. C. (1985). Similar distribution of monoamine oxidase (MAO) and parkinsonian toxin (MPTP) binding sites in human brain. *Neurology*, **35**, 1415–19

Ricaurte, G. A., Langston, J. W., DeLaney, L. E., Irwin, I. and Brooks, J. O. (1985). Dopamine uptake blocks protect against the dopamine depleting effect of 1-methyl-4-phenyl-1,2,3,6-tetrahydropyridine (MPTP) in the mouse striatum. *Neurosci. Lett.*, **59**, 259–64

Rinne, U. K. (1982). Brain neurotransmitter receptors in Parkinson's disease. In: *Movement Disorders* (ed. C. D. Marsden and S. Fahn), Butterworths, London, pp. 59–74

Saghal, A., Andrews, J. S., Biggins, J. A., Candy, J. M., Edwardson, J. A., Keith, A. B., Turner, J. D. and Wright, C. (1984). N-methyl-4-phenyl-1,2,3,6-tetrahydropyridine (MPTP) affects locomotor activity without producing a nigrostriatal lesion in the rat. *Eur. J. Pharmacol.*, **48**, 179–84

Salach, J. I., Singer, T. P., Castagnoli, N. Jr and Trevor, A. (1984). Oxidation of the neurotoxic amine 1-methyl-4-phenyl-1,2,3,6-tetrahydropyridine (MPTP) by monoamine oxidases A and B; suicide inactivation of the enzymes by MPTP. *Biochem. Biophys. Res. Comm.*, **125**, 831–5

Schmidt, C. J., Matsuda, L. A. and Gibb, J. W. (1984). *In vitro* release for tritiated monoamines from rat CNS tissue by the neurotoxic compound 1-methyl-phenyl-tetrahydropyridine. *Eur. J. Pharmacol.*, **103**, 255–60

Schneider, J. S., Yuviler, A. and Markham, C. H. (1985). Behavioural, histological and biochemical characteristics of the MPTP model of Parkinson's disease in the cat. Presented at symposium on MPTP: A parkinsonian syndrome producing neurotoxin, Bethesda, Maryland.

Sershen, H., Mason, M. F., Hashim, A. and Lajtha, A. (1985a). Effect of N-methyl-4-phenyl-1,2,3,6-tetrahydropyridine (MPTP) on age related changes in dopamine turnover and transporter function on the mouse striatum. *Eur. J. Pharmacol.*, **113**, 135–6

Sershen, H., Reith, M. E. A., Hashim, A. and Lajtha, A. (1985b). Protection against 1-methyl-4-phenyl-1,2,3,6-tetrahydropyridine neurotoxicity by the antioxidant ascorbic acid. *Neuropharmacology*, **24**, 1257–9

Sheehy, M. P., Schachter, M., Parkes, J. D. and Marsden, C. D. (1981). GABA-mimetics, Parkinson's disease and other movement disorders. In: *Research Progress in Parkinson's Disease* (ed. F. Clifford Rose and R. Capildeo), Pitman Medical, London, pp. 309–17

Shen, R-S., Abell, C. W., Gressner, W. and Brossi, A. (1985). Serotonergic conversion of MPTP and dopaminergic accumulation of MPP$^+$. *Febs Lett.*, **189**, 225–30

Steranka, L. R., Polite, L. N., Perry, K. W. and Fuller, R. W. (1983). Dopamine depletion in rat brain by MPTP (1-methyl-4-phenyl-1,2,3,6-tetrahydropyridine). *Res. Comm. Substance Abuse*, **4**, 315–23

Sundstrom, E. and Jonsson, G. (1985). Pharmacological interference with the neurotoxic action of 1-methyl-4-phenyl-1,2,3,6-tetrahydropyridine (MPTP) on central catecholamine neurons in the mouse. *Eur. J. Pharmacol.*, **110**, 293–9

Testa, B., Naylor, R., Costall, B., Jenner, P. and Marsden, C. D. (1985). Does an endogenous methylpyridinium analogue cause Parkinson's disease. *J. Pharm. Pharmac.*, **37**, 679–80

Uhl, G. R., Javitch, J. A. and Snyder, S. H. (1985). Normal MPTP binding sites in Parkinsonian substantia nigra: Evidence for extraneuronal toxin conversion in human brain. *Lancet*, **1**, 956–7

Wagner, G. C., Jarvis, M. F. and Carelli, R. M. (1985). Ascorbic acid reduces the dopamine depletion induced by MPTP. *Neuropharmacology*, **24**, 1261–2

Wallace, R. A., Boldry, R., Schmittgen, T., Miller, D. and Uretsky, N. (1984). Effect of 1-methyl-4-phenyl-1,2,3,6-tetrahydropyridine (MPTP) on monoamine neurotransmitters in mouse heart and brain. *Life Sci.*, **35**, 285–91

Weissman, J., Trevor, A., Chiba, K., Peterson, L. A., Caldera, P., Castagnoli, N. Jr and Baillie, T. (1985). Metabolism of the nigrostriatal toxin 1-methyl-4-phenyl-1,2,3,6-tetrahydropyridine by lower homogenate fractions. *J. Med. Chem.*, **28**, 997–1001

Wieczorek, C. M., Parsons, B. and Rainbow, T. C. (1984). Quantitative autoradiography of ^{3}H-MPTP binding sites in rat brain. *Eur. J. Pharmacol.*, **98**, 453–4

Youngster, S. K. and Heikkila, R. E. (1986). Studies on the mechanism of MPTP-MPP$^+$-induced neurotoxicity. In: *MPTP: A Neurotoxin Producing A Parkinsonian Syndrome* (ed. S. P. Markey, N. Castagnoli Jr, A. J. Trevor and I. J. Kopin), Academic Press, New York (in press)

Youngster, S. K., Duvoisin, R. C., Hess, A., Sonsalla, P. K., Kindt, M. V. and Heikkila, R. E. (1986). 1-methyl-4-(2'-methylphenyl)-1,2,3,6-tetrahydropyridine (2'-CH$_2$-MPTP) is a more potent dopaminergic neurotoxin than MPTP in mice. *Eur. J. Pharmacol.*, in press

Zamir, N., Skofitsch, G., Bannon, M. J., Helke, C. J., Kopin, I. J. and Jacobowitz, D. M. (1984). Primate model of Parkinson's disease: Alteration in multiple opioid systems in the basal ganglia. *Brain Res.*, **322**, 356–60

10

Hexane Neuropathy: Studies in Experimental Animals and Man

Anthony P. DeCaprio

INTRODUCTION

n-Hexane is a straight-chain hydrocarbon solvent which currently enjoys wide industrial and commercial application. The US National Institute of Occupational Safety and Health (NIOSH) has estimated that over 2 million workers per year in the US are exposed to significant levels of n-hexane in the course of their workday (NIOSH, 1977). NIOSH has also named more than 40 industrial classifications and processes in which n-hexane is commonly employed. A discussion of n-hexane neurotoxicity must necessarily include the two related compounds methyl n-butyl ketone (MnBK) and 2,5-hexanedione (2,5-HD) (figure 10.1). All three compounds produce an identical neurotoxic syndrome and differ only in their relative potencies as neurotoxic agents. MnBK is itself a useful solvent, while 2,5-HD has only minor commercial use.

Human neuropathy due to n-hexane exposure was first reported amongst Japanese using the solvent in household sandal-making operations, where poor ventilation commonly resulted in high ambient air levels (Yamada, 1967; Yamamura, 1969). These early reports were generally ignored until a large outbreak of neuropathy in an Ohio textile plant was traced to use of the related solvent MnBK (Billmaier et al., 1974; Allen et al., 1975). Typical symptoms of exposure included body weight loss, fatigue, and distal sensory paraesthesia, followed eventually by muscular weakness in the extremities. Human neuropathy was also found to be associated with inhalation of vapours containing n-hexane during solvent abuse ('glue-sniffing') (Goto et al., 1974; Altenkirch et al., 1977).

Early experimental work in a number of species revealed characteristic changes in peripheral nerves as a result of MnBK exposure (Duckett et al., 1974; Mendell et al., 1974). These changes included focal giant axonal swellings in distal nerve

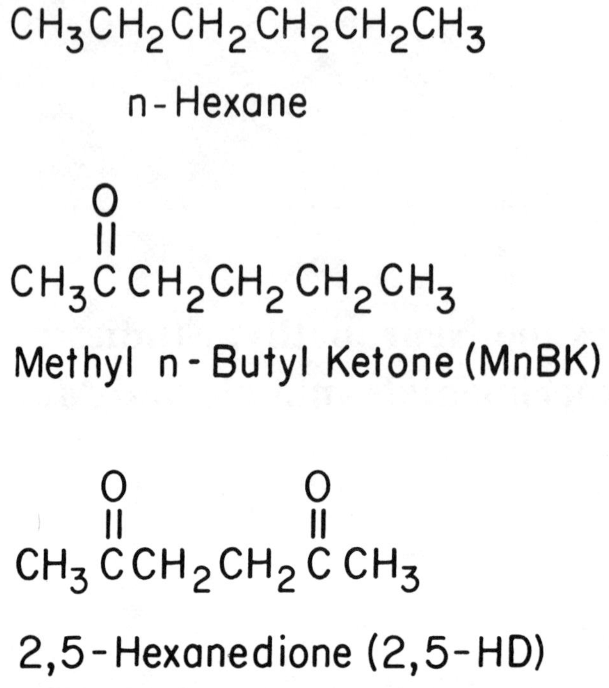

$$CH_3CH_2CH_2CH_2CH_2CH_3$$

n-Hexane

$$CH_3 \overset{\overset{\displaystyle O}{\|}}{C} CH_2CH_2 CH_2CH_3$$

Methyl n-Butyl Ketone (MnBK)

$$CH_3 \overset{\overset{\displaystyle O}{\|}}{C} CH_2CH_2 \overset{\overset{\displaystyle O}{\|}}{C} CH_3$$

2,5-Hexanedione (2,5-HD)

Figure 10.1   Chemical structures of n-hexane and related neurotoxic derivatives.

regions accompanied by paranodal retraction of the myelin sheath. Subsequent investigation revealed that the neurotoxic effects of n-hexane in rats were identical to those produced by MnBK, although a more prolonged exposure time was required with the former compound (Schaumburg and Spencer, 1976). Similar alterations were reported in certain long and large diameter myelinated nerve fibres in the central nervous system. Based on these pathological findings, n-hexane and MnBK were included among the class of compounds able to produce the neurotoxic syndrome known as 'central-peripheral distal axonopathy' (CPDA) (Spencer and Schaumburg, 1976).

In vivo studies in rats and guinea pigs revealed that the metabolic pathways of n-hexane and MnBK were linked through the common metabolites 2-hexanol and 5-hydroxy-2-hexanone (Abdel-Rahman *et al.*, 1976; DiVincenzo *et al.*, 1977; Couri *et al.*, 1978). The latter metabolite was found to undergo additional conversion to detoxified products including CO_2, urea, γ-valerolactone, and 2,5-dimethylfuran. n-Hexane and MnBK were also converted to hexanoic acid and norleucine, products which could be utilised in normal intermediary metabolism. In contrast to these detoxification pathways, a major metabolic product of 5-hydroxy-2-hexanone was the γ-diketone 2,5-HD, which was suggested as the actual neurotoxic agent (DiVincenzo *et al.*, 1976). This was confirmed by reports that animals administered pure 2,5-HD developed a neuropathy indistinguishable from that produced by either n-hexane or MnBK in a significantly shorter period of time (Spencer and Schaumburg, 1975). Thus, the neurotoxic syndrome induced by n-hexane, MnBK and 2,5-HD is now generally referred to as 'γ-diketone neuropathy'.

DISTINGUISHING FEATURES OF γ-DIKETONE NEUROPATHY

Target organ specificity

The neurotoxic diketones exhibit an organ-specific toxicity in that only the nervous system and testicular germinal epithelium are affected during exposure to these compounds (Spencer et al., 1980). Even at high dose levels with wide tissue distribution of the diketone there is no histological or clinical evidence of damage to other organ systems. Although body weight loss is frequently observed following 2,5-HD administration, Gillies et al. (1980) have shown that this is primarily an effect of decreased food and water consumption. The phenomenon does not appear to be related to neurotoxicity, since neuropathy in hens (DeCaprio et al., 1983) and in mice (Mennear, 1982) administered 2,5-HD has been reported without accompanying body weight loss. The nervous system specificity of these compounds has been attributed to the unique structural characteristics and energy requirements of the nerve fibre as compared with other tissues (Spencer et al. 1980; Cavanagh, 1982; DeCaprio et al., 1983).

Structure/activity relationships

Following reports that 2,5-HD was the active neurotoxic agent in n-hexane neuropathy (Spencer and Schaumburg, 1975), Spencer et al. (1978) demonstrated that only those compounds with a γ-diketone structure (i.e. two carbon spacing between the carbonyl groups), or which could be metabolised to a γ-diketone, were capable of inducing the syndrome. Thus, 2,5-HD and 2,5-hexanediol were neurotoxic, whereas 2,4-HD, 2,3-HD, and 1,6-hexanediol were not. Later studies demonstrated the neurotoxicity of the γ-diketones 2,5-heptanedione and 3,6-octanedione, and of 5-nonanone, which was shown to be metabolised to MnBK and 2,5-HD (O'Donoghue and Krasavage, 1979; DiVincenzo et al., 1982). The methylated γ-diketone derivatives 3-methyl-2,5-HD and 3,4-dimethyl-2,5-hexanedione (DMHD) produce a similar neuropathy (Anthony et al., 1983a; Monaco et al., 1985). However, the axonal lesions induced by these compounds appear to be more proximally-localised than those with 2,5-HD. All γ-diketones examined to date appear to cause a neuropathy similar to that produced by 2,5-HD, and this finding has led to several mechanistic hypotheses based on the unique chemical reactivity of these compounds.

Neurofilament accumulation and distal axonal degeneration

A pathological hallmark of γ-diketone neuropathy is axonal swelling due to massive accumulation of neurofilaments within the axoplasm of selected nerve fibres

(Spencer and Schaumburg, 1977a). These swellings are typically localised to the distal, non-terminal regions of long, large diameter myelinated nerve fibres, on the proximal side of nodes of Ranvier. Both peripheral (PNS) and central nervous system (CNS) fibres may be involved concurrently, and fibre diameter appears to be a more important determinant of vulnerability than fibre length (Spencer and Schaumburg, 1977b). Changes resembling Wallerian degeneration are often seen distal to areas of neurofilament (NF) accumulation, particularly in the PNS. Disorientation of neurofilaments with arrangement into whorled patterns is frequently observed, along with segregation of microtubules and other organelles within a channel near the centre or at the periphery of the axon (Powell *et al.*, 1978; Sahenk and Mendell, 1983). Other studies have demonstrated a reduced rate of fast axoplasmic transport through areas of NF accumulation along the nerve fibre (Griffin *et al.*, 1977; Mendell and Sahenk, 1980).

Recent reports have shown that NF accumulations are widespread in CNS nerve fibres from rats receiving 2,5-hexanediol in the drinking water, and are not necessarily restricted to the most distal regions of the nerve fibre (Cavanagh and Bennetts, 1981). In addition, frank nerve degeneration does not follow NF accumulation in CNS fibres until relatively late in the syndrome. This phenomenon has been attributed to the more ready passage of NF masses into nerve terminals for subsequent degradation in CNS as compared to PNS fibres (Cavanagh, 1982; Jones and and Cavanagh, 1982). The nodes of Ranvier in peripheral fibres appear to be much more restrictive to the passage of NF accumulations than CNS nodes (Jones and Cavanagh, 1983). It is currently unclear whether altered NF structure and subsequent aggregation represents a primary cause of the neurotoxic syndrome or is a secondary effect of some other critical biochemical lesion within the axon.

In vivo protein binding

DiVincenzo *et al.* (1977) reported the presence of protein-bound radiolabel in liver, kidney and brain from rats receiving a single oral dose of $[1\text{-}^{14}\text{C}]$ MnBK. Peak tissue protein levels occurred just after maximum blood levels of 2,5-HD (8 h versus 6 h after dosing), suggesting a covalent reaction of metabolically-derived 2,5-HD with protein. Radiolabel in protein remained the same or decreased only slightly between 8 and 24 h after dosing, again indicating covalent binding. Administration of $[^{14}\text{C}]$ 2,5-HD (8 mg/kg) to rats via a single ip injection resulted in residual label in both spinal cord and sciatic nerve 48 h after dosing (Spencer *et al.*, 1980). A later study reported high-affinity binding of $[1,6\text{-}^{14}\text{C}]$ 2,5-HD to myelin and other subcellular fractions of sciatic nerve from rats after intraneural injection of the diketone (Sabri and Spencer, 1981). These results provided evidence for chemical reaction of 2,5-HD with tissue macromolecules *in vivo*, and suggested that such binding may be critical to the evolution of γ-diketone neuropathy.

Direct action

The γ-diketones appear to act directly upon axonal components. Politis *et al.* (1980) demonstrated that application of 2,5-HD to areas of intact exposed rat sciatic nerve resulted in typical axonal swellings and NF accumulations localised to the treated regions. Unexposed contralateral nerves displayed no alterations, and nerves exposed to non-neurotoxic 2,4-HD or 1,6-hexanediol developed only non-specific fibre breakdown and Schwann cell necrosis. Experiments utilising a struc-turally- and functionally-coupled explanted mouse spinal cord, dorsal root ganglion, and skeletal muscle tissue culture system were also able to reproduce γ-diketone neuropathy *in vitro* (Veronesi *et al.*, 1983). Axonal swellings in motor nerve fibres were produced by nutrient fluid containing 2,5-HD (and metabolic precursors of 2,5-HD) but not by fluid containing 2,4-HD. Recent studies have shown that the direct intrafascicular injection of 2,5-HD into rat sciatic nerve induces a rapid (within 5 min) reorganisation of axonal organelles (Griffin *et al.*, 1983; Zagoren *et al.*, 1983), whereas non-neurotoxic 2,4-HD produces no alterations.

MECHANISMS OF ACTION

The unique characteristics of γ-diketone neuropathy described above have led to a number of proposed molecular mechanisms of action for these compounds. While they differ in detail, the various hypotheses all postulate covalent reaction of γ-diketones with one or more axonal proteins as the critical initiating event in the neuropathy. Although space does not permit a detailed presentation of each hypo-thesis here, a general discussion of their respective merits is possible. The interested reader is referred to several current reviews of the proposed mechanisms (DeCaprio, 1985; Sayre *et al.*, 1985; Spencer *et al.*, 1985).

Inhibition of axonal energy-producing enzymes

An early suggestion was made by Spencer and Schaumburg (1978) that the mech-anism of γ-diketone neuropathy involved inhibition of axonal glycolytic enzymes. This was visualised to proceed via covalent reaction with active-site cysteine sul-phydryl groups. They proposed that such inhibition would compromise the normal flow of nutrients carried within fast axoplasmic transport, a process requiring glycolytic energy sources. This would conceivably result in a selective degeneration of long, large-diameter nerve fibres, as these contain a relatively greater volume of axoplasm and would therefore have the greatest energy requirements. The distal areas of such fibres were suggested to be the most vulnerable, since they lie the furthest from the nerve cell body (Spencer *et al.*, 1979).

A number of *in vitro* studies have examined this hypothesis. Incubation with 2,5-HD appears to result in selective inhibition of certain glycolytic enzymes, including glyceraldehyde-3-phosphate dehydrogenase (GAPDH), phosphofructo-kinase (PFK), and enolase (Sabri *et al.*, 1979a,b; Howland *et al.*, 1980; Sabri, 1984a). Similar studies utilising nervous tissue homogenates and isolated intact nerve fibres have also indicated glycolytic enzyme inhibition. However, such effects generally require either unphysiologically high concentrations of γ-diketone or prolonged incubation, and may therefore be irrelevant to the actual mechanism *in vivo*. In addition, 2,5-HD appears to be only a weak sulphydryl inhibitor compared to such classical reagents as N-ethylmaleimide and iodoacetate (Graham and Abou-Donia, 1980).

The results of *in vivo* studies related to this hypothesis have been inconclusive. Sabri *et al.* (1979b) reported a moderate (31%) decrease in brain PFK activity in rats administered 2,5-HD in the drinking water. A similar decrease in sciatic nerve (but not brain) GAPDH activity was observed in a later experiment (Sabri, 1984b). Animals in both studies exhibited evidence of substantial clinical neuropathy and body weight loss at the time of assay, so the possibility cannot be excluded that the enzyme inhibition may have been related more to general debilitation than to a specific neurotoxic action. Other investigators demonstrated little or no change in kinetic parameters (K_m, V_{max}) for glucose-dependent lactate production in nervous tissue from 2,5-HD-treated rats (LoPachin *et al.*, 1984). Some indirect evidence of glycolytic inhibition *in vivo* has been reported. Decreased O_2 uptake in sciatic nerves was observed in rats administered 2,5-HD, although the decrease was not dose-related (Couri and Nachtman, 1979). A reduction in local glucose utilisation in the superior colliculus of rats following 2,5-HD exposure was reported by Griffiths *et al.* (1981), who suggested a lowered energy demand due to decreased impulse conduction rather than a primary inhibition of axonal glycolysis.

A number of considerations argue against a molecular mechanism involving axonal glycolytic inhibition in γ-diketone neuropathy. Although marked inhibition of fast axoplasmic transport could undoubtedly result in eventual nerve degeneration, NF accumulation would not necessarily accompany this process. Neurofilaments are an integral part of the slow transport component (Lasek and Hoffman, 1976), and no evidence has been provided that this process requires energy from glycolysis. An inhibition of glycolysis might be expected to produce widespread systemic effects, yet γ-diketone toxicity appears to be restricted to the nervous system and testicular germinal epithelium. The rapid disorganisation of axonal neurofilaments and microtubules following direct exposure of nerve fibres to 2,5-HD (Griffin *et al.*, 1983; Zagoren *et al.*, 1983) is also difficult to account for via this mechanism. This finding implicates direct reaction of the compound with cyto-skeletal elements as a more likely mechanism. Recently, the glycolytic inhibition hypothesis has been modified to postulate a requirement for metabolic energy in the maintenance of normal NF-microtubule (MT) interaction (Spencer *et al.*, 1985). However, no such requirement has been demonstrated in mammalian axons, and the cytoskeletal network can be reproduced in the absence of energy-producing systems (Aamodt and Williams, 1984).

Pyrrole adduct formation in axonal cytoskeletal protein

Several years ago, DeCaprio and Weber (1980, 1981) demonstrated the reaction of 2,5-HD with protein lysine ε-amine moieties to yield 2,5-dimethylpyrrole adducts (figure 10.2). This reaction was shown to occur not only *in vitro* using various model systems (DeCaprio *et al.*, 1982), but also *in vivo* following systemic exposure to the diketone (DeCaprio *et al.*, 1982, 1983). Based on this evidence, pyrrole adduct formation was proposed as the critical initiating event in γ-diketone neuro-

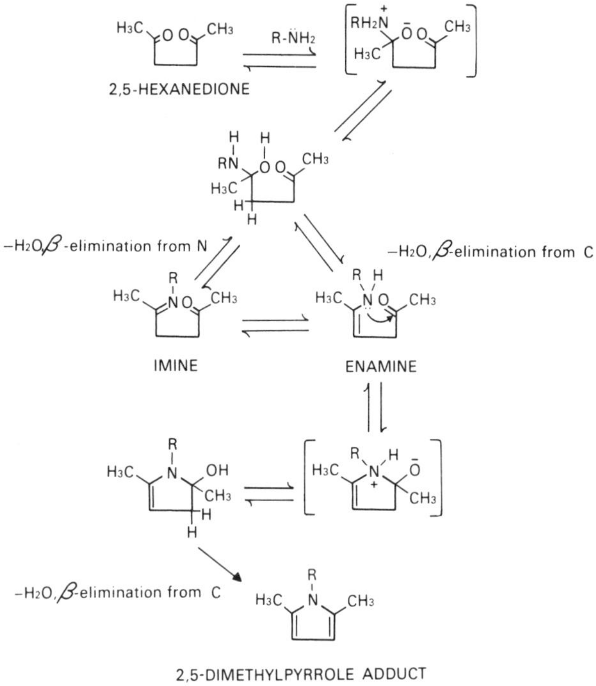

Figure 10.2 Mechanism of pyrrole formation from the reaction of 2,5-hexanedione with primary amines.

pathy (DeCaprio *et al.*, 1982, 1983). Such a reaction could account for the structure/activity relationships in the neuropathy, since only γ-diketones can form the pyrrole ring (Jones and Bean, 1977). Several hypotheses have since been proposed to link the phenomenon of pyrrole formation in NF protein to the ultimate NF accumulation and nerve fibre degeneration in the neuropathy, and these are discussed below and summarised in figure 10.3.

Enhancement of neurofilament hydrophobicity

In view of the hydrophobic nature of the 2,5-dimethylpyrrole adduct, DeCaprio *et al.* (1983), proposed an increase in hydrophobic interactions between neurofilaments with a resultant accumulation and aggregation of these cytoskeletal elements in γ-diketone neuropathy. Aggregated NF masses were then hypothesised to become lodged at areas of axonal constriction (i.e. nodes of Ranvier), thus inducing a physical blockade to nutrient transport into the distal axon. In addition to explaining the various characteristic observations in the neuropathy, this mechanism could account for the enhanced neurotoxicity (relative to 2,5-HD) of the γ-diketone DMHD (Anthony *et al.*, 1983a,b). The 2,3,4,5-tetramethylpyrrole

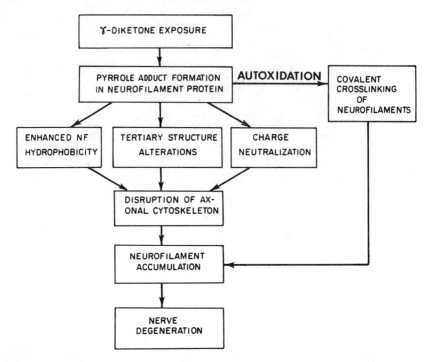

Figure 10.3 Proposed mechanisms linking pyrrole adduct modification of neurofilament protein with nerve degeneration in γ-diketone neurotoxicity.

moiety formed by this derivative would be substantially more hydrophobic than the dimethyl adduct from 2,5-HD.

Current evidence indicates that pyrrole adduct concentrations in axonal cytoskeletal protein preparations from rat brain following 2,5-HD exposure average 1-2 adducts/molecule of protein (DeCaprio and O'Neill, 1985). Although these apparently low average conversion levels might not result in substantial increases in NF hydrophobicity, pyrrole concentrations in the individual NF subunit proteins could be substantially higher. Efforts are currently underway in this laboratory to quantitate pyrrole formation and hydrophobicity in specific NF subunit proteins.

Neurofilament crosslinking

Prior to the elucidation of pyrrole adduct formation by 2,5-HD, Graham (1980) had proposed a mechanism of NF accumulation in γ-diketone neuropathy involving covalent crosslinking of neurofilaments via 'conjugated Schiff base' derivatives (Chio and Tappel, 1969). This proposal was based upon studies demonstrating the formation of an orange chromophore (λ_{max} = 475 nm) in incubation mixtures of protein and 2,5-HD. In this scheme, progressive, covalent crosslinking of neurofilaments was visualised to occur during transport of the structures along the axon.

The proposed result of such NF modification was the lodging of crosslinked masses of neurofilaments at nodes of Ranvier in the distal axon and distal nerve degeneration (Graham, 1980).

Early studies on the pyrrole-forming reaction had also revealed the presence of chromophores in 2,5-HD:protein mixtures, along with dimers, trimers and higher polymers of the protein (DeCaprio and Weber, 1980, 1981; DeCaprio *et al.*, 1982). Since these products could be minimised by incubation under N_2, they were attributed to secondary autoxidative modification of the pyrrole adduct, a well-known phenomenon in pyrrole chemistry (Jones and Bean, 1977). In view of the above findings and the lack of structural data in support of a 'conjugated Schiff base' mechanism, Graham *et al.* (1982a,b) proposed a modified hypothesis based on autoxidative covalent crosslinking of NF proteins modified by pyrrole adduct formation. The enhanced neurotoxicity of the DMHD derivative was later attributed to an increased susceptibility of the tetramethylpyrrole adduct to autoxidative reactions (Anthony *et al.*, 1983b).

Recent studies have confirmed the formation of NF protein polymers both *in vitro* and *in vivo* following 2,5-HD exposure (Graham *et al.*, 1984; DeCaprio and O'Neill, 1985). However, other evidence suggests that such crosslinking may be unrelated to the ultimate neurotoxic mechanism. For example, the rapid rearrangement of axonal cytoskeletal elements following local exposure of nerve fibres to 2,5-HD (Griffin *et al.*, 1983; Zagoren *et al.*, 1983) is more likely a direct consequence of pyrrole adduct formation rather than progressive secondary autoxidation. In addition, other known protein crosslinking agents do not produce neurotoxic syndromes characterised by NF accumulations (Spencer *et al.*, 1978).

Disruption of axonal cytoskeletal architecture

Reports of NF-MT disorganisation following direct exposure of nerve fibres to 2,5-HD led to the initial suggestion that this compound acts via disruption of axonal cytoskeletal architecture (Griffin *et al.*, 1983). However, the specific chemical nature or target site of such 2,5-HD:cytoskeletal interaction was not addressed. DeCaprio and O'Neill (1985) elaborated on this theme by suggesting that tertiary structure alterations accompanying pyrrole adduct formation at certain critical lysine ε-amine functions in the NF subunit proteins were responsible for the observed changes. In this mechanism, conversion of even a single amine might be sufficiently deleterious to induce axonal cytoskeletal disorganisation. They further proposed the NF(H) subunit protein as a particularly appropriate target in γ-diketone neuropathy. The lysine-rich carboxy-terminal 'tail' of this protein is thought to be responsible for interactions between neurofilaments and other axonal cytoskeletal elements (Ellisman and Porter, 1980; Geisler *et al.*, 1983). Thus, specific pyrrole adduct formation at one or more sites within this region could result in cytoskeletal disruption, changes in slow transport, and eventual nerve degeneration. Some support for selective vulnerability of the NF(H) protein during 2,5-HD exposure in rats has been reported (DeCaprio and O'Neill, 1985).

A related hypothesis was recently put forth by Sayre *et al.* (1985), who proposed a mechanism involving 'charge neutralisation' of the NF proteins. This scheme implicates the loss of positive charge following the γ-diketone:lysine reaction rather than the specific formation of pyrrole adduct *per se* as the critical molecular lesion. Loss of charge is postulated to either directly alter NF–MT interactions or to disrupt NF phosphorylation, a process believed to be critical to normal integration of neurofilaments into the axonal cytoskeleton (Julien and Mushynski, 1982).

FUTURE PROSPECTS

Research progress in the area of n-hexane neurotoxicity has been rapid since the early reports of neuropathy in humans exposed to this important solvent. In fact, this is one instance where we may be close to demonstrating a molecular mechanism for a specific type of chemically-induced axonopathy. Current evidence indicates that the nerve degeneration is almost certainly a consequence of pyrrole adduct modification of axonal cytoskeletal protein, most likely involving the NF subunit proteins. However, the temporal sequence of events between pyrrole formation in cytoskeletal protein and ultimate axonal degeneration remains obscure. Final elucidation of these events may not be achieved until more data are available on the metabolic and structural characteristics of the normal axonal cytoskeleton, an area where progress has fortunately also been rapid. It must be recognised that the various proposed mechanisms (i.e. enhanced NF hydrophobicity, tertiary structure alterations, NF charge neutralisation, neurofilament crosslinking) may not be mutually exclusive, and may all play some role in γ-diketone neuropathy.

Other aspects of this neuropathy demand further attention. The observed dependence of the axonal localisation of NF swellings (i.e. distal versus proximal) on both γ-diketone structure and relative dose is an important finding (Anthony *et al.*, 1983a,b; Sayre *et al.*, 1985). Such a dependence has been accounted for in a number of ways; by the enhanced tendency to autoxidation (Anthony *et al.*, 1983b) or hydrophobicity (DeCaprio *et al.*, 1983) of highly alkylated pyrrole adducts, by increased penetration of methylated γ-diketone derivatives into the axoplasm (DeCaprio, 1985), or by unequal distribution of the diketone to various areas of the axon (DeCaprio, 1984). Resolution of this question should aid in understanding not only the mechanism of γ-diketone neuropathy but also the distal versus proximal dependence of the NF alterations present in certain naturally-occurring disorders (Pena, 1982).

A related phenomenon is the potentiation of n-hexane, MnBK, and 2,5-HD neuropathies by co-administration of a non-neurotoxic ketone such as methyl ethyl ketone (MEK) (Altenkirch *et al.*, 1982; Ralston *et al.*, 1985). Evidence has been provided that much of this effect may be due to either induction of cytochrome P-450 (in the case of n-hexane and MnBK) or to competitive inhibition of conjugating enzymes (in the case of 2,5-HD) by the MEK, thus raising the effective serum level ·of 2,5-HD. An alternative explanation might be competition between MEK and 2,5-HD for non-critical protein binding sites, allowing more of the neurotoxic derivative to reach presumably more critical axonal target sites (DeCaprio, 1984). A further understanding of this potentiation is important, in view of the increasing use of MEK as a co-solvent in various commercial and industrial hexanebased preparations.

Recently, several investigators have proposed unifying hypotheses in an attempt to define a generalised mechanism for xenobiotics producing axonal degeneration accompanied by NF accumulation (CPDA) (Spencer *et al.*, 1979; Graham *et al.*, 1982b; Griffin *et al.*, 1983; Spencer *et al.*, 1985; Sayre *et al.*, 1985). These chemicals constitute a structurally-diverse group, including not only the γ-diketones but such derivatives as carbon disulphide, acrylamide, β,β'-iminodipropionitrile, aluminium salts, and disulphiram (Antabuse). Several members of this group are widely used in industrial and commercial applications. While it is beyond the scope of the present review to discuss the various aspects of these hypotheses, it is significant that the neurotoxins are all postulated to act directly upon one or more axonal cytoskeletal components. Thus, they may serve as valuable tools in examining the pathogenesis of certain naturally-occurring neurological syndromes (e.g. congenital giant axonal neuropathy, Alzheimer's disease) which are characterised by cytoskeletal disorganisation within the nerve cell.

ACKNOWLEDGEMENT

This work was supported by a research grant (OH-01972) from the US National Institute of Occupational Safety and Health.

REFERENCES

Aamodt, E. J. and Williams, R. C. (1984). Microtubule-associated proteins connect microtubules and neurofilaments *in vitro. Biochemistry*, 23, 6031–5

Abdel-Rahman, M. S., Hetland, L. B. and Couri, D. (1976). Toxicity and metabolism of methyl n-butyl ketone. *Am. Ind. Hyg. Assoc. J.*, 37, 95–102

Allen, N., Mendell, J. R., Billmaier, D. J., Fontaine, R. E. and O'Neill, J. (1975). Toxic polyneuropathy due to methyl n-butyl ketone: An industrial outbreak. *Arch. Neurol.*, 32, 209–18

Altenkirch, H., Mager, J., Stoltenburg, G. and Helmbrecht, J. (1977). Toxic polyneuropathies after sniffing a glue thinner. *J. Neurol.*, 214, 137–52

Altenkirch, H., Wagner, H. M., Stoltenburg-Didinger, G. and Steppat, R. (1982). Potentiation of hexacarbon-neurotoxicity by methyl-ethyl-ketone (MEK) and other substances: Clinical and experimental aspects. *Neurobehav. Toxicol. Teratol.*, 4, 623–7

Anthony, D. C., Boekelheide, K. and Graham, D. G. (1983a). The effect of 3,4-dimethyl substitution on the neurotoxicity of 2,5-hexanedione. I. Accelerated clinical neuropathy is accompanied by more proximal axonal swellings. *Toxicol. appl. Pharmacol.*, 71, 362–71

Anthony, D. C., Boekelheide, K., Anderson, C. W. and Graham, D. G. (1983b). The effect of 3,4-dimethyl substitution on the neurotoxicity of 2,5-hexanedione. II. Dimethyl substitution accelerates pyrrole formation and protein crosslinking. *Toxicol. appl. Pharmacol.*, **71**, 372–82

Billmaier, D., Vee, H. T., Allen, N., Craft, B., Williams, N., Epstein, S. and Fontaine, R. (1974). Peripheral neuropathy in a coated fabrics plant. *J. Occup. Med.*, **16**, 665–71

Cavanagh, J. B. (1982). The pattern of recovery of axons in the nervous system of rats following 2,5-hexanediol intoxication: A question of rheology? *Neuropathol. appl. Neurobiol.*, **8**, 19–34

Cavanagh, J. B. and Bennetts, J. B. (1981). On the pattern of changes in the rat nervous system produced by 2,5-hexanediol: A topographical study by light microscopy. *Brain*, **104**, 297–318

Chio, K. S. and Tappel, A. L. (1969). Synthesis and characterization of the fluorescent products derived from malonaldehyde and amino acids. *Biochemistry*, **8**, 2821–7

Couri, D. and Nachtman, J. P. (1979). Biochemical and biophysical studies of 2,5-hexanedione neuropathy. *Neurotoxicology*, **1**, 269–83

Couri, D., Abdel-Rahman, M. S. and Hetland, L. B. (1978). Biotransformation of n-hexane and methyl n-butyl ketone in guinea pigs and mice. *Am. Ind. Hyg. Assoc. J.*, **39**, 295–300

DeCaprio, A. P. (1984). Molecular mechanisms of n-hexane neurotoxicity. In: *Proc. 14th Ann. Conf. Environ. Toxicol.*, Dayton, Ohio. AFAMRL-TR-83-099, pp. 40–59

DeCaprio, A. P. (1985). Molecular mechanisms of diketone neurotoxicity. *Chem-Biol. Interact.*, **54**, 257–70

DeCaprio, A. P. and O'Neill, E. A. (1985). Alterations in rat axonal cytoskeletal proteins induced by *in vitro* and *in vivo* 2,5-hexanedione exposure. *Toxicol. appl. Pharmacol.*, **78**, 235–47

DeCaprio, A. P. and Weber, P. (1980). *In vitro* studies on the amino group reactivity of a neurotoxic hexacarbon solvent. *Pharmacologist*, **22**, 222

DeCaprio, A. P. and Weber, P. (1981). Conversion of lysine ε-amino groups to substituted pyrrole derivatives by 2,5-hexanedione: A possible mechanism of protein binding. *Toxicologist*, **1**, 134

DeCaprio, A. P., Olajos, E. J. and Weber, P. (1982). Covalent binding of a neurotoxic n-hexane metabolite: Conversion of primary amines to substituted pyrrole adducts by 2,5-hexanedione. *Toxicol. appl. Pharmacol.*, **65**, 440–50

DeCaprio, A. P., Strominger, N. L. and Weber, P. (1983). Neurotoxicity and protein binding of 2,5-hexanedione in the hen. *Toxicol. appl. Pharmacol.*, **68**, 297–307

DiVincenzo, G. D., Kaplan, C. J. and Dedinas, J. (1976). Characterization of the metabolites of methyl n-butyl ketone, methyl iso-butyl ketone, and methyl ethyl ketone in guinea pig serum and their clearance. *Toxicol. appl. Pharmacol.*, **36**, 511–22

DiVincenzo, G. D., Hamilton, M. L., Kaplan, C. J. and Dedinas, J. (1977). Metabolic fate and disposition of ^{14}C-labelled methyl n-butyl ketone in the rat. *Toxicol. appl. Pharmacol.*, **41**, 547–60

DiVincenzo, G. D., Zeigler, D. A., O'Donoghue, J. L. and Krasavage, W. J. (1982). Possible role of metabolism in 5-nonanone neurotoxicity. *Neurotoxicology*, **3**, 55–63

Duckett, S., Williams, N. and Francis, S. (1974). Peripheral neuropathy associated with inhalation of methyl n-butyl ketone. *Experentia*, **30**, 1283–4

Ellisman, M. H. and Porter, K. R. (1980). Microtrabecular structure of the axoplasmic matrix: Visualization of cross-linking structures and their distribution. *J. Cell. Biol.*, **87**, 464–79

Geisler, N., Kaufmann, E., Fischer, S., Plessmann, U. and Weber, P. (1983). Neuro-filament architecture combines structural principles of intermediate filaments with carboxy-terminal extensions increasing in size between triplet proteins. *EMBO. J.*, 2, 1295–1302

Gillies, P. J., Norton, R. M. and Bus, J. S. (1980). Effect of 2,5-hexanedione on lipid biosynthesis in sciatic nerve and brain of the rat. *Toxicol. appl. Pharmacol.*, 54, 210–16

Goto, I., Matsumara, M., Inoue, N., Murai, Y., Shida, K., Santa, T. and Ruroiwa, Y. (1974). Toxic polyneuropathy due to glue sniffing. *J. Neurol. Neurosurg. Psych.*, 37, 848–53

Graham, D. G. (1980). Hexane polyneuropathy: A proposal for the pathogenesis of a hazard of occupational exposure and inhalant abuse. *Chem.-Biol. Interact.*, 32, 339–45

Graham, D. G. and Abou-Donia, M. B. (1980). Studies of the molecular pathogenesis of hexane neuropathy. I. Evaluation of the inhibition of glyceraldehyde-3-phosphate dehydrogenase by 2,5-hexanedione. *J. Toxicol. Environ. Hlth*, 6, 621–31

Graham, D. G., Anthony, D. C., Boekelheide, K., Maschmann, N. A., Richards, R. G., Wolfram, J. W. and Shaw, B. R. (1982a). Studies of the molecular pathogenesis of hexane neuropathy. II. Evidence that pyrrole derivatization of lysyl residues leads to protein crosslinking. *Toxicol. appl. Pharmacol.*, 64, 415–22

Graham, D. G., Anthony, D. C. and Boekelheide, K. (1982b). *In vitro* and *in vivo* studies of the molecular pathogenesis of n-hexane neuropathy. *Neurobehav. Toxicol. Teratol.*, 4, 629–34

Graham, D. G., Szakal-Quin, G., Priest, J. W. and Anthony, D. C. (1984). *In vitro* evidence that covalent crosslinking of neurofilaments occurs in γ-diketone neuropathy. *Proc. Nat. Acad. Sci. USA*, 81, 4979–82

Griffin, J. W., Price, D. L. and Spencer, P. S. (1977). Fast axonal transport through giant axonal swellings in hexacarbon neuropathy. *J. Neuropathol. Exp. Neurol.*, 36, 603

Griffin, J. W., Fahnestock, K. E., Price, D. L. and Cork, L. C. (1983). Cytoskeletal disorganization induced by local application of β,β'-iminodipropionitrile and 2,5-hexanedione. *Ann. Neurol.*, 14, 55–61

Griffiths, I. R., Kelly, P. A. T., Carmichael, S., McCulloch, M. and Waterston, M. (1981). The relationship of glucose utilization and morphological change in the visual system in hexacarbon neuropathy. *Brain Res.*, 222, 447–51

Howland, R. D., Vyas, I. L., Lowndes, H. E. and Argentiers, T. M. (1980). The etiology of toxic peripheral neuropathies: *In vitro* effects of acrylamide and 2,5-hexanedione on brain enolase and other glycolytic enzymes. *Brain Res.*, 202, 131–42

Jones, H. B. and Cavanagh, J. B. (1982). Recovery from 2,5-hexanediol intoxication of the retinotectal tract of the rat. An ultrastructural study. *Acta Neuropathol.*, 58, 286–90

Jones, H. B. and Cavanagh, J. B. (1983). Distortions in the nodes of Ranvier from axonal distention by filamentous masses in hexacarbon intoxication. *J. Neurocytol.*, 12, 439–589

Jones, R. A. and Bean, G. P. (1977). *The Chemistry of Pyrroles*, Academic Press, New York

Julien, J. P. and Mushynski, W. E. (1982). Multiple phosphorylation sites in mammalian neurofilament polypeptides. *J. Biol. Chem.*, 257, 10467–70

Lasek, R. J. and Hoffman, P. N. (1976). The neuronal cytoskeleton, axonal transport and axonal growth. In: *Cell Motility* (eds R. Golden, T. Pollard and J. Rosenbaum), Cold Spring Harbor Conf. Cell Proliferation, Vol. 3, Cold Spring Harbor Laboratory, New York, pp. 1021–49

LoPachin, R. M., Moore, R. W., Menahan, L. A. and Peterson, R. E. (1984). Glucose-dependent lactate production by homogenates of neuronal tissues prepared from rats treated with 2,4-dithiobiuret, acrylamide, p-bromophenylacetylurea, and 2,5-hexanedione. *Neurotoxicology*, **5**, 25–36

Mendell, J. R. and Sahenk, Z. (1980). Interference of neuronal processing and axoplasmic transport by toxic chemicals. *Experimental and Clinical Neurotoxicology*, (eds P. S. Spencer and H. H. Schaumburg), William and Wilkins, Baltimore, pp. 139–60

Mendell, J. R., Saida, K., Ganansia, M. F., Jackson, D. B., Weiss, H., Gardier, R. W., Chrisman, C., Allen, N., Couri, D., O'Neill, J., Marks, B. and Hetland, L. (1974). Toxic polyneuropathy produced by methyl n-butyl ketone. *Science*, **185**, 787–9

Mennear, J. H. (1982). A short-lived effect of 2,5-hexanedione on thermal perception in mice. *Toxicol. appl. Pharmacol.*, **62**, 205–10

Monaco, S., Autilio-Gambetti, L., Zabel, D. and Gambetti, P. (1985). Giant axonal neuropathy: acceleration of neurofilament transport in optic axons. *Proc. Nat. Acad. Sci. (USA)*, **82**, 920–4

NIOSH (1977). Occupational exposure to alkanes (C5-C8). DHEW Publication No. 77–151, Government Publication Office, Washington, D.C.

O'Donoghue, J. L. and Krasavage, W. J. (1979). Hexacarbon neuropathy: A γ-diketone neuropathy? *J. Neuropathol. Exp. Neurol.*, **38**, 333

Pena, S. D. J. (1982) Giant axonal neuropathy: An inborn error of organization of intermediate filaments. *Muscle Nerve*, **5**, 166–72

Politis, M. J., Pelligrino, R. G. and Spencer, P. S. (1980). Ultrastructural studies of the dying-back process. V. Axonal neurofilaments accumulate at sites of 2,5-hexanedione application: Evidence for nerve fiber dysfunction in experimental hexacarbon neuropathy. *J. Neurocytol.*, **9**, 505–16

Powell, H. C., Koch, T., Garrett, R. and Lampert, P. W. (1978). Schwann cell abnormalities in 2,5-hexanedione neuropathy. *J. Neurocytol.*, **7**, 517–28

Ralston, W. H., Hilderbrand, R. L., Uddin, D. E., Andersen, M. E. and Gardier, R. W. (1985). Potentiation of 2,5-hexanedione neurotoxicity by methyl ethyl ketone. *Toxicol. appl. Pharmacol.*, **81**, 319–27

Sabri, M. I. (1984a). *In vitro* effect of n-hexane and its metabolites on selected enzymes in glycolysis, pentose phosphate pathway and citric acid cycle. *Brain Res.*, **297**, 145–50

Sabri, M. I. (1984b). Further observations on *in vitro* and *in vivo* effects of 2,5-hexanedione on glyceraldehyde-3-phosphate dehydrogenase. *Arch. Toxicol.*, **55**, 191–4

Sabri, M. I. and Spencer, P. S. (1981). Sites of 2,5-hexanedione binding in mammalian peripheral nerve. *Soc. Neurosci. Abstr.*, **7**, 601

Sabri, M. I., Moore, C. L. and Spencer, P. S. (1979a). Studies on the biochemical basis of distal axonopathies. I. Inhibition of glycolysis by neurotoxic hexacarbon compounds. *J. Neurochem.*, **32**, 683–9

Sabri, M. I., Ederle, K., Holdsworth, C. E. and Spencer, P. S. (1979b). Studies on the biochemical basis of distal axonopathies. II. Specific inhibition of fructose-6-phosphate kinase by 2,5-hexanedione and methyl butyl ketone. *Neurotoxicology*, **1**, 285–97

Sahenk, Z. and Mendell, J. R. (1983). Studies on the morphologic alterations of axonal membranous organelles in neurofilamentous neuropathies. *Brain Res.*, **268**, 239–48

Sayre, L. M., Autilio-Gambetti, L. and Gambetti, P. (1985). Pathogenesis of experimental giant neurofilamentous axonopathies: A unified hypothesis based on chemical modification of neurofilaments. *Brain Res. Rev.*, **10**, 69–83

Schaumburg, H. H. and Spencer, P. S. (1976). Degeneration in central and peripheral nervous systems produced by pure n-hexane: An experimental study. *Brain*, **99**, 183–92

Spencer, P. S. and Schaumburg, H. H. (1975). Experimental neuropathy produced by 2,5-hexanedione – A major metabolite of the neurotoxic industrial solvent methyl n-butyl ketone. *J. Neurol. Neurosurg. Psych.*, **38**, 771-5

Spencer, P. S. and Schaumburg, H. H. (1976). Central-peripheral distal axonopathy – The pathology of dying-back polyneuropathies. In: *Progress in Neuropathology*, Vol. 3, (ed. H. Zimmerman), Grune and Stratton, New York, pp. 253-95

Spencer, P. S. and Schaumburg, H. H. (1977a). Ultrastructural studies of the dying-back process. III. The evolution of experimental peripheral giant axonal degeneration. *J. Neuropathol. Exp. Neurol.*, **36**, 276-99

Spencer, P. S. and Schaumburg, H. H. (1977b). Ultrastructural studies of the dying-back process. IV. Differential vulnerability of PNS and CNS fibers in experimental central-peripheral distal axonopathies. *J. Neuropathol. Exp. Neurol.*, **36**, 300-20

Spencer, P. S. and Schaumburg, H. H. (1978). Pathobiology of neurotoxic axonal degeneration. In: *Physiology and Pathobiology of Axons* (ed. S. G. Waxman), Raven Press, New York, pp. 265-82

Spencer, P. S., Bischoff, M. C. and Schaumburg, H. H. (1978). On the specific molecular configuration of neurotoxic aliphatic hexacarbon compounds causing central-peripheral distal axonopathy. *Toxicol. appl. Pharmacol.*, **44**, 17-28

Spencer, P. S., Sabri, M. I., Schaumburg, H. H. and Moore, C. L. (1979). Does a defect of energy metabolism in the nerve fiber underlie axonal degeneration in polyneuropathies? *Ann. Neurol.*, **5**, 501-7

Spencer, P. S., Schaumburg, H. H., Sabri, M. I. and Veronesi, B. (1980). The enlarging view of hexacarbon neurotoxicity. *CRC Crit. Rev. Toxicol.*, **4**, 279-356

Spencer, P. S., Miller, M. S., Ross, S. M., Schwab, B. W. and Sabri, M. I. (1985). Biochemical mechanisms underlying primary degeneration of axons. In: *Handbook of Neurochemistry*, Vol. 9 (ed. A. Lajtha), Plenum Press, New York, pp. 31-65

Veronesi, B., Peterson, E. R., Bornstein, M. B. and Spencer, P. S. (1983). Ultrastructural studies of the dying-back process. VI. Examination of nerve fibers undergoing giant axonal degeneration in organotypic culture. *J. Neuropathol. Exp. Neurol.*, **42**, 153-65

Yamada, S. (1967). Intoxication polyneuritis in the workers exposed to n-hexane. *Japan J. Ind. Hlth*, **9**, 651-9

Yamamura, Y. (1969). n-Hexane polyneuropathy. *Folia Psych. Neurol. Japan*, **23**, 45-57

Zagoren, J. C., Politis, M. J. and Spencer, P. S. (1983). Rapid reorganization of the axonal cytoskeleton induced by a gamma-diketone. *Brain Res.*, **270**, 162-4

11

Toxicology of Impurities in Malathion: Potentiation of Malathion Toxicity and Lung Toxicity Caused by Trialkyl Phosphorothioates

W. N. Aldridge, D. Dinsdale, B. Nemery and R. D. Verschoyle

INTRODUCTION

Organophosphorus compounds were first synthesised in the 1930s and because of their high toxicity were initially considered for use as chemical warfare agents. Since that time they have been developed for peaceful purposes and their effects on biological systems have been intensively studied. They are well known for their inhibition of acetylcholinesterase and there is considerable knowledge on their structure–activity relationships. The variety of directly toxic compounds is very large. Many compounds, although inactive *in vitro*, are metabolised *in vivo* to active inhibitors of esterases; this has greatly extended the range of toxic organophosphorus structures. It is not surprising therefore that amongst these structures, compounds are found with biological activities other than, and in addition to, those depending on inactivation of acetylcholinesterase. The range of structures and biological reactions are illustrated in figures 11.1 and 11.2.

POTENTIATION OF MALATHION TOXICITY BY OTHER ORGANOPHOSPHORUS COMPOUNDS

During a large World Health Organisation malaria eradication programme in Pakistan in 1976 2800 out of 7500 spraymen became poisoned and 5 died using malathion (OO-(dimethyl diethylmercaptosuccinyl phosphorothionate)) in a water dispersible formulation (Baker *et al.*, 1978). The symptoms were those expected from inhibition

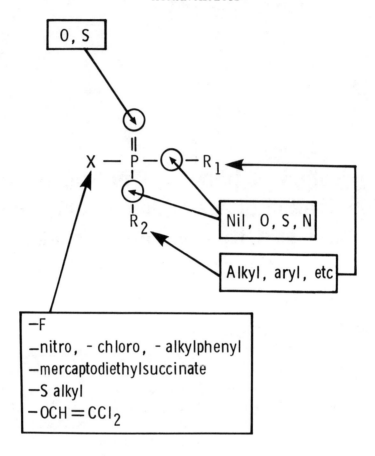

Figure 11.1 Diagrammatic representation of the various chemical structures of organophosphorus compounds

of acetylcholinesterase. After extensive investigation it was found that the main cause of the high toxicity was the presence of an impurity, isomalathion (Aldridge *et al.*, 1979; Miles *et al.*, 1979; for chemical structures, cf. figure 11.4). The published oral toxicity of technical malathion in rats is 1–2 g/kg body wt, but even these preparations contain impurities, since the toxicity of pure recrystallised malathion is approximately 10–12 g/kg body wt (Aldridge *et al.*, 1979; Umetsu *et al.*, 1977). Some of the stored samples of malathion used in Pakistan were toxic at doses as low as 0.15 g/kg body wt, indicating an isomalathion content of around 8–10% (Aldridge *et al.*, 1979). The isomalathion content was undoubtedly caused by isomerisation of malathion at high temperatures in an incorrectly formulated wettable dispersible powder (Miles *et al.*, 1979, 1980). With other formulations the isomerisation is much slower. While there is no doubt that isomalathion as an impurity in the sprayed malathion was the cause of the poisoning episode, the relationship between the number of spraymen poisoned and working practices of

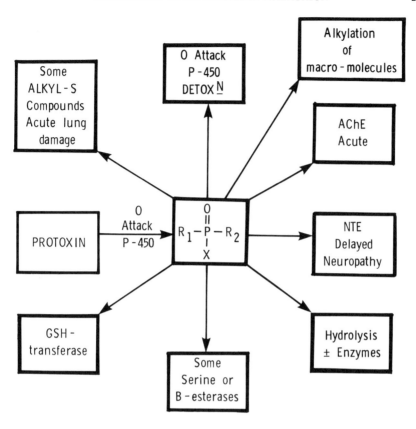

Figure 11.2 Various biological activities of organophosphorus compounds. P-450 = Cyto-chrome P-450, AChE = acetylcholinesterase, NTE = neuropathy target esterase

these spraymen is not known. As a result of this episode an accelerated storage test for formulated water dispersible malathion has been devised to check potentiality for isomerisation under adverse climatic conditions (WHO, 1979).

The enhanced toxicity of malathion is due to other organophosphorus compounds which inhibit the detoxification of malathion by carboxylesterases in the liver, blood and other tissues of the rat. This detoxification is normally brought about by removal of either or both ethyl groups from the diethylmercaptosuccinyl moiety in the molecule (Frawley *et al.*, 1957; Murphy and DuBois, 1957; Toia *et al.*, 1980; Talcott *et al.*, 1979a,b). Although the phenomenon of the potentiation of the toxicity of malathion by other organophosphorus compounds in experimental animals has been known for almost 30 years (Murphy and DuBois, 1957) the poisoning episode in Pakistan is its first demonstration in man.

In figure 11.3 are shown the action of carboxylesterases on malathion, malaoxon and isomalathion. Malathion is not itself an inhibitor of acetylcholinesterase and must be metabolised to malaoxon, probably mainly in the liver, by cytochromes

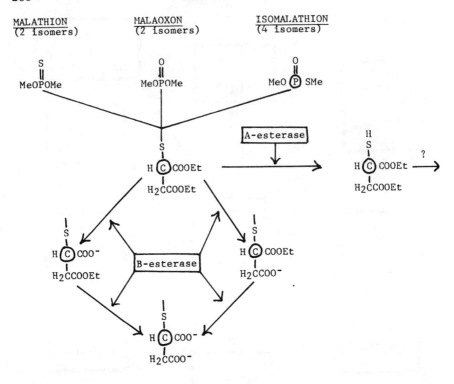

Figure 11.3 The possible routes of hydrolysis of malathion, malaoxon and isomalathion. Chiral centres are circled. The group –S– Ⓒ –C etc., is common to all the phosphorus-containing compounds. Note that the site of attack by A-esterase is different from that by B-esterase

P-450. Metabolism by B-esterase introduces an ionisable group(s) into the molecule, which will be more water soluble and metabolism of P=S to P=O will probably be slower; should this occur, the product, with its negative charge, will be a rather poor inhibitor of acetylcholinesterase. The efficiency of detoxification by carboxyl-esterases is shown by the observation that inhibition of these enzymes by pretreatment of rats with compounds such as tri-2-tolyl phosphate reduce the LD_{50} to 7.5 mg/kg body wt, i.e. over 10^3 times based on the toxicity of pure malathion (Main and Braid, 1962). Malaoxon is a substrate for and an inhibitor of the carboxyl-esterases (Main and Hastings, 1966; Dauterman and Main, 1966). Isomalathion would also be expected to be a substrate of carboxylesterases but in this case the rates of inhibition and detoxification are presumably in favour of inhibition. The *in vivo* rates of the removal of ethyl groups from malathion, malaoxon and iso-malathion will depend on their relative concentrations in the liver (delivery of malathion and isomalathion via the blood to the liver and production of malaoxon from malathion in the liver) and their relative K_m's for carboxylesterase. The structure–activity relationships for these compounds even *in vitro* are very complex.

As shown in figure 11.3 malathion and malaoxon exist in two chiral forms due to optical isomerism around a carbon in the diethylmercaptosuccinyl moiety. Removal of one or other ethyl group will lead theoretically to four different monoesters and two succinyl moieties. Isomalathion possesses two chiral centres, that is a phosphorus and a carbon atom and will yield theoretically eight different monoesters and four succinyl moieties. The chiral atoms in the initial compounds will influence all their interactions with carboxylesterases and also for malaoxon and isomalathion their reaction with acetylcholinesterase (for discussion cf. Aldridge *et al.*, 1979). In the rat it has been shown that two carboxylesterases exist in the liver showing a preference for attack on the α- or β-carboxyethyl group (Mallipudi *et al.*, 1980). Some of the complexities of the *in vivo* situation have been illustrated by measurements of α and β monoacid and diacid excretion in the urine after administration of [14C]-malathion or [14C]-malaoxon following pretreatment with isomalathion or OSS-trimethyl phosphorodithioate (OSS-Me(O)) (Ryan and Fukuto, 1984). The interplay between oxidation of malathion to malaoxon, and detoxification by carboxylesterase and a GSH dependent process (probably O-demethylation by glutathione S-transferases) have also been shown by experiments on isolated rat hepatocytes (Malik and Summer, 1982).

Many other compounds besides isomalathion have been found in technical malathion stored under a variety of conditions (figure 11.4; Miles *et al.*, 1980). Those not containing phosphorus and the diesters of phosphoric acid (Verschoyle *et al.*, 1982) (see figure 11.4) are probably irrelevant to toxicity. One compound, OSS-Me(O) is 2–3 times more active than isomalathion in the potentiation of the toxicity of malathion to rats (Aldridge *et al.*, 1979). Trialkyl phosphorothioates are potential impurities produced during the synthesis of many organophosphorus thionates including malathion. Storage of malathion can also, under certain conditions, lead to the increased formation of trimethyl phosphorothioates (Miles *et al.*, 1980) possibly by reaction of S-dimethyl esters breakdown products with malathion (Verschoyle *et al.*, 1982).

It is not known whether OSS-Me(O) has any significance in the potentiation of malathion toxicity to man. It has been suggested that only one detoxifying carboxylesterase exists in human liver, in contrast to rat liver which has two, and this human esterase is less sensitive to inhibition by OSS-Me(O) than by isomalathion (Talcott *et al.*, 1979b). This point requires more experimental work on postmortem samples of human liver, using separation methods for esterases which allow recovery in the isolated fractions of most of the activity found in the liver homogenate (Cain *et al.*, 1983; Cain and Clothier, 1986; Clothier and Cain, 1986). If the results of Talcott *et al.* (1979a,b) are confirmed, then a difference between man and several other species in the potentiation of malathion toxicity by trialkyl phosphorothioates will be found (table 11.1).

TOXICITY OF TRIALKYL PHOSPHOROTHIOATES TO THE LUNG

When OSS-Me(O) was examined (without malathion), it was found to be unexpectedly toxic. Oral LD_{50} was 26 mg/kg body wt and the rats died several days after

NOT CONTAINING PHOSPHORUS

NEUTRAL ORGANOPHOSPHORUS COMPOUNDS

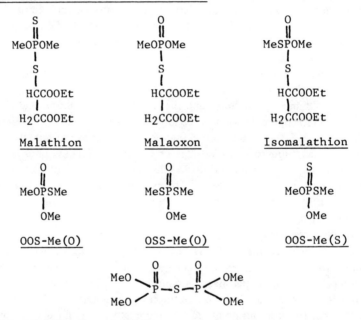

DIESTERS OF PHOSPHORIC ACID

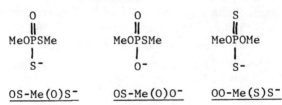

Figure 11.4 Chemical structures identified in technical and formulated malathion. Common names or abbreviations for organophosphorus compounds are included and indicate the style for other abbreviations in this paper. Information is taken from Miles *et al.* (1980)

Table 11.1 Potentiation of the Toxicity of Malathion by OSS-Me(O) and Isomalathion in Various Animal Species

	Oral LD_{50} (g/kg body wt)		
	Malathion	Malathion +2% OSS-Me(O)	Malathion +4% Isomalathion
Rat	3–4	0.35–0.45	0.35–0.45
Guinea-pig	1–2	$\simeq$ 0.65	0.45–0.65
Hamster	2	0.15–0.25	0.25–0.35
Pheasant	< 2	< 0.15	0.15
Mouse	6.1	0.6[a]	—
	3.2	—	1.15[b]
	3.2	—	0.9[c]

[a] Predosed with 50 mg OSS-Me(O)/kg body weight (Toia *et al.*, 1980)
[b] Malathion containing 2% isomalathion (Umetsu *et al.*, 1977)
[c] Predosed with 20 mg OSS-Me(O)/kg body weight (Talcott *et al.*, 1977)

dosing having shown only minor early cholinergic symptoms (Aldridge *et al.*, 1979; Verschoyle *et al.*, 1980; Umetsu *et al.*, 1981). The toxicity is due to lung damage (Verschoyle *et al.*, 1980; Verschoyle and Cabral, 1982; Dinsdale *et al.*, 1982); this has now been confirmed in another laboratory (Imamura *et al.*, 1983). Measurements of arterial p_{O_2} and p_{CO_2} 4 days following a LD_{50} dose of OSS-Me(O) indicate that the cause of death is respiratory failure.

In some early publications the time to death after various trialkyl phosphorothioates was much longer than the 3–5 days found in our laboratories and in some cases was as long as 22 days (Mallipudi *et al.*, 1979; Ali and Fukuto, 1982). It seems probable that this difference is due to intercurrent disease in the rat colony used for the above studies which is exacerbated by treatment of the animals with lung damaging agents.

The trimethyl and triethyl phosphorothioates are direct inhibitors of acetylcholinesterase with relatively low second order rate constants (Clothier *et al.*, 1981; Ali and Fukuto, 1982). With some compounds the symptoms due to inhibition of acetylcholinesterase are mild and occur early. However with others they can be severe, followed by recovery and several days later by lung damage. This aspect may be important when the effect of substances which affect disposal of the compound is being examined. In those cases when toxicity at 3–5 days is reduced the larger dose of the phosphorothioate required sometimes leads to early cholinergic symptoms sufficiently severe to cause death within 1 day; the few survivors may, however, develop lung effects several days later (Verschoyle and Cabral, 1982; Aldridge and Nemery, 1984).

Cellular specificity of lung damage

OSS-Me(O) and OOS-Et(O) primarily attack the type I pneumocyte (Dinsdale *et al.*, 1982). The impaired lung function and respiratory insufficiency at death result from a massive alveolar oedema and cellular responses following the selective destruction of type I pneumocytes. Proliferation of type II pneumocytes produces an epithelium with large cells and a consequent thickening of the blood/alveolus barrier. Debris from the damaged type 1 cells also leads to cellular infiltration of the interstitial tissue and to an increase in the number of alveolar macrophages.

It has been reported (Imamura *et al.*, 1983) that injury to the Clara cell is the primary event after treatment with OOS-Me(O). In another study changes in Clara cells have also been seen after a LD_{50} dose of OSS-Me(O) but these do not seem to be relevant to the alveolar damage (Dinsdale *et al.*, 1984). The changes do not involve cell injury or death and may be physiological and simply represent a cholinergic response in the lung.

Biochemical evidence is available which is consistent with the type I pneumocyte hypothesis. Putrescine is taken up by an active transport system into type I and type II pneumocytes (Smith, 1982). This transport system regards paraquat as 'putrescine-like' and transports paraquat into these cell types so that its concentration is much higher than in the plasma. This is why these cells are selectively damaged. No such explanation is possible for OSS-Me(O) or other trialkyl phosphorothioates (see later; Aldridge *et al.*, 1984). Putrescine uptake into lung slices taken from rats pretreated with OSS-Me(O) is lowered within a few hours and significantly reduced by 1 day (Nemery *et al.*, 1986). At 4-6 days the rate of uptake is 50-60% of the controls and remains depressed thereafter. The early reduction at a time when lung weights are unchanged is consistent with the electron microscopical studies indicating primary attack on type I pneumocytes.

Thus, while it is often unwise to generalise from one compound to another, even in a homologous series, our current hypothesis is that trimethyl and triethyl phosphorothioates cause lung damage by a similar mechanism involving a primary attack on type 1 pneumocytes.

Structure–activity relationships

As knowledge of mechanisms of toxicity increases, structure–activity relationships at levels of biological organisation other than for the whole animal may be perceived. When the primary target is known and its reaction with the toxin can be measured, the contribution of the many other factors which influence toxicity *in vivo* may be quantitatively assessed, e.g. disposal by various means, distribution and the degree of reaction with the target leading to no clinical response (threshold).

In table 11.2 is shown the LD_{50} of the trimethyl and triethyl phosphorothioates and two related pesticides, methamidophos and ethoprophos (Verschoyle and Cabral, 1982). Lung weight at 3-4 days is a good indicator of the severity of the damage. Those compounds producing no increase in lung weight show no lung

Table 11.2 Structure–Activity Relationships of Various Sulphur-containing Alkylphosphates in the Rat (Lung weights are those 4 days after the oral administration of the compounds. For abbreviations of names of compounds, cf. figure 11.4)

Compound	LD_{50} (μmol/kg)	Dose (μmol/kg)	Lung weight (mg/100 g) Mean $\pm$ S.E.M.
OOO-Me(O)	–	7140	494 $\pm$ 15
OOS-Me(O)	385	320	1234 $\pm$ 118
OSS-Me(O)	151	145	1456 $\pm$ 116
SSS-Me(O)	159	106	1134 $\pm$ 87
OOS-Et(O)	136	126	1348 $\pm$ 143
OSS-Et(O)	654	560	952 $\pm$ 97
SSS-Et(O)	>870	870	485 $\pm$ 10
OOS-Me(S)	3710	2320	530 $\pm$ 12
(MeO) (MeS)P(O) NH$_2$ (methamidophos)	113	85 354[a]	481 $\pm$ 12 557 $\pm$ 20
(EtO) (n-PrS)$_2$P(O) (ethoprophos)	145	116	521 $\pm$ 14
Controls	–	–	518 $\pm$ 8

[a]This dose, more than the LD_{50}, was given to rats protected from cholinergic death by atropine.

damage either by post mortem or by histological examination. In the methyl series with increasing substitution of the oxygen atom of methoxy by sulphur there is a decrease in LD_{50} with a change of 1-2 atoms of sulphur, but with 2 or 3 sulphur atoms the LD_{50} is approx. 150–160 μmol/kg. Trimethyl phosphate [OOO-Me(O)] produces no lung damage. In the ethyl series as sulphur atoms are progressively introduced toxicity decreases; at the maximum tolerated dose of 870 μmol/kg, SSS-Et(O) produced no lung damage. The two pesticides, methamidophos and ethoprophos, are also inert in this respect at the maximum tolerated doses; these doses are however relatively low due to cholinergic toxicity.

Other studies have been carried out (Mallipudi *et al.*, 1979; Ali and Fukuto, 1982) using OOS-Me(O) and OOS-Et(O) and a series of OO-dimethyl and OO-diethyl S-alkyl esters. In table 11.3 the relationship between structure, LD_{50} and time to death are shown. These results are difficult to interpret except that the compounds containing the highest number of carbon atoms do not cause delayed deaths. In this work no lung weight measurements or morphological examinations were carried out. However, in a recent paper (Gandy *et al.*, 1984) some of these compounds have been re-examined by scanning electron microscopy and changes were found in morphology of the bronchiolar epithelium (fewer apical bulges of

Table 11.3 Structure–Activity Relationships for Various OO-dimethyl and OO-diethyl S-alkyl Phosphorothioate Esters (Oral administration. Animals kept for 25 days)

Compounds	Time range for death (days)	LD_{50} (μmol/kg)	(a) Dose causing changes in bronchiolar epithelium (μmol/kg)
OO-dimethyl series			
S-methyl	4–22	96–128	128
S-ethyl	3–11	107	88
S-n-propyl	1–3	60	–
S-iso-propyl	1–7	590	293
S-n-butyl	1–2	270	–
S-t-butyl	2–6	320	–
S-n-pentyl	1–3	1470	–
S-n-hexyl	–	>3320	–
OO-diethyl series			
S-methyl	1–7	256	359
S-ethyl	1–8	252–430	480
S-n-propyl	1–3	230	–
S-iso-propyl	1	845	–
S-t-butyl	1–3	560	–
S-n-hexyl	–	>1380	–

Data taken from Ali and Fukuto (1982) except column marked (a) which is from Gandy *et al.* (1984).

Clara cells). Such changes appeared to be correlated with loss of body weight. Some compounds required rather high doses (cf. tables 11.2 and 11.3). No examination by transmission electron microscopy of the alveolar epithelium is reported.

The conclusions from all of these studies are that for toxicity a sulphur atom is necessary in a position linking an alkyl group to phosphorus. Toxicity is not appreciably increased when there is more than one sulphur atom in this position in the molecule. Indeed in the ethyl series toxicity to the lung decreases. As the number of carbons in the molecule increases the ability to cause lung damage decreases. This latter conclusion must be qualified due to the acute toxicity of some compounds, e.g. the *in vitro* inhibitory power against acetylcholinesterase also increases as the number of carbons increases (Ali and Fukuto, 1982).

Two unexpected findings in table 11.2 are the inactivity of OOS-Me(S) on the one hand, and of methamidophos and ethoprophos on the other, to produce changes in the lung (Verschoyle and Cabral, 1982).

Absorption, distribution and disposal

In the preceding section structure–activity relationships for the whole animal have been considered. From a mechanistic point of view it would be useful to know the concentration of compounds reaching the lung and whether the doses received by the lung even in a restricted series of structurally related compounds differ markedly.

A highly sensitive and accurate capillary gas-chromatographic method has been devised for the determination of OSS-Me(O) in blood and other tissues (Bailey *et al.*, 1981a), and has been shown to be adaptable for the determination of all the trimethyl and triethyl phosphorothioates. Following intravenous injection the initial concentration in the plasma can be extrapolated from disposal curves and compared with that expected if the compound mixes uniformly with the body water (Aldridge *et al.*, 1984). In table 11.4 the compounds are arranged in decreasing order of the determined/calculated ratio of their initial plasma concentrations. The compounds OOS-Me(O), OOS-Et(O) and OSS-Me(O) mix uniformly with the body water but SSS-Me(O), OSS-Et(O) and SSS-Et(O) must be distributed nonuniformly. For SSS-Et(O) the actual initial concentration found in the plasma is only 2–3% of that calculated assuming a uniform distribution in the body water. This change may well be due to the lipophilic character and low solubility in water of SSS-Et(O). The low molecular weight members of the series are miscible in water and lipophilic solvents (Aldridge and Nemery, 1984; Aldridge *et al.*, 1984). Experience of their use in the laboratory has shown that as the molecular weight increases from methyl to ethyl and from oxygen to sulphur the compounds become less soluble in water and more lipophilic.

The results shown in table 11.5 indicate that the plasma concentrations are a reliable measure of concentrations in lung and often in other tissues, although there is a tendency for the more lipophilic compounds to have a higher concentration in the brain, than in plasma or lung.

Table 11.4 Determined and Predicted Plasma Concentrations of Trialkyl Phosphorothioates after Intravenous Injection in the Rat (The calculated plasma concentration is that expected from a uniform mixing with the body water (70% of body weight). The determined value is that obtained by extrapolation of the linear logarithmic plot to zero time. The compounds are arranged in order of decreasing detd/calc. ratio (column 5)

Compound	Dose (μmol/kg)	Initial concentration (nmol/g plasma water)		$\dfrac{\text{Detd}}{\text{Calc.}}$
		Detd	Calc	
OOS-Me(O)	288	415	411	1.01
OOS-Et(O)	125	187	178	1.05
OSS-Me(O)	146	179	208	0.86
SSS-Me(O)	160	147	228	0.64
OSS-Et(O)	374	325	534	0.61
SSS-Et(O)	869	29	1241	0.02

Table 11.5 Comparison of Concentrations of Trialkyl Phosphorothioates in Plasma, Lung and Brain of the Rat (All results (means
± S.E.M. of the number of observations in parenthesis) are from
table 11.4, except for SSS-Et(O) which was given at 217 μmol/kg)

Compound	nmol/g tissue water		
	Plasma	Lung	Brain
OOS-Me(O)	360 ± 6　(4)	338 ± 8　(4)	340 ± 11　(4)
OSS-Me(O)	68.8 ± 1.8 (8)	77.3 ± 3.4 (4)	–
SSS-Me(O)	63.9 ± 5.5 (4)	61.1 ± 7.3 (4)	84.6 ± 7.4 (4)
OOS-Et(O)	21.0 ± 1.6 (6)	17.5 ± 1.4 (6)	–
OSS-Et(O)	114 ± 13　(4)	115 ± 24　(4)	170 ± 19　(4)
SSS-Et(O)	10.6 ± 0.8 (3)	15.2 ± 4.4 (4)	25.7 ± 3.4 (3)

Disposal curves have been determined for most of the trimethyl and triethyl phosphorothioates. A typical set of data is shown in figure 11.5. The analytical method used is sensitive enough to follow disposal curves until the concentration has decreased 10^3 fold from the initial value. The rate of disposal seems to be different after oral and intravenous dosing (figure 11.5; Aldridge et al., 1984). This probably indicates that although the rate of absorption is rapid, the measured rate of disposal after oral dosing is a composite of disposal and absorption. Nevertheless, whatever is the true meaning of the apparent first order constant, it is derived from measured concentrations in the plasma and does allow the doses presented to the lung over particular time periods to be calculated. As shown in figure 11.5 the first order rate rapidly declines at low concentrations and becomes much slower. The reason for this is not clear but it is not due to self destruction of the metabolising system. The introduction of a second dose of compound when the rate is slow, results in a return to the initial more rapid rate of metabolism (Aldridge et al., 1984).

In table 11.6 the LD$_{50}$ (death due to lung damage) is compared with both the initial circulating concentration and to the integrated dose presented to the lung via the circulation. For both oral and intravenous administration the compounds are arranged in order of decreasing toxicity; it is clear that neither parameter follows the same order. However the inability to produce lung damage or death with SSS-Et(O) is undoubtedly due to the fact that it is not possible, even with intravenous injection, to produce a sustained concentration as high as that for other compounds.

The disposal rates for these compounds are rather fast (table 11.6); for example the half-lives derived from the first order rate constants after intravenous injection for OSS-Me(O) and OOS-Et(O) are 0.8 h and 0.33 h respectively. Several mechanisms for disposal are known. If rats are pretreated with phenobarbitone then the rate of disposal of OSS-Me(O) and OSS-Et(O) from the plasma is increased ten-fold.

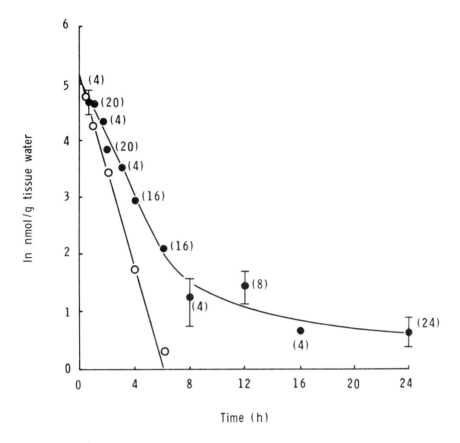

Figure 11.5 Plasma concentrations of OSS-Me(O) as a function of time after administration of a dose of 145 μmol/kg body weight. ○, intravenous; ● oral. Results taken from Aldridge *et al.* (1984). Numbers in brackets represent the numbers of animals

It therefore seems that the main pathway for disposal is oxidative and involves the cytochrome P-450 system. Increase in disposal by systems induced by phenobarbitone is a detoxification pathway, for the LD_{50} increases in direct proportion to the increase in the rate of disposal (figure 11.6; Aldridge *et al.*, 1984).

Detailed studies (Nemery, 1986) have established that OSS-Me(O) is metabolised by lung and liver slices to diesters. This work has been recently summarised (Aldridge *et al.*, 1985b). Both tissues metabolise OSS-Me(O) to OS-Me(O)O⁻ and SS-Me(O)O⁻ through loss of −SCH₃ and −OCH₃, respectively. The ratio of the concentration of the two diesters produced by lung or liver slices shows that −SCH₃ is preferentially eliminated by the lung when compared to the liver.

The reaction by tissue slices is temperature dependent and metabolism by microsomal fractions from lung and liver was NADPH dependent. However microsomal metabolism resulted in OS-Me(O)O⁻ with little of the SS-Me(O)O⁻ diester; therefore microsomal metabolism is almost exclusively via loss of −SCH₃.

Table 11.6 Comparison of the Relative Order of Toxicity to the Rat of Trialkyl
Phosphorothioates with the Initial Plasma Concentration and the Integrated
Dose Presented to the Lung

Compound	LD_{50} (μmol/kg)	Initial plasma conc. (nmol/ml)	Integrated dose (nmol/h/ml)	Disposal rate constant (k/h: mean ± S.E.M.)
Intravenous administration				
OOS-Et(O)	192	287	137	2.09 ± 0.11
OSS-Me(O)	244	299	343	0.87 ± 0.02
OOS-Me(O)	288	415	2231	0.19 ± 0.01
OSS-Et(O)	443	385	386	1.00 ± 0.03
SSS-Et(O)	217[a]	29	–	0.82 ± 0.10[b]
Oral administration				
OOS-Et(O)	136	67	74	0.91 ± 0.12
OSS-Me(O)	151	157	314	0.50 ± 0.03
SSS-Me(O)	159	81	72	1.13 ± 0.07
OOS-Me(O)	385	314	2180	0.14 ± 0.03
OSS-Et(O)	654	176	652	0.27 ± 0.03
SSS-Et(O)	870	8	–	–

[a]Maximum tolerated dose.
[b]This rate is that after a very rapid decrease in concentration over the first 40 min.

The trialkyl phosphorothioates are substrates for the soluble glutathione S-transferases from rat liver (Aldridge *et al.*, 1985a). The highest rate was obtained with
OSS-Me(O) but the other compounds are also metabolised. OSS-Me(O) is a substrate for the transferases 1-1, 1-2, 2-2, 3-3 and 3-4 but due to the relative abund-
ance of isozymes in rat liver cytosol most of the breakdown is due to the isozymes
1-1, 3-4 and 1-2 (for nomenclature cf. Jakoby *et al.*, 1984). The diesters produced
by this reaction have been identified by proton NMR and the reaction pathway
shown to be via the transfer of the methyl from $-OCH_3$ yielding SS-Me(O)O$^-$
and S-methylglutathione (Aldridge *et al.*, 1985a).

Trialkyl phosphorothioates react with esterases directly (Clothier *et al.*, 1981;
Ali and Fukuto, 1982; Talcott *et al.*, 1979a; Lee and Fukuto, 1982; Casida *et al.*,
1963). When OSS-Me(O) reacts with bovine erythrocyte cholinesterase the leaving
group is $-SCH_3$ and the (MeO)(MeS)P(O)- ligand becomes attached to the enzyme
(Clothier *et al.*, 1981; cf. also De Jong *et al.*, 1982). Although it has not been
established that an S-alkyl group is the leaving group for reaction with other esterases, this seems likely on theoretical grounds. Since there are many esterases in
mammals which react with organophosphorus compounds (Aldridge, 1981) this
reaction may provide a significant detoxification pathway for the trialkyl phosphorothioates. The complete reaction sequence has been worked out for bovine
erythrocyte acetylcholinesterase (figure 11.7).

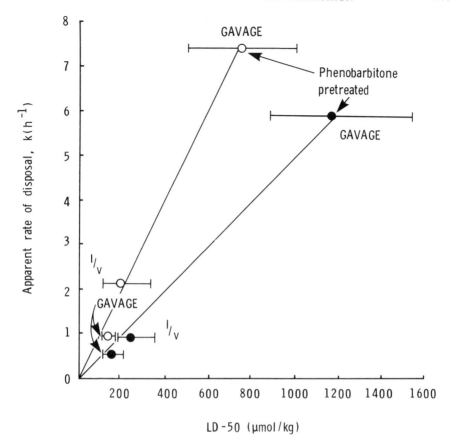

Figure 11.6 Relationship between rate of disposal of OSS-Me(O) and OOS-Et(O) phosphoro-thioates and toxicity to the rat. •, OSS-Me(O); ○, OOS-Et(O). Taken from Aldridge *et al.* (1984). Compounds were administered either intravenously (i/v) or by gavage as indicated and where shown to rats pretreated with phenobarbitone before dosing

Detailed work with OSS-Me(O) and OOS-Et(O) has demonstrated the presence of three routes for the detoxification of trialkyl phosphorothioates (figure 11.8). The relative contributions of each pathway *in vivo* is not known and it has not yet been possible to link rates determined *in vitro* with those expected *in vivo*.

Mechanisms of toxicity in the lung

Death of rats after OSS-Me(O) and probably other trimethyl and triethyl phos-phorothioates is due to respiratory failure resulting from alveolar oedema and proliferation of granular (type II) pneumocytes in response to an initial drug-induced damage of squamous (type I) pneumocytes. It is important to establish

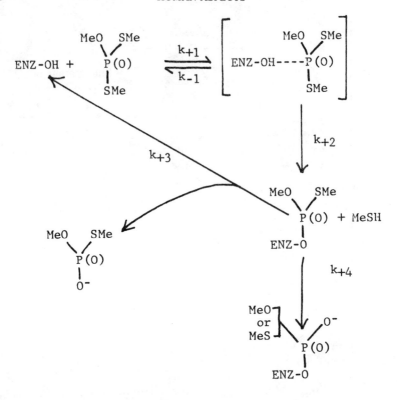

Figure 11.7 Reaction sequence for the reaction of esterases with OSS-Me(O). k_{+1}, k_{-1}, k_{+2} and k_{+4} are the rate constants for the reaction of 1 mol of OSS-Me(O) with 1 mol of esterase. k_{+1}, k_{-1}, k_{+2} and k_{+3} are the rate constants for the reaction sequence with catalytic hydrolysis of OSS-Me(O) as a substrate. The reaction sequence was worked out by Clothier *et al.* (1981). The products of the ageing reaction (k_{+4}) are not known, i.e. whether reaction occurs on the P–S–Me or P–O–Me.

if the proximal toxin for the type I alveolar cells is the parent compound or a metabolite. The diester phosphorus-containing metabolites are not toxic (Verschoyle *et al.*, 1982) and need not be considered.

There are accepted experimental methods of modifying the rate of metabolism mediated by the cytochrome P-450 systems. The results of experiments with several such modifying agents on LD_{50} are shown in table 11.7. Piperonyl butoxide is a competitive substrate for cytochrome P-450 systems (Wilkinson and Hicks, 1969; Kamienski and Casida, 1970; Philpot and Hodgson, 1972; Marshall and Wilkinson, 1973; Casida, 1970) and also depletes liver glutathione concentrations (James and Harbison, 1982). p-Xylene when given in large doses to rats or rabbits results in selective destruction of the cytochrome P-450 system in lung but not in liver and a decrease in microsomal NADPH-cytochrome reductase with little change in lung or liver glutathione (Patel *et al.*, 1978, 1979; Buckpitt and Warren, 1983).

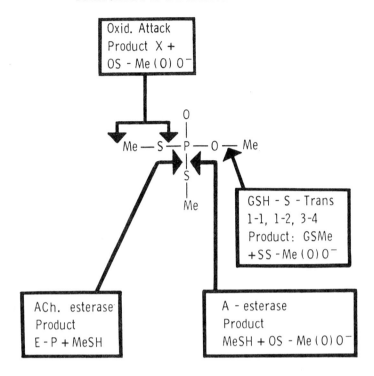

Figure 11.8 Routes of metabolism of OSS-Me(O). Oxidative attack can be either on the S or Me of Me–S–P. One product is the diester OS-Me(O)O⁻ and the other(s) is unknown. Reaction with acetylcholinesterase (AChE) yields phosphorylated enzyme (E-P) and MeSH. Glutathione S-transferases (1–1, 1–2, 3–4) yield methyl-S-glutathione (GS-Me) and the diester SS-Me(O)O⁻. A-esterase hydrolyses OSS-Me(O) to yield MeSH and the diester OS-Me(O)O⁻ (Reiner, 1985, unpublished)

Table 11.7 Toxicity of OSS-Me(O) and OOS-Et(O) to the Rat after Various Pretreatments (data taken from Aldridge *et al.*, 1984, 1985b)

Compound and route of administration	No pretreatment	Phenobarbitone	LD$_{50}$ (μmol/kg)	
			Piperonyl butoxide	p-xylene
OSS-Me(O)				
Oral	151	1162	732	–
Intravenous	308	–	814	791
OOS-Et(O)				
Oral	136	500–1000	121	–
Intravenous	230	–	81	386

When metabolism in the liver is increased by pretreatment of rats with pheno-barbitone, the LD_{50} is also increased, i.e. the doses must be increased so that the dose presented to the lung is the same with and without phenobarbitone. This has been established for both OSS-Me(O) and OOS-Et(O) (table 11.7 and figure 11.6). After pretreatment with p-xylene, toxicity to the lung is decreased (table 11.7) and this would suggest that OSS-Me(O) must be metabolised to a more reactive compound in the lung. The results with piperonyl butoxide are equivocal and cannot be reliably interpreted; they may suggest that metabolism to a reactive compound is essential but that differing degrees of inhibition of metabolism of OSS-Me(O) or OOS-Et(O) in the liver, lung and perhaps other tissues complicate the situation.

As previously discussed, protection of rats by pretreatment requires higher doses at the LD_{50} with consequent increased inhibition of acetylcholinesterase. Where necessary rats have been protected by treatment with atropine and pyridine 2-aldoxime methiodide (PAM) so that they survive early cholinergic symptoms. A 2–2.5-fold increase in lung weight at 3–4 days is indicative of death due to res-piratory failure.

Using [^{3}H] OSS-Me(O) radiolabelled in the $-SCH_3$ groups it has been shown that [^{3}H] becomes bound to the protein when OSS-Me(O) is metabolised by lung or liver slices or microsomal fractions from lung and liver. Binding was prevented at low temperatures ($0°C$) or by omission of NADPH, the cofactor essential for micro-somal mono-oxygenation. The specific activity (dpm/mg protein) in each case was greater for lung than liver (Nemery, 1986; Aldridge et al., 1985b).

During studies in Fukuto's laboratory in Riverside, California, USA, it was found that the toxicity to rats of OOS-Me(O) varied with different methods of isolation following synthesis (Umetsu et al., 1979). The cause of this variability was the presence of differing amounts of trimethyl phosphorothionate (OOO-Me(S)) as an impurity. Vacuum distillation yielded a sample of OOS-Me(O) containing OOO-Me(S) which could be dosed to rats at doses of 200 mg/kg (1280 μmol/kg) without mortality whereas after isolation of OOS-Me(O) by column chromatography the administration of 60 mg/kg (380 μmol/kg) caused death within 7 days of all of a group of six rats. A concentration of 1% OOO-Me(S) in OOS-Me(O) was found to be sufficient to cause the above differences in toxicity.

This important finding has been extended later (Hammond et al., 1982; Umetsu et al., 1981). Protection from delayed deaths is obtained only by pretreatment and is ineffective if given after OOS-Me(O). Trimethyl phosphate (OOO-Me(O)) is inef-fective as is OOO-Et(S) (Umetsu et al., 1981). Other combinations of thionates and thioates have been examined and recent work (Aldridge et al., 1985b) has shown that addition of 5% OOO-Me(S) to OOS-Me(O), OSS-Me(O) or OOS-Et(O) is able to prevent or reduce the increase in lung weight after intravenous injection. Using lung weight at 3 days as an indicator of lung damage, a dose–response relationship between pretreatment with various compounds and their ability to protect against lung damage by OSS-Me(O) has been determined (table 11.8). Other compounds have been screened using a similar pretreatment schedule for this property and are included in table 11.9.

Table 11.8 Prevention of the Toxicity of OSS-Me(O) to Rats by Pretreatment with OOO-Trimethyl Phosphorothionate (OOO-Me(S)) (OOO-Me(S) was administered by the oral route as a solution in glycerol formal 2 h before the intravenous challenge dose of 290 μmol OSS-Me(O)/kg)

OOO-Me(S) (μmol/kg)	Intravenous challenge with OSS-Me(O)	Lung weight at 3 days (mg/100 g rat)[a]
0	–	557 ± 7 (5)
0	+	1491 ± 62 (13)
3.2	+	941 ± 96 (4)
8	+	618 ± 29 (5)
16	+	542 ± 14 (5)
80	+	557 ± 9 (5)

[a]Results are given as means ± S.E.M. of the number of observations in parenthesis.

From other work with sulphur-containing organophosphorus compounds (Neal, 1985 and see chapter by De Matteis in this volume), a reasonable hypothesis is that OOO-Me(S) is metabolised by the lung to products which damage the metabolising system and thus prevent the metabolism of trialkyl phosphorothioates such as OSS-Me(O). Pretreatment with OOO-Me(S) is a controlled experimental procedure to examine this hypothesis.

7-Ethoxycoumarin O-deethylase is a substrate for the cytochrome P-450 dependent enzymes in both lung and liver. As shown in table 11.10, over the same range of pretreatment doses, OOO-Me(S) is effective in protecting against lung damage produced by OSS-Me(O) and causing inhibition of 7-ethoxycoumarin O-deethylase in lung but not in liver microsomes. Thus the dose-response for protection against lung damage, and inhibition of 7-ethoxycoumarin O-deethylase in the lung (but not in liver) is similar (compare tables 11.8 and 11.10).

The tissue specificity may be further examined by a study of the metabolism of $[^{14}C]$–OSS-Me(O) by lung and liver slices (table 11.11). As previously shown the diesters OS-Me(O)O$^-$ and SS-Me(O)O$^-$ are produced by both lung and liver slices with a preference for OS-Me(O)O$^-$ in the lung. When tissue slices from animals pretreated with OOO-Me(S) were examined the production of SS-Me(O)O$^-$ by both lung and liver were unaffected. However the production of OS-Me(O)O$^-$ by lung slices was inhibited but not by liver slices. Binding of $[^{14}C]$ to protein was also inhibited in lung but not in liver slices.

Table 11.9 Pretreatment of Rats with Various Organophosphorus Compounds and Carbon Disulphide and Prevention of Subsequent Lung Damage after Administration of OSS-Me(O)

Pretreatment compound	Effective dose (μmol/kg)
1. OOO-Me(S)	8
2. OOS-Me(S)	14

3.

Fenitrothion (LD$_{50}$ 3000 μmol/kg) < 14

4.

Bromophos (LD$_{50}$ 10 200–22 000 μmol/kg) < 14

5.

< 73

6. Malathion	> 24
7. OOO-Me(O)	> 710
8. OSS-Me(O)	> 58
9. Carbon disulphide	> 660

Effective doses are those where the lung weight was not significantly different from control. Doses marked $<$ indicate the lowest dose tested and which gave complete protection. Doses marked $>$ indicate maximum dose tested and which gave no protection. All organophosphorus compounds were administered by the oral route in glycerol formal 2 h prior to the intravenous challenge dose of 290 μmol OSS-Me(O)/kg.

Table 11.10 Influence of OOO-trimethyl Phosphorothionate (OOO-Me(S)) on the 7-ethoxycoumarin O-
deethylase Activity of Rat Lung and Liver (OOO-Me(S)
was administered by the oral route as a solution in
glycerol formal 2 h prior to removal of tissues from
the rat)

OOO-Me(S) (μmol/kg)	7-Ethoxycoumarin O-deethylase activity in microsomal fraction (pmol of product/min/mg protein)[a]	
	Lung	Liver
0	72 ± 4 (18)	201 ± 15 (18)
3.2	38 ± 2 (6)	—
8	31 ± 4 (6)	—
16	16 ± 2 (6)	—
80	9 ± 1 (6)	160 ± 19 (6)

[a]Results are means $\pm$ S.E.M. of the number of observations in
parenthesis.

CONCLUSIONS

Trialkyl phosphorothioates in rats cause lung damage. Morphological changes can
be seen in type I pneumocytes at early times after administration of OSS-Me(O).
Following this insult alveolar oedema and proliferation of type II pneumocytes
results in respiratory insufficiency and animals generally die 3-4 days after dosing.
Evidence for the primary damage being due to the type I pneumocyte is morphological and is confirmed by changes in putrescine uptake by lung slices, a process
characteristic of type I and II pneumocytes (Smith, 1982).

The distribution of OSS-Me(O) and some other trialkyl phosphorothioates is
uniform within the body water; measurement of concentrations in the plasma are
a reliable measure of the dose presented to the l   g. It is probable that inhibition of
esterases and cholinergic symptoms are caused by the parent compounds (Aldridge
et al., 1985b). The early results of administration of OSS-Me(O) to piperonyl
butoxide pretreated rats suggested that a reactive metabolite rather than the parent
compound was responsible for the delayed toxicity.

The discovery that OOO-Me(S) prevents the production of lung damage by
OOS-Me(O) and other trialkyl phosphorothioates (Umetsu *et al.*, 1979), has allowed
experiments to be designed to determine the dose–response relationships between
the pretreatment of rats with OOO-Me(S) and the subsequent production of lethal
lung damage 3 days later. This dose–response relationship is the same in the lung as
that for inhibition of 7-ethoxycoumarin O-deethylase, inhibition of the metabolism of

Table 11.11 Metabolism of [^{14}C]OSS-Me(O) by Lung and Liver Slices from Rats Pretreated with OOO-Me(S) and Binding to Protein (OOO-Me(S) was administered by the oral route as a solution in glycerol formal 2 h prior to removal of tissues from the rat. Results are mean ± S.E. from tissue from 3 rats and are after metabolism of mM [^{14}C]OSS-Me(O) for 1 h and are taken from Nemery (1986))

OOO-Me(S) (μmol/kg)	Metabolism of OSS-Me(O)	
	Diester produced	
	OS-Me(O)O$^-$	SS-Me(O)O$^-$
	(dpm/mg tissue)	
Lung slices		
0	630 ± 40	580 ± 30
3.2	540 ± 110	650 ± 120
16	180 ± 50	500 ± 40
80	120 ± 30	470 ± 60
Liver slices		
0	220 ± 15	920 ± 10
3.2	270 ± 30	1080 ± 50
16	260 ± 40	810 ± 60
80	200 ± 20	890 ± 40

^{14}C binding from OSS-Me(O)

OOO-Me(S) (μmol/kg)	Binding to protein	
	Lung	Liver
	(dpm/mg at 60 min)	
0	271 ± 19	68 ± 2
3.2	202 ± 30	65 ± 2
16	101 ± 8	84 ± 4
80	75 ± 19	62 ± 7

OSS-Me(O) to OS-Me(O)O$^-$ and the binding to protein from [^{14}C]SCH$_3$ radiolabelled compound. These experiments indicate that it is highly probable that OSS-Me(O) is metabolised by the lung to the more reactive proximal lung damaging toxin. Presumably OOO-Me(S) is metabolised (Neal, 1985) in a way which inhibits the activating metabolism of OSS-Me(O) *in vivo* in the rat lung, while disposal of OSS-Me(O) by the other pathways continues. Thus, over the early few hours when OSS-Me(O) is being presented to the lung it cannot metabolise it to the lung damaging toxin; when the lung's ability to metabolise has returned, the circulating concentrations of the compound are low due to metabolism by the liver to inactive metabolites.

In studies of the structure–activity relationships of the phosphorothionates two types of experiments have been done. The thionate has been administered at the same time as a mixture with the trialkyl phosphorothioate, or by pretreatment with the thionate followed by the lung damaging trialkyl phosphorothioate. For the former procedure even among closely related thionates there are considerable differences in apparent activity (Hammond *et al.*, 1982; Umetsu *et al.*, 1981). Different thionates give various degrees of protection against the same thioate and the same thionates yield differing degrees of protection for different thioates (Aldridge *et al.*, 1985b). These results would be expected on the basis of competition between oxidative attack on the sulphur of P=S and P–S–CH$_3$. For the second type of experiment the same degree of protection should be found against all lung damaging thioates by the same doses of thionate. This has not been established yet but it is clear that the ability to protect is widespread amongst organophosphorus thionate structures. The results presented in table 11.9 are preliminary but some were unexpected. For example, the doses of the two thionate pesticides, fenitrothion and bromophos, which were effective in protecting against a challenge dose of 290 μmol OSS-Me(O)/kg were 200 and 1000 times less than their LD$_{50}$ — the mechanism of lethality involves oxidation of the thionate to the oxon, the proximal anticholinesterase toxin. OOS-Trimethyl phosphorodithionate [OOS-Me(S)] does not cause lung damage (table 11.2) even though it contains a P–S–CH$_3$. It also possesses a P=S and has been shown at low doses of pretreatment to protect animals from the toxicity of subsequent administration of OSS-Me(O) (table 11.9). It would therefore appear that preferential oxidative attack occurs on the P=S rather than –S–CH$_3$ (see later).

The reason for the tissue selectivity of OOO-Me(S) between the liver and lung (tables 11.10 and 11.11) is not understood. For the other protective compounds shown in table 11.9 experiments have not yet been completed but it is known that diethyl phenyl phosphorothionate does cause depression of cytochrome P-450 and changes in liver morphology (Seawright *et al.*, 1976) associated with metabolism of the P=S to P=O. However liver changes were described after administration of 1600 μmol/kg to phenobarbitone pretreated rats; in control rats 1600 μmol/kg produced no histological changes in the liver. In contrast, in table 11.9, 73 μmol/kg was effective in protecting against OSS-Me(O) lung toxicity. Similarly carbon disulphide can produce depression of cytochrome P-450 in the liver both in control and phenobarbitone-pretreated rats, but only phenobarbitone-pretreated animals will also develop histological liver damage. Carbon disulphide pretreatment, however, did not protect against OSS-Me(O) lung toxicity. At this early stage in the investigation it is clear that there are many unexplained differences between liver and lung; these may be in the metabolism of the thionates and thiolates but also in the responses of the cells to the products.

Most research in mechanisms of toxicity follows a biological response to a chemical seen in man or experimental work. Many subsequent investigations use *in vitro* systems; it is often a difficult task to establish that the changes measured *in vitro* are relevant to the whole animal situation. In these studies this gap has been bridged as shown by the summary in table 11.12. The production of changes in the lung has been linked to changes measured in tissues taken from animals; the link has been made by common dose–response curves for pretreatment with OOO-Me(S) and other compounds. It will also be possible to examine the influence of *in vitro* treatment of tissues on the subsequent metabolism of the lung damaging trialkyl

Table 11.12 Comparison of Relative Changes Produced by Pretreatment of Rats with Various Doses of OOO-Me(S) and OOS-Me(S) (OOO-Me(S) and OOS-Me(S) pretreatments were given orally in glycerol formal and rats were challenged with OSS-Me(O) or tissues examined 2 h later. The increase in lung weight was measured 3 days after an intravenous challenge of 290 μmol OSS-Me(O)/kg and is expressed as a percentage of the increase obtained in control rats. Ethoxycoumarin O-deethylase was determined in the lung microsomal fraction and the metabolism of [^{14}C]OSS-Me(O) was measured using lung slices)

Dose of compound (μmol/kg)	Lung weight (% increase)	Lung microsomal ethoxycoumarin O-deethylase (% decrease)	Metabolism of [^{14}C]OSS-Me(O) by lung slices	
			Binding to protein	Diester OS-Me(O)O$^-$ produced
			(% decrease)	
0	100	100	100	100
OOO-Me(S)				
3.2	41	53	74	86
8	6	43	—	—
16	0	22	33	28
80	0	12	5	19
OOS-Me(S)				
2.9	58	75	—	—
14.5	9	29	—	—
73	0	32	—	—

phosphorothioates. In this way the complete bridge between *in vitro* and whole animal will have been made. The molecular basis for tissue selectivity and species selectivity may then be examined with confidence and in a fundamental way. A cell specific toxin and a selective antagonist are invaluable tools for the solution of such a problem.

For lung damage to be produced by organophosphorus compounds the compound must contain a P–S-alkyl group. Trialkyl phosphates and thionophosphates are inactive and SSS-Me(O) is as active as OSS-Me(O). Thionophosphates at rather low doses prevent trialkyl phosphorothioates from causing lung damage and appear to do so by reducing the activity of cytochrome P-450 dependent enzymes in the lung.

The present hypothesis is that a metabolite of OSS-Me(O) and probably other trialkyl phosphorothioates are involved in the cell specific toxicity to type I pneumocytes in the lung. The identity of the metabolite is not known or whether the organ specificity between the lung and the liver is due to a different metabolite or very different rates of further metabolism (detoxification). Oxidative attack is possible on carbon or sulphur (Eto *et al.*, 1977; Wing *et al.*, 1983, 1984; Casida,

1984). Preliminary work (P. Farmer, unpublished work) in which haemoglobin and lung protein have been examined for methylcysteine after treatment with OSS-Me(O) suggest that the active metabolite is unlikely to be a methylating agent (table 11.13).

Both the lung and liver metabolise OSS-Me(O) to the same diester OS-Me(O)O$^-$; in the lung the route of metabolism is correlated with morphological change in the lung. The question therefore arises why the liver is not affected. It could be a matter of the dose of active metabolite per cell. The following preliminary experiment has been carried out (Verschoyle and Sparrow, 1986, unpublished) designed to increase the dose per liver cell. The rate of disposal of OSS-Me(O) in the rat, presumably by the liver, may be markedly increased by pretreatment by phenobarbitone (Aldridge *et al.*, 1984). The experimental groups were: (1) 25 mg OSS-Me(O)/kg to control rats; (2) 150 mg OSS-Me(O) to phenobarbitone pretreated rats; (3) phenobarbitone pretreated rats. Even with the 6-fold increase in dose of OSS-Me(O) changes in the liver (cytoplasmic vacuolation, perivascular (portal) oedema and cytoplasmic shrinkage) were minimal and occurred in all three groups (Verschoyle and Sparrow, 1986, unpublished). This result requires confirmation, but, if it is confirmed, must suggest that either the rates of detoxification of the active metabolite differ in lung and liver and/or that the routes of metabolism in these tissues are different.

Table 11.13 Methylcysteine in Protein from Rat Erythrocytes, Haemoglobin and Lung after Exposure to OSS-Me(O) *in vitro* and *in vivo* (Integrated doses were calculated from the plasma disposal rates. The methylcysteine was determined by the method of Bailey *et al.* (1980, 1981b))

Integrated dose of OSS-Me(O) (nmol/ml/h) (time)	Methylcysteine (nmol/g protein)	
In vitro (erythrocytes)	Erythrocyte	
Control	149	
1163 (1 h incubation)	297	
232 (1 h incubation)	165	
In vivo (151 μmol/kg)		
122 (1 h after dose)	140	
315 (24 h after dose)	165	
	Haemoglobin	Lung
In vivo (581 μmol/kg)		
Control	82 ± 5 (3)	135 ± 21 (3)
932 (4.5 h after dose)	181 ± 8 (3)	166 ± 8 (3)
In vitro (lung slices)		
1000 (1 h incubation)	−	320

The research described and summarised in this paper has several aspects of direct relevance to human toxicology.

(1) It is now known that potentiation of the toxicity of malathion by isomalathion occurs in man.

(2) An accelerated storage test has been devised to establish the stability of water-dispersible malathion powders before they are used in hot countries.

(3) Further research on carboxylesterases should establish whether the trialkyl phosphorothioates can potentiate the toxicity of malathion in man.

(4) It should now be possible to establish whether the metabolic pathways associated with lung toxicity of trialkyl phosphorothioates to rats also occur in human post-mortem tissue.

(5) Although trialkyl phosphorothioates occur in many phosphorothionate pesticides, their presence in many pesticides may have no potential to cause lung toxicity because the parent pesticide or other thiono impurities may prevent this action.

(6) The significance to man of the observations that very low concentrations of thionate pesticides affect the drug metabolising potential of the lung is not known but should be investigated.

In addition to these important practical issues the trialkyl phosphorothioates are and will provide tools for experimental research to establish the basis for selective cell damage in man and animals and to define the biochemical and biological properties of these cells. Effective collaborative research utilising the skills from many disciplines is required (Smith *et al.*, 1986).

ACKNOWLEDGEMENTS

We are very grateful to Dr P. Farmer for the synthesis of compounds and also for permission to use the results shown in table 11.13. One of us (B.N.) was supported during the course of this research by the Fonds National de la Recherche Scientifique, Belgium, the European Science Foundation and NATO.

REFERENCES

Aldridge, W. N. (1981). Organophosphorus compounds: molecular basis for their biological properties. *Sci. Progr. Oxf.*, **67**, 131–47

Aldridge, W. N. and Nemery, B. (1984). Toxicology of trialkyl phosphorothioates with particular reference to lung toxicity. *Fund. appl. Toxicol.*, **4**, S215–S223

Aldridge, W. N., Miles, J. W., Mount, D. L. and Verschoyle, R. D (1979). The toxicological properties of impurities in malathion. *Arch. Toxicol.*, **42**, 95–106

Aldridge, W. N., Verschoyle, R. D. and Peal, J. A. (1984). OSS-Trimethyl phosphorodithioate and OOS-triethyl phosphorothioate: pharmacokinetics in rats and effect of pretreatment with compounds affecting drug processing systems. *Pest. Biochem. Physiol.*, **21**, 265–74

Aldridge, W. N., Grasdalen, H., Aarstad, K., Street, B. W. and Norkov, T. (1985a). Trialkyl phosphorothioates and glutathione S-transferases. *Chem. Biol. Interactions*, **54**, 243–56

Aldridge, W. N., Dinsdale, D., Nemery, B. and Verschoyle, R. D. (1985b). Some aspects of the toxicology of trimethyl and triethyl phosphorothioates. *Fund. appl. Toxicol.*, **5**, S47–S60

Ali, F. A. F. and Fukuto, T. R. (1982). Toxicity of OOS-trialkyl phosphorothioates in the rat. *J. Agric. Food Chem.*, **30**, 126–30

Bailey, E., Farmer, P. B. and Lamb, J. H. (1980). The enantiomer as internal standard for the quantitation of the alkylated amino acid S-methyl-L-cysteine in haemoglobin by gas chromatography-chemical ionisation mass spectrometry with single ion detection. *J. Chromatogr.*, **200**, 145–52

Bailey, E., Peal, J. A. and Verschoyle, R. D. (1981a). The determination of OSS-trimethyl phosphorodithioate in the plasma and various tissues of rats using high-resolution gas chromatography with nitrogen–phosphorus detection. *J. Chromatogr.*, **219**, 285–90

Bailey, E., Connors, T. A., Farmer, P. B., Gorf, S. M. and Rickard, J. (1981b). Methylation of cysteine in haemoglobin following exposure to methylating agents. *Cancer Res.*, **41**, 2514–17

Baker, E. L., Zack, M., Miles, J. W., Alderman, L., Warren, McW., Dobbin, R. D., Miller, S. and Teeters, W. R. (1978). Epidemic malathion poisoning in Pakistan malaria workers. *Lancet*, **I**, 31–3

Buckpitt, A. R. and Warren, D. L. (1983). Evidence for hepatic formation, export and covalent binding of reactive naphthalene metabolites in extra hepatic tissues *in vivo*. *J. Pharmacol. exp. Ther.*, **225**, 8–15

Cain, K. and Clothier, B. (1986). The identification, characterisation and partial purification of two separate carboxylesterases in guinea pig serum. *Human Toxicology*, Abstract to British Toxicology Society, September 1985

Cain, K., Reiner, E. and Williams, D. G. (1983). The identification and characterisation of two separate carboxylesterases in guinea pig serum. *Biochem. J.*, **215**, 91–9

Casida, J. E. (1970). Mixed function oxidases involvement in the biochemistry of insecticide synergists. *J. Agric. Food Chem.*, **18**, 753–72

Casida, J. E. (1984). Oxidative bioactivation of acetylcholinesterase inhibitors with emphasis on S-alkyl phosphorothiolate pesticides. In: *Cholinesterases*, Walter de Gruyter & Co., Berlin, pp. 427–40

Casida, J. E., Baron, R. L., Eto, M. and Engel, J. L. (1963). Potentiation and neurotoxicity induced by certain organophosphates. *Biochem. Pharmacol.*, **12**, 73–83

Clothier, B. and Cain, K. (1986). Kinetic properties of two separate carboxylesterases isolated from guinea pig serum. *Human Toxicology*. Abstract to British Toxicology Society, September 1985

Clothier, B., Johnson, M. K. and Reiner, E. (1981). Interaction of some trialkyl phosphorothiolates with acetylcholinesterase. Characterisation of inhibition, aging and reactivation. *Biochim. Biophys. Acta*, **660**, 306–16

Dauterman, W. C. and Main, A. R. (1966). Relationship between acute toxicity and *in vitro* inhibition and hydrolysis of a series of carbalkoxy homologs of Malathion. *Toxicol. appl. Pharmacol.*, **9**, 408–17

De Jong, L. P. A., Wolring, G. Z. and Benschop, H. P. (1982). Reactivation of acetylcholinesterase inhibited by methamidophos and analogous (Di)methyl-phosphoramidates. *Arch. Toxicol.*, **49**, 175–83

Dinsdale, D., Verschoyle, R. D. and Cabral, J. R. P. (1982). Cellular responses to trialkyl phosphorothioate induced injury in rat lung. *Arch. Toxicol.*, **51**, 79–89

Dinsdale, D., Verschoyle, R. D. and Ingham, J. E. (1984). Ultrastructural change in rat Clara cells induced by a single dose of OSS-trimethyl phosphorodithioate. *Arch. Toxicol.*, **56**, 59–65

Eto, M., Okabe, S., Ozoe, Y. and Mackawa, K. (1977). Oxidative activation of OS-dimethyl phosphoramidothiolate. *Pestic. Biochem. Physiol.*, **7**, 367–77

Frawley, J. P., Fuyat, H. N., Hajan, E. C., Blake, J. R. and Fitzhugh, O. G. (1957). Marked potentiation in mammalian toxicity from simultaneous administration of two anticholinesterase compounds. *J. Pharmacol.*, **121**, 96–106

Gandy, J., Ali, F. A. F., Hasegawa, L. and Imamura, T. (1984). Morphological alterations of rat lung bronchiolar epithelium produced by various trialkyl phosphorothioates. *Toxicology*, **32**, 37–46

Hammond, P. S., Badawy, S. M. A., March, R. B. and Fukuto, T. R. (1982). Delayed acute toxicity of OSS-trimethyl phosphorodithioate and OOS-trimethyl phosphorothioate to the rat. *Pestic. Biochem. Physiol.*, **8**, 90–100

Imamura, T., Gandy, J., Fukuto, T. R. and Talbot, P. (1983). An impurity of malathion alters the morphology of rat lung bronchiolar epithelium. *Toxicology*, **26**, 73–9

Jakoby, W. B., Ketterer, B. and Mannervik, B. (1984). Glutathione transferases: Nomenclature. *Biochem. Pharmacol.*, **33**, 2539–40

James, R. C. and Harbison, R. D. (1982). Hepatic glutathione and hepatotoxicity. Effects of cytochrome P-450 complexing compounds SKF 525-A, 1-αacetyl methadol (LAAM), nor LAAM and piperonyl butoxide. *Biochem. Pharmacol.*, **31**, 1829–35

Kamienski, F. X. and Casida, J. E. (1970). Importance of demethylenation in the metabolism *in vivo* and *in vitro* of methylene dioxyphenyl synergists and related compounds in mammals. *Biochem. Pharmacol.*, **19**, 91–112

Lee, S. G. K. and Fukuto, T. R. (1982). Inhibition of rat liver and plasma carboxyl-esterases by impurities present in technical phenthoate. *J. Toxicol. Environ. Hlth*, **10**, 717–28

Main, A. R. and Braid, P. E. (1962). Hydrolysis of malathion by aliesterases *in vitro* and *in vivo*. *Biochem. J.*, **84**, 255–63

Main, A. R. and Hastings, F. L. (1966). A comparison of acylation, phosphorylation and binding in related substrates and inhibitors of serum cholinesterase. *Biochem. J.*, **101**, 584–90

Malik, J. K. and Summer, K. H. (1982). Toxicity and metabolism of malathion and its impurities in isolated rat hepatocytes: role of glutathione. *Toxicol. appl. Pharmacol.*, **66**, 69–76

Mallipudi, N. M., Umetsu, N., Toia, R. F., Talcott, R. E. and Fukuto, T. R. (1979). Toxicity of OOS-Trimethyl and Triethyl Phosphorothioate to the rat. *J. Agric. Food Chem.*, **27**, 463–6

Mallipudi, N. M., Talcott, R. E., Ketterman, A. and Fukuto, T. R. (1980). Properties and inhibition of rat malathion carboxylesterases. *J. Toxicol. Environ. Hlth*, **6**, 585–96

Marshall, R. S. and Wilkinson, C. F. (1973). The interaction of insecticide synergists with non-enzymic model systems. *Pestic. Biochem. Physiol.*, **2**, 425–36

Miles, J. W., Mount, D. L., Staiger, M. A. and Teeters, W. R. (1979). The S-methyl isomer content of stored malathion and fenitrothion water-dispersible powders and its relationship to toxicity. *J. Agric. Food Chem.*, **27**, 421–5

Miles, J. W., Mount, D. L. and Churchill, F. C. (1980). The effect of storage on the formation of minor components in malathion powders. *CIPAC Proceedings Symposium* (ed. F. Sanchez-Rasero), Series 2, pp. 176–92

Murphy, S. D. and DuBois, K. P. (1957). Quantitative measurement of inhibition of the enzymic detoxification of malathion by EPN (ethyl p-nitrophenyl thiono-benzenephosphonate). *Proc. Soc. exp. Biol. Med.*, **96**, 813–18

Neal, R. A. (1985). Thiono-sulphur compounds. In: *Bioactivation of Foreign Compounds* (ed. M. W. Anders), Academic Press, Orlando, pp. 519-37

Nemery, B. (1986). Ph.D. thesis. Council for National Academic Awards, London.

Nemery, B., Smith, L. L. and Aldridge, W. N. (1986). Assessment of cell selectivity in toxic lung damage by simultaneous measurement of putrescine and 5-hydroxy-tryptamine uptake in rat lung slices: OSS-trimethyl phosphorodithioate and other pneumotoxins. Submitted for publication

Patel, J. M., Harper, C. and Drew, R. T. (1978). The biotransformation of p-xylene to a toxic aldehyde. *Drug Metab. Dis.*, **6**, 368-74

Patel, J. M., Wolf, C. R. and Philpot, R. M. (1979). Interaction of 4-methylbenz-aldehyde with rabbit pulmonary cytochrome P-450 in the intact animal, microsomes and purified systems. *Biochem. Pharmacol.*, **28**, 2031-6

Philpot, R. M. and Hodgson, E. (1972). Effect of piperonyl butoxide concentration on the formation of cytochrome P-450 difference spectra in hepatic microsomes from mice. *Molec. Pharmacol.*, **8**, 204-14

Ryan, D. L. and Fukuto, T. R. (1984). The effect of isomalathion and OSS-tri-methyl phosphorodithioate on the *in vivo* metabolism of malathion in rats. *Pestic. Biochem. Physiol.*, **21**, 349-57

Seawright, A. A., Hrdlika, J. and De Matteis, F. (1976). The hepatotoxicity of O,O-diethyl O-phenyl phosphorothionate (SV1) for the rat. *Brit. J. exp. Pathol.*, **57**, 16-22

Smith, L. L. (1982). The identification of an accumulation system for diamines and polyamines into the lung and its relevance to paraquat toxicity. *Arch. Toxicol.* (Suppl. 5), 1-14

Smith, L. L., Cohen, G. M. and Aldridge, W. N. (1986). Morphological and bio-chemical correlates of chemical induced injury in the lung. A discussion. *Arch. Toxicol.*, **58**, 214-18

Talcott, R. E., Mallipudi, N. M. and Fukuto, T. R. (1977). Malathion carboxyl-esterase titer and its relationship to malathion toxicity. *Toxicol. appl. Pharmacol.*, **50**, 501-4

Talcott, R. E., Mallipudi, N. M., Umetsu, N. and Fukuto, T. R. (1979a). Inactivation of esterases by impurities isolated from technical malathion. *Toxicol. appl. Pharmacol.*, **49**, 107-12

Talcott, R. E., Denk, H. and Mallipudi, N. M. (1979b). Malathion carboxylesterase activity in human liver and its inactivation by isomalathion. *Toxicol. appl. Pharmacol.*, **49**, 373-6

Toia, R. F., March, R. B., Umetsu, N., Mallipudi, N. M., Allahyari, R. and Fukuto, T. R. (1980). Identification and toxicological evaluation of impurities in technical malathion and fenthion. *J. Agric. Food Chem.*, **28**, 599-604

Umetsu, N., Grose, F. H., Allahyari, R., Abu-El-Haj, S. and Fukuto, T. R. (1977). Effect of impurities on the mammalian toxicity of technical malathion and acephate. *J. Agric. Food Chem.*, **25**, 946-53

Umetsu, N., Toia, R. F., Mallipudi, N. M., March, R. B. and Fukuto, T. R. (1979). Novel antagonistic effect to the toxicity in the rat of O,O,S-trimethylphosphoro-thioate by its phosphorothionate isomer. *J. Agric. Food Chem.*, **27**, 1423-5

Umetsu, N., Mallipudi, N. M., Toia, R. F., March, R. B. and Fukuto, T. R. (1981). Toxicological properties of phosphorothioate and related esters present as impurities in technical organophosphorus insecticides. *J. Toxicol. Environ. Hlth*, **7**, 481-97

Verschoyle, R. D. and Cabral, J. R. P. (1982). Investigation of the acute toxicity of some trimethyl and triethyl phosphorothioates with particular reference to those causing lung damage. *Arch. Toxicol.*, **51**, 221-31

Verschoyle, R. D., Aldridge, W. N. and Cabral, J. R. P. (1980). Toxicology of tri-methyl and triethyl phosphorothioates. In: *Mechanisms of Toxicity and Hazard*

Evaluation (ed. B. Holmstedt, R. Lauwerys, M. Mercier and M. Roberfroid), Elsevier/North Holland Biomedical Press, Amsterdam, pp. 631–4

Verschoyle, R. D., Reiner, E., Bailey, E. and Aldridge, W. N. (1982). Dimethylphosphorothioates. Reaction with malathion and effect on malathion toxicity. *Arch. Toxicol.*, **49**, 293–301

Wilkinson, C. F. and Hicks, L. T. (1969). Microsomal metabolism of the 1,3-benzodioxole ring and its probable significance in synergistic action. *J. Agric. Food Chem.*, **17**, 829–36

Wing, K. D., Glickman, A. H. and Casida, J. E. (1983). Oxidative bioactivation of S-alkyl phosphorothiolate pesticides: stereospecificity of profenofos insecticide activation. *Science, N.Y.*, **219**, 63–5

Wing, K. D., Glickman, A. H. and Casida, J. E. (1984). Phosphorothiolate pesticides and related compounds: oxidative bioactivation and aging of the inhibited acetylcholinesterase. *Pestic. Biochem. Physiol.*, **21**, 22–30

World Health Organisation (1979). Specification for pesticides used in public health. Geneva, pp. 102–14

Index

Abrin, 105–112

Acetylcholine, 125

Acetylcholinesterase (AChE)
  inhibition by trialkyl phosphorothiolates, 265–268, 271, 274, 278, 282
  mechanism of ageing after inhibition by organophosphates, 125–147
  relevance to organophosphate-induced delayed neuropathy, 29, 30, 35, 37, 40
    42, 48–49

Acetylene, as a suicide substrate of cytochrome P-450, 188, 194

A-chains, role in toxicity of plant lectins, 110–117

Acrylamide, 259

Ah locus, 92

2-Aldoxime methiodide (PAM), 128, 138, 282

2-Allyl-2-isopropyl acetamide (AIA), 193, 195, 200

Alveolar capillary endothelial cells, damage by oxygen, 4

Alveolar type I epithelial cells
  active transport of paraquat and polyamines, 14, 272, 285
  damage by butylated hydroxytoluene, 11, 18
  damage by oxygen, 4
  damage by paraquat, 13
  damage by trialkylphosphorothioates, 15, 17, 19, 272, 279–280, 288

Alveolar type II epithelial cells
  active transport of paraquat and polyamines, 14, 285
  damage by 4-ipomeanol, 9
  damage by paraquat, 13
  proliferation following butylated hydroxytoluene, 11
  proliferation following oxygen toxicity, 4
  proliferation following trialkylphosphorothioates, 272, 279, 285

2-Aminoethylisothiouronium bromide, 7

5-Aminolaevulinate synthase (ALA-S)
  induction by AIA, 193, 196
  induction by DDC, 193, 199